D1806973

World Scientific
Series in Advanced
Manufacturing

Volume 2: Recent Advances in Industrial Robotics

Manufacturing in the Era of 4th Industrial Revolution

A World Scientific Reference

World Scientific Series in Advanced Manufacturing

Print ISSN: 2717-5901
Online ISSN: 2717-591X

Editor-in-Chief: Prof. Satyandra K. Gupta *(University of Southern California)*

The World Scientific Series in Advanced Manufacturing aims to disseminate the new knowledge being created in the area of advanced manufacturing. Books in this series are expected to serve as a reference for practicing engineers and textbooks for new courses. This series has a broad scope and will cover all potential areas related to Advanced Manufacturing technologies.

Published

Manufacturing in the Era of 4th Industrial Revolution — A World Scientific Reference (in 3 Volumes)

Volume 1: Recent Advances in Additive Manufacturing
edited by Hugh A. Bruck, Yong Chen, and Satyandra K. Gupta

Volume 2: Recent Advances in Industrial Robotics
edited by Satyandra K. Gupta, Venkat N. Krovi, and Craig Schlenoff

Volume 3: Augmented, Virtual and Mixed Reality Applications in Advanced Manufacturing
edited by Monica Bordegoni, Satyandra K. Gupta, and James Ritchie

Editor-in-chief: **Satyandra K Gupta**

World Scientific
Series in Advanced
Manufacturing

Volume 2: Recent Advances in Industrial Robotics

Manufacturing in the Era of 4th Industrial Revolution

A World Scientific Reference

editors

Satyandra K Gupta
University of Southern California, USA

Venkat N Krovi
Clemson University, USA

Craig Schlenoff
National Institute of Standards and Technology, USA

 **World Scientific**

NEW JERSEY · LONDON · SINGAPORE · BEIJING · SHANGHAI · HONG KONG · TAIPEI · CHENNAI · TOKYO

Published by

World Scientific Publishing Co. Pte. Ltd.

5 Toh Tuck Link, Singapore 596224

USA office: 27 Warren Street, Suite 401-402, Hackensack, NJ 07601

UK office: 57 Shelton Street, Covent Garden, London WC2H 9HE

Library of Congress Cataloging-in-Publication Data
Names: Gupta, Satyandra K, editor.
Title: Manufacturing in the era of 4th industrial revolution / editor-in-chief, Satyandra K Gupta.
Other titles: Manufacturing in the era of fourth industrial revolution
Description: Hackensack, NJ : World Scientific, 2020. | Series: A World Scientific reference |
    Includes bibliographical references and index. | Contents: volume 1. Recent advances in
    additive manufacturing / editors, Hugh Bruck, University of Maryland, College Park, USA, Yong Chen,
    University of Southern California, USA, Satyandra K Gupta, University of Southern California, USA --
    volume 2. Recent advances in industrial robotics / editors, Satyandra K Gupta,
    University of Southern California, USA, Venkat N Krovi, Clemson University, USA,
    Craig Schlenoff, National Institute of Standards and Technology, USA --
    volume 3. Augmented, virtual and mixed reality applications in advanced manufacturing /
    editors, Monica Bordegoni, Politecnico di Milano, Italy, Satyandra K Gupta,
    University of Southern California, USA, James Ritchie, Heriot-Watt University, UK.
Identifiers: LCCN 2020034693 | ISBN 9789811222818 (v. 1 ; hardcover) |
    ISBN 9789811222832 (v. 2 ; hardcover) | ISBN 9789811222856 (v. 3 ; hardcover) |
    ISBN 9789811222788 (hardcover ; set) | ISBN 9789811222825 (v. 1 ; ebook for institutions) |
    ISBN 9789811222849 (v. 2 ; ebook for institutions) | ISBN 9789811222863 (v. 3 ; ebook for institutions) |
    ISBN 9789811222801 (ebook for individuals) | ISBN 9789811222795 (ebook for institutions ; set)
Subjects: LCSH: Manufacturing processes--Technological innovations.
Classification: LCC TS183 .M353 2020 | DDC 670--dc23
LC record available at https://lccn.loc.gov/2020034693

British Library Cataloguing-in-Publication Data
A catalogue record for this book is available from the British Library.

Copyright © 2020 by World Scientific Publishing Co. Pte. Ltd.

All rights reserved. This book, or parts thereof, may not be reproduced in any form or by any means, electronic or mechanical, including photocopying, recording or any information storage and retrieval system now known or to be invented, without written permission from the publisher.

For photocopying of material in this volume, please pay a copying fee through the Copyright Clearance Center, Inc., 222 Rosewood Drive, Danvers, MA 01923, USA. In this case permission to photocopy is not required from the publisher.

For any available supplementary material, please visit
https://www.worldscientific.com/worldscibooks/10.1142/11898#t=suppl

Printed in Singapore

© 2020 World Scientific Publishing Company
https://doi.org/10.1142/9789811222849_fmatter

Contents

About the Editors   vii

About the Contributors   ix

1. Introduction   1
   Satyandra K. Gupta, Venkat Krovi, and Craig Schlenoff

2. Agile Industrial Robots   7
   Craig Schlenoff, Zeid Kootbally, William Shackleford, Fred Proctor,
   Brian Antonishek, William Harrison, and Anthony Downs

3. State-of-the-Art in Human-Robot Interaction   43
   Jeremy A. Marvel, Megan Zimmerman, and Shelly Bagchi

4. Human-Robot Collaboration for Advanced Manufacturing by   87
   Learning from Multi-Modal Human Demonstrations
   Weitian Wang, Yi Chen, Rui Li, Zhujun Zhang,
   Venkat Krovi, and Yunyi Jia

5. Collaborative Industrial Robot Control: From Safe Motion to   117
   Multi-Robot Manipulation
   John T. Wen, John Wason, Daniel Kruse, Yuan-Chih Peng,
   and Shuyang Chen

6. Blended Shared Control in Collaborative Robotics   153
   Zongyao Jin and Prabhakar R. Pagilla

7. Learning and Coordination of Movement Primitives for Bimanual   187
   Manipulation Tasks Using Concurrent Synchronization
   Ashwin Dani, Iman Salehi, Harish Ravichandar, and Gang Yao

8. Advances in Robot Technology Supporting Low-Volume/High-Mix   215
    Small Part Assembly Operations
    Joe Falco, Karl Van Wyk, and Kenneth Kimble

9. A Smart Companion Robot for Automotive Assembly   239
    Jasprit Singh Gill, Yi Chen, Farbod Akhavan Niaki,
    Mark Tomaszewski, Weitian Wang, Laine Mears, Pierluigi Pisu,
    Yunyi Jia, and Venkat Krovi

10. Collaborative Robotics for Deformable Object Manipulation with   267
    Use Cases from Food Processing Industry
    Philip Long, Philippe Martinet, and Taskin Padir

11. Collaborative Robots for Assembly of Large-Scale Structures   297
    Ashis G. Banerjee

12. Robotic Finishing of Geometrically Complex Parts   315
    Ariyan M. Kabir, Prahar M. Bhatt, Brual C. Shah, and
    Satyandra K. Gupta

13. Advancing Capabilities of Industrial Robots Through Evaluation,   337
    Benchmarking, and Characterization
    Adam Norton, Elena Messina, and Holly Yanco

© 2020 World Scientific Publishing Company
https://doi.org/10.1142/9789811222849_fmatter

About the Editors

Satyandra K. Gupta

Dr. Satyandra K. Gupta is Smith International Professor in the Department of Aerospace and Mechanical Engineering and Department of Computer Science in Viterbi School of Engineering at the University of Southern California. He served as a program director for the National Robotics Initiative at the National Science Foundation from September 2012 to September 2014. Dr. Gupta's interests are in the area of physics-aware decision making to facilitate and advance the state of automation. He has published more than 350 technical articles. He is a fellow of the American Society of Mechanical Engineers (ASME), Institute of Electrical and Electronics Engineers (IEEE), and Society of Manufacturing Engineers (SME). He serves as editor of the *ASME Journal of Computing and Information Science in Engineering*. Dr. Gupta has received numerous honors and awards for his scholarly contributions. Representative examples include a Young Investigator Award from the Office of Naval Research in 2000, Robert W. Galvin Outstanding Young Manufacturing Engineer Award from the Society of Manufacturing Engineers in 2001, CAREER Award from the National Science Foundation in 2001, Presidential Early Career Award for Scientists and Engineers in 2001, Invention of the Year Award at the University of Maryland in 2007, Kos Ishii-Toshiba Award from ASME in 2011, Excellence in Research Award from ASME Computers and Information in Engineering Division in 2013, and Distinguished Alumnus Award from Indian Institute of Technology, Roorkee in 2014. He has also received ten best paper awards at international conferences.

Venkat Krovi

Prof. Venkat N. Krovi is currently the Michelin Endowed SmartState Chair Professor of Vehicle Automation at Clemson University – International Center for Automotive Research. His research focuses on intelligent modulation of distributed physical-power-interactions (motions/forces) between humans and autonomous-systems to unlock the "power of the many". Research activities focus on the life-cycle treatment (design, modeling, analysis, control, implementation and verification) of a new generation of systems for realizing Human-Autonomy synergy with applications in vehicle automation, plant-automation, and defense arenas. He currently serves as the Editor-in-Chief of the ASME *Journal of Mechanisms and Robotics* and was the Founding Editor-in-Chief of the *SAE Journal of Connected and Automated Vehicles*. He has also taken significant leadership roles within multiple professional societies (ASME, IEEE) and currently serves on the Executive Committee of the IEEE Robotics and Automation Society.

Craig Schlenoff

Dr. Craig Schlenoff is the Group Leader of the Cognition and Collaboration Systems Group, the Associate Program Manager of the Measurement Science for Manufacturing Robotics Program, and the Project Leader of the Agility Performance of Robotic Systems project in the Intelligent Systems Division at the National Institute of Standards and Technology. His research interests include knowledge representation/ontologies, intention recognition, and performance evaluation of autonomous systems and industrial robotics. He has led multiple million-dollar projects addressing performance evaluation of advanced military technologies and agility performance of manufacturing robotic systems. He has published over 150 journal and conference papers, guest edited three journals, guest edited three books, and written four book chapters. He is currently the Associate Vice President for Standardization in the IEEE Robotics and Automation Society and the co-chair of the IEEE Robot Task Representation Working Group, was previously the chair of the IEEE Ontology for Robotics and Automation Working Group and has served as the Program Manager for the Process Engineering Program at NIST and the Director of Ontologies at VerticalNet. He also teaches two courses at the University of Maryland, College Park: "Calculus" and "Building a Manufacturing Robot Software System." He received his Bachelor's degree from the University of Maryland, his Master's degree from Rensselaer Polytechnic Institute, and his PhD from the University of Burgundy (France).

© 2020 World Scientific Publishing Company
https://doi.org/10.1142/9789811222849_fmatter

About the Contributors

1. *Introduction*

Satyandra K. Gupta

Dr. Satyandra K. Gupta is Smith International Professor in the Department of Aerospace and Mechanical Engineering and Department of Computer Science in Viterbi School of Engineering at the University of Southern California. He served as a program director for the National Robotics Initiative at the National Science Foundation from September 2012 to September 2014. Dr. Gupta's interests are in the area of physics-aware decision making to facilitate and advance the state of automation. He has published more than three hundred fifty technical articles. He is a fellow of the American Society of Mechanical Engineers (ASME), Institute of Electrical and Electronics Engineers (IEEE), and Society of Manufacturing Engineers (SME). He serves as editor of the *ASME Journal of Computing and Information Science in Engineering*. Dr. Gupta has received numerous honors and awards for his scholarly contributions. Representative examples include a Young Investigator Award from the Office of Naval Research in 2000, Robert W. Galvin Outstanding Young Manufacturing Engineer Award from the Society of Manufacturing Engineers in 2001, CAREER Award from the National Science Foundation in 2001, Presidential Early Career Award for Scientists and Engineers in 2001, Invention of the Year Award at the University of Maryland in 2007, Kos Ishii-Toshiba Award from ASME in 2011, Excellence in Research Award from ASME Computers and Information in Engineering Division in 2013, and Distinguished Alumnus Award from Indian Institute of Technology, Roorkee in 2014. He has also received ten best paper awards at international conferences.

Venkat Krovi

Prof. Venkat N. Krovi is currently the Michelin Endowed SmartState Chair Professor of Vehicle Automation at Clemson University – International Center for Automotive Research. His research focuses on intelligent modulation of distributed physical-power-interactions (motions/forces) between humans and autonomous-systems to unlock the "power of the many". Research activities focus on the life-cycle treatment (design, modeling, analysis, control, implementation and verification) of a new generation of systems for realizing Human-Autonomy synergy with applications in vehicle automation, plant-automation, and defense arenas. He currently serves as the Editor-in-Chief of the ASME Journal of Mechanisms and Robotics and was the Founding EiC of the SAE Journal of Connected and Automated Vehicles. He has also taken significant leadership roles within multiple professional societies (ASME, IEEE) and currently serves on the Executive Committee of the IEEE Robotics and Automation Society.

Craig Schlenoff

Dr. Craig Schlenoff is the Group Leader of the Cognition and Collaboration Systems Group, the Associate Program Manager of the Measurement Science for Manufacturing Robotics Program, and the Project Leader of the Agility Performance of Robotic Systems project in the Intelligent Systems Division at the National Institute of Standards and Technology. His research interests include knowledge representation/ontologies, intention recognition, and performance evaluation of autonomous systems and industrial robotics. He has led multiple million-dollar projects addressing performance evaluation of advanced military technologies and agility performance of manufacturing robotic systems. He has published over 150 journal and conference papers, guest edited three journals, guest edited three books, and written four book chapters. He is currently the Associate Vice President for Standardization in the IEEE Robotics and Automation Society and the co-chair of the IEEE Robot Task Representation Working Group, was previously the chair of the IEEE Ontology for Robotics and Automation Working Group and has served as the Program Manager for the Process Engineering Program at NIST and the Director of Ontologies at VerticalNet. He also teaches two courses at the University of Maryland, College Park: "Calculus" and "Building a Manufacturing Robot Software System." He received his Bachelor's degree from the University of Maryland, his Master's degree from Rensselaer Polytechnic Institute, and his PhD from the University of Burgundy (France).

2. *Agile Industrial Robots*

Craig Schlenoff

Dr. Craig Schlenoff is the Group Leader of the Cognition and Collaboration Systems Group, the Associate Program Manager of the Measurement Science for Manufacturing Robotics Program, and the Project Leader of the Agility Performance of Robotic Systems project in the Intelligent Systems Division at the National Institute of Standards and Technology. His research interests include knowledge representation/ontologies, intention recognition, and performance evaluation of autonomous systems and industrial robotics. He has led multiple million-dollar projects addressing performance evaluation of advanced military technologies and agility performance of manufacturing robotic systems. He has published over 150 journal and conference papers, guest edited three journals, guest edited three books, and written four book chapters. He is currently the Associate Vice President for Standardization in the IEEE Robotics and Automation Society and the co-chair of the IEEE Robot Task Representation Working Group, was previously the chair of the IEEE Ontology for Robotics and Automation Working Group and has served as the Program Manager for the Process Engineering Program at NIST and the Director of Ontologies at VerticalNet. He also teaches two courses at the University of Maryland, College Park: "Calculus" and "Building a Manufacturing Robot Software System." He received his Bachelor's degree from the University of Maryland, his Master's degree from Rensselaer Polytechnic Institute, and his PhD from the University of Burgundy (France).

Zeid Kootbally

Zeid Kootbally is currently a Senior Research Associate with the Department of Aerospace and Mechanical Engineering at the University of Southern California, LA, U.S. His research interests are in automated robotic systems and more specifically in knowledge representation, control systems, and task planning for agile industrial robotics. Prior to his current research efforts, Dr. Kootbally worked at NIST (National Institute of Standards and Technology) on the PRIDE (Predictions In Dynamic Environments) project for which he modeled a level of situation awareness for autonomous ground vehicles so they are able to plan a path while avoiding any collision with static and moving objects on the road. In 2018, Dr. Kootbally received a Distinguished Associate Award from NIST (National Institute of Standards and Technology) for his contributions in the development of an international standard and supporting messaging language to enable enhanced robot agility in manufacturing applications. Dr. Kootbally also helped in many DARPA (Defense Advanced Research Projects Agency) projects for which he also received Distinguished Associate Awards from NIST. Dr. Kootbally's roles in these projects include 1) his contributions (2015) in the development of innovative techniques to secure and measure the performance of smartphones for field-deployed military applications in the ASSIST (Advanced Soldier Sensor Information System and Technology) program and 2) for his contributions (2012) in the evaluation of the performance of technologies used for the TRANSTAC (The Spoken Language Communication and Translation System for Tactical Use) program in 2012.

William P Shackleford

Mr. William P Shackleford is an Electronics Engineer in the Intelligent Systems Division of the Engineering Laboratory of the National Institute of Standards and Technology. He received the Department of Commerce Silver Medal for Scientific or Engineering Achievement in 2017 for being part of the team recognized for their technical leadership in the development of ISO/TS 15066, the first international technical specification for safe operation of collaborative industrial robot systems in workspaces shared with humans. He currently works on the Agility Performance of Robotic Systems (APRS) project. Past projects include the Real-time Control Systems (RCS) library, the Neutral Messaging Language (NML), DARPA's Learning Applied to Ground Robotics (LAGR), and the Enhanced Machine Controller (EMC) which later became LinuxCNC. He completed an MS in Computer Science from Johns Hopkins University in 2013 after a BS in Electrical Engineering from the University of Maryland in 1993.

Fred Proctor

Frederick M. Proctor was the Group Leader of the Networked Control Systems group at the U.S. National Institute of Standards and Technology (NIST) in Gaithersburg, Maryland, until his retirement in 2019. He received a BS in electrical engineering from the University of Maryland in 1986, and an MS in computer science from the Johns Hopkins University in 1993. His research interests include real-time operating systems, motion control, modeling and simulation, manufacturing process planning, industrial control cybersecurity, and support for standards activities for machine tools, robots, and industrial automation. A Past Chair of the Computers and Information in Engineering Division and the Systems and Design Technical Group of the American Society of Mechanical Engineers (ASME), he received the Dedicated Service Award. He is a recipient of the Department of Commerce Gold Medal and the Jacob Rabinow Applied Research Award. He is the developer of the Real-time Control Systems (RCS) software tool suite for distributed heterogeneous control, the Real-Time Linux Tutorial, and the founder of the open-source controller for machine tools and robots hosted at LinuxCNC.org.

Brian Antonishek

Brian Antonishek is on the staff of the Cognition and Collaboration Systems Group in the Intelligent Systems Division of the Engineering Laboratory at the National Institute of Standards and Technology. Antonishek received the Bachelor of Science degree in computer science from the University of Pittsburgh, Johnstown, Pennsylvania, in 1990 and the Master of Science degree in computer science from the University of Pittsburgh, Pittsburgh, Pennsylvania, in 1996. Before coming to NIST in 1997, he developed user interaction and scientific visualization techniques for viewing and analyzing 3D engineering data. While at NIST, he has performed research in a wide variety projects including areas such as mobile device security testing, speech translation, medical visualization and video analytics. His research areas include human robot interaction, mobile devices, video processing and analysis, and 3D web interactions.

William Harrison

William S. Harrison III is a Mechanical Research Engineer in the Department of Commerce's National Institute of Standards and Technology (NIST). William started in November of 2013 and works in the Intelligent Systems Division on the Robot Agility Framework project. William's specialty within the project is Virtual Fusion; which is the mix simulated and real components for process validation and training. His interests include virtual reality, game engines, augmented reality, and CG modeling among other things.

Anthony Downs

Anthony J. Downs is a Mechanical Engineer at the National Institute of Standards and Technology, working in the Intelligent Systems Division. He is one of the designers of the Agile Robotics for Industrial Automation Competition (ARIAC) which is currently running its fourth year in 2020 and has served as one of the

Judges for the ARIAC competition during the 2019 competition. He is the lead in the IEEE Standards Association (IEEE SA) Study Group on Robot Agility, which is currently working towards becoming a Working Group under the Robotics and Automation Society (IEEE RAS) for developing standards and test metrics for Robot Agility. He is also part of the IEEE SA Robot Task Representation Working Group which is working to develop a representation of robot tasks that is independent of the nature of the task being performed. He has received awards for his efforts contributing to the testing of robots and technology, including the 2011 TARDEC Director's Coin award for the NIST Efforts in support of the Multi Autonomous Ground-robotic International Challenge (MAGIC), the "Outstanding Information Technology Achievement in Government" from the Government Computer News (GCN) and a NIST/Department of Commerce Gold Medal for the NIST Efforts in developing and performing tests and evaluations for the DARPA Transformative Applications Project, and the 2014 NIST Edward Bennett Rosa Award for "Outstanding Achievement in or contributions to the development of meaningful and significant engineering, scientific or documentary standards either within NIST or in cooperation with other government agencies or private groups" for the work on the DHS/NIST/ASTM Standard Test Methods for Response Robots Project.

3. *State-of-the-Art in Human-Robot Interaction*

Jeremy A. Marvel

Jeremy A. Marvel is a research scientist and project leader at the U.S. National Institute of Standards and Technology (NIST) in Gaithersburg, MD. Dr. Marvel received the bachelor's degree in Computer Science from Boston University, Boston, MA, the master's degree in Computer Science from Brandeis University, Waltham, MA, and the PhD degree in Computer Engineering from Case Western Reserve University, Cleveland, OH. Prior to NIST, Dr. Marvel was a research scientist at the Institute for Research in Engineering and Applied Physics at the University of Maryland, College Park, MD. He joined the Intelligent Systems Division at NIST in 2012 and has over 15 years of robotics research experience in industry, academia, and government. His research interests include intelligent and adaptive solutions for robot applications, with particular attention paid to human-robot and robot-robot collaborations, multirobot coordination, industrial robot safety, machine learning, perception, and automated parameter optimization. Dr. Marvel currently leads a team of scientists and engineers in metrology efforts at NIST that works towards the performance evaluation of human-robot teaming, and developing tools to enable small and medium-sized enterprises to effectively deploy robot solutions.

Megan Zimmerman

Megan Zimmerman has been a computer science researcher at NIST since 2016 and has been involved in the HRI community since 2015. She received her Bachelors in Computer Science from UMBC in 2016 and is currently pursuing a Masters in Computer Science from Johns Hopkins University. Megan's primary area of expertise is in human robot interaction and alternative robot control interfaces, including Virtual Reality and Tangible User Interfaces. Currently, she is leading efforts at NIST to generate public datasets for human robot interaction research.

Shelly Bagchi

Shelly Bagchi is an Electrical Engineer at the National Institute of Standards and Technology in Gaithersburg, Maryland. She received her Masters in Electrical Engineering from the Georgia Institute of Technology in 2015, and her Bachelors in Computer Engineering from the George Washington University in 2013. Her research interests are in human-robot interaction, situational awareness, and augmented reality. She previously co-taught the introductory Artificial Intelligence class in Georgia Tech's Online Masters in Computer Science program. She has presented at several symposia and workshops, including the annual AAAI Fall Symposium Series, and participates in the ASTM Standards Committee E57 on 3D Imaging Systems. She also serves as an organizer for the "Test Methods and Metrics for HRI" Workshop which occurs annually at the ACM/IEEE International Conference on Human-Robot Interaction.

4. Human-Robot Collaboration for Advanced Manufacturing by Learning from Multi-Modal Human Demonstrations

Weitian Wang

Dr. Weitian Wang is currently a tenure-track assistant professor in the Department of Computer Science at Montclair State University. He was a postdoc in the Collaborative Robotics and Automation (CRA) Lab at Clemson University. His research focuses on collaborative robotics and smart systems, including collaborative robotics, smart manufacturing, human-robot interaction, advanced sensing technology, and machine learning. The results of Dr. Wang's work have been published in multiple peer-reviewed international journals and conference proceedings. He received several awards in his research activities such as ASME Dynamic Systems and Control Conference Robotics TC Best Paper Award (DSCC 2018). Dr. Wang is enthusiastic about STEM education and participates in numerous education and outreach programs for K-12, undergraduate, and graduate students.

Yi Chen

Yi Chen is currently pursuing a PhD degree with the Collaborative Robotics and Automation (CRA) Lab, Department of Automotive Engineering, Clemson University, Greenville, SC, USA. His research interests include collaborative robotics, machine intelligence, and autonomous driving.

Rui Li

Rui Li received her PhD degree from the University of Science and Technology of China, Hefei, China, in 2016. She is currently a Research Scholar at Clemson University International Center for Automotive Research, Greenville, SC, U.S. Her research interests include Multimodal Human-Computer Interaction, Virtual Reality, Machine Perception, Computer Vision, and Autonomous Vehicles/Robots.

Zhujun Zhang

Zhujun Zhang is currently a PhD candidate in Mechanical Engineering at Harbin Institute of Technology. His research interests focus on machine learning, computer vision, defect detection, robotics, and intelligent manufacturing.

Venkat Krovi

Prof. Venkat N. Krovi is currently the Michelin Endowed SmartState Chair Professor of Vehicle Automation at Clemson University – International Center for Automotive Research. His research focuses on intelligent modulation of distributed physical-power-interactions (motions/forces) between humans and autonomous-systems to unlock the "power of the many". Research activities focus on the life-cycle treatment (design, modeling, analysis, control, implementation and verification) of a new generation of systems for realizing Human-Autonomy synergy with applications in vehicle automation, plant-automation, and defense arenas. He currently serves as the Editor-in-Chief of the *ASME Journal of Mechanisms and Robotics* and was the Founding EiC of the SAE *Journal of Connected and Automated Vehicles*. He has also taken significant leadership roles within multiple professional societies (ASME, IEEE) and currently serves on the Executive Committee of the IEEE Robotics and Automation Society.

Yunyi Jia

Dr. Yunyi Jia is currently the McQueen Quattlebaum assistant professor in the Department of Automotive Engineering at Clemson University. He directs the Collaborative Robotics and Automation (CRA) Lab and his research focuses on robotics, autonomous vehicles, and advanced sensing systems. He has been the recipient of the 2020 SAE Ralph R. Teetor Educational Award, 2019 NSF CAREER Award, 2018 NSF CPS CRII Award, and 2017 SAE Trevor O. Jones Outstanding Paper Award. He received his PhD in Electrical Engineering from Michigan State University in 2014, MS in Control Theory and Control Engineering from South China University of Technology in 2008, and BS in Automation from National University of Defense Technology in 2005. He is a member of the IEEE, ASME, and SAE.

5. *Collaborative Industrial Robot Control: From Safe Motion to Multi-Robot Manipulation*

John T. Wen

John T. Wen is the Russell Sage Professor and Head of the Department of Electrical, Computer, and Systems Engineering at Rensselaer Polytechnic Institute. He has joint appointments in the Department of Mechanical, Aerospace, and Nuclear Engineering and the Department of Industrial and Systems Engineering. He has served as the Director of the Center for Automation Technologies and Systems (CATS), a New York State designated Center for Advanced Technology, from 2005-2013; and the Interim Director of the NSF Smart Lighting Engineering Research Center (ERC) in 2009. He was the Rensselaer representative on the Advanced Manufacturing Partnership (AMP) 2.0 operating committee from 2013 to 2014. He led the Rensselaer participation in the

Advanced Robotics for Manufacturing (ARM) Institute, a Manufacturing USA Institute awarded by the Department of Defense in 2017. He has served on the ARM Technical Advisory Council since 2017. He is the co-inventor of the Adaptive Scanning Optical Microscope (ASOM), which was licensed to Thorlabs in 2007. He has received numerous honors and awards, including the 2013 IEEE Control Systems Society Transition to Practice Award, the Overseas Assessor for the Chinese Academy of Sciences from 2004 to 2009, a Senior Visiting Scientist of the Japan Society for the Promotion of Science (JSPS) in 1997, and IEEE Fellow since 2001. John Wen's research is in the area of control theory and applications, particularly for challenging problems that lie at the intersection of multiple disciplines, including robotics, material processing, thermal management, and circadian rhythm regulation.

John Wason

John Wason is the founder of Wason Technology, LLC. He received his PhD in Mechanical Engineering from Rensselaer Polytechnic Institute in 2011. He has worked on numerous projects involving complex, distributed, multidisciplinary systems. He specializes in development of automation control software, mechatronic interfaces between mechanical hardware and computer control systems, dynamic simulation, microtechnology, and control design.

Daniel Kruse

Daniel Kruse received his BS from Virginia Commonwealth University in 2011 and PhD from Rensselaer Polytechnic Institute in 2016, both in Electrical Engineering. He has been with SRI Robotics since 2017 where he is a Control Research Engineer. His research interest is in kinematic and dynamic controls, humanoid robotics, and perception engineering.

Yuan-Chih Peng

Yuan-Chih Peng received his BS in Electrical Engineering from National Chiao Tung University, Taiwan, in 2009, and MS from National Taiwan University in 2011. From 2012 to 2016, he worked as an Algorithm Engineer for capacitive touch panels at ILITEK cooperation in Taiwan. He is currently a PhD candidate at Rensselaer Polytechnic Institute in the Electrical, Computer, and Systems Engineering department. Peng is also the recipient of the Hung Hai (Foxconn)

2019 Tech Award. His research interests include multi-robot coordination, human-robot cooperation, and industrial automation.

Shuyang Chen

Shuyang Chen received his MSE degree from Johns Hopkins University in 2016. Currently he is pursuing his PhD degree in the Department of Mechanical, Aerospace, and Nuclear Engineering at Rensselaer Polytechnic Institute. His research interests lie in the intersection between machine learning and robotics control, and practical applications in an industrial environment. He is a student member of Institute of Electrical and Electronics Engineers (IEEE).

6. Blended Shared Control in Collaborative Robots

Zongyao Jin

Zongyao Jin received his BS degree in Mechanical Engineering from Harbin Engineering University, Harbin, Heilongjiang, China. He is pursuing a PhD with the Department of Mechanical Engineering, Texas A&M University, College Station, TX, U.S. His research interests include robotics, machine learning, human-robot interaction, and human-machine shared control. At Harbin Engineering University, he received the Outstanding Undergraduate Student Award of Heilongjiang Province and the Chinese National Fellowship. Before going to Texas A&M University, he was a research engineer at the Institute of Spacecraft System Engineering (ISSE) of China Academy of Space Technology (CAST). His research and teaching work at Texas A&M University has led him to the James J. Cain Award for Outstanding Graduate Student Achievement and the James J. Cain Graduate Student Teaching Award.

Prabhakar R. Pagilla

Prabhakar Pagilla received his PhD in mechanical engineering from the University of California at Berkeley in 1996. He is currently the Associate Department Head and James J. Cain Professor II of Mechanical Engineering at Texas A&M University, College Station, TX, U.S. His research interests include modeling and control-related problems in robotics/mechatronics, roll-to-roll manufacturing systems, connected and autonomous vehicles, and large-scale nonlinear dynamic systems.

7. Learning and Coordination of Movement Primitives for Bimanual Manipulation Tasks Using Concurrent Synchronization

Ashwin P. Dani

Dr. Ashwin P. Dani received the MS and PhD degrees from the University of Florida (UF), Gainesville, FL, U.S., in 2008 and 2011, respectively. He was a Postdoctoral Research Associate at the University of Illinois at Urbana–Champaign, IL, U.S. In 2013, he joined the Faculty of Electrical and Computer Engineering (ECE), University of Connecticut, Storrs, CT, U.S., as an Assistant Professor, where he is currently an Associate Professor. He has authored over 50 technical journal and conference papers and several book chapters. His current research interests include machine learning for control, human–robot collaboration, and perception. He serves as a member of conference editorial board of the IEEE Control Systems Society (CSS). His work has been recognized by the Tammy L. Blair Best Student Paper Award–1st Runner-up in 2016, the ASME Dynamics Systems and Controls Conference Best Student Robotics Paper Award in 2015, the IEEE CSS Video Contest Award in 2015, the UConn's Outstanding Teaching Award from ECE in 2015, and the AAUP-UConn Chapter's Teaching Innovation Award.

Iman Salehi

Iman Salehi received his Master's degree from the Department of Electrical and Computer Engineering at the University of Hartford in 2015. He is currently a Graduate Fellow of the UTC Institute for Advanced Systems Engineering, working toward his PhD in the Robotics and Controls Lab at the University of Connecticut, Storrs, CT, U.S. His research interests include safe learning for control, human-robot interaction and system identification and robot learning.

Harish Ravichandar

Dr. Harish Ravichandar is currently a Research Scientist in the School of Interactive Computing at Georgia Institute of Technology, where he joined as a Postdoctoral Fellow in 2018. He received his PhD in 2018 from the University of Connecticut, where he was a Graduate Fellow of the UTC Institute for Advanced Systems Engineering, and his MS from the University of Florida in 2014. Dr. Ravichandar's research interests include robot learning, human-robot interaction, and multi-agent systems. His work has been recognized by an Outstanding

Postdoctoral Research Award (2019) at Georgia Tech, a Best Robotics Student Paper Award (2015) at the ASME Dynamic Systems and Control Conference, and an IEEE CSS Video Contest Award (2015).

Gang Yao

Gang Yao received the MS degree from the University of Connecticut Storrs, CT, U.S., where he is currently pursuing a PhD with the Department of Electrical and Computer Engineering. His current research interests are object tracking, machine learning, and robotics. He was a recipient of the Tammy L. Blair Best Student Paper Award, First Runner-up at the 2016 19th International Conference on Information Fusion.

8. *Advances in Robot Technology Supporting Low-Volume/High-Mix Small Part Assembly Operations*

Joe Falco

Joe Falco is an engineer in the Intelligent Systems Division of the National Institute of Standards and Technology (NIST) within the United States Department of Commerce. He holds a BS in Mechanical Engineering from the University of Massachusetts and an MS in Computer Science from Johns Hopkins University. His most recent work has been performed within the NIST Measurement Science for Manufacturing Robotics Program and is focused on robot standards and performance metrics in the areas of robotic grasping, manipulation and assembly as well as the safety aspects of human-robot collaboration. He is a member of the IEEE RAS TC on Robotic Hands, Grasping, and Manipulation where he leads an effort in the development of performance benchmarks. He was a co-organizer of the IEEE IROS 2016, 2017, and 2019 Robotic Grasping and Manipulation Competitions. He is a member of the RIA R15 Robot Standards Approval Committee and serves as an ANSI Technical Advisor to ISO 299 with a focused effort on industrial robot safety.

Karl Van Wyk

Karl Van Wyk received the bachelor's degree in mechanical engineering from Vanderbilt University, Nashville, TN, U.S. in 2009, and the MS and PhD degrees in mechanical engineering from the University of Florida, Gainesville, FL, U.S. in

2011 and 2014, respectively. During his graduate research, he developed tactile-based grasp control with NASA's Robonaut 2 and Valkyrie humanoid platforms. From 2014 to 2018, he was a Research Scientist with the Intelligent Systems Division, National Institute of Standards and Technology, Gaithersburg, MD, U.S. During this time, he researched forced-based grasping and manipulation control algorithms and helped develop end-effector performance tests and task-level performance tests. Currently, he is a Research Scientist for Nvidia where he pursues his research interest in dynamics and control of robotic systems, machine learning, and highly sensorized and actuated robotic hands.

Kenneth Kimble

Kenneth Kimble is a Mechanical Engineer working for the National Institute of Standards and Technology (NIST). He received his BS degree in 2014 from Frostburg State University with a major in Materials Engineering and a minor in Physics. He works on the Grasping, Manipulation, and Contact safety performance of robotic systems designing test methods that benchmark performance of collaborative robot systems. His recent work has been in developing a low-cost test dummy artifact that can be used to test potentially dangerous interactions between a collaborative robot and a human. He has developed three task boards for benchmarking robotic arm performance on industrial assembly-based tasks that are being adopted by researchers and manufactures world-wide. He also works on the Standard Test Methods for Response Robots Project where he designs, models, and prototypes test methods to be used for testing a variety of disaster response robots.

9. A Smart Companion Robot for Automotive Assembly

Jasprit Singh Gill

Dr. Jasprit Singh Gill is a Senior Software Engineer for Motion Planning at BlueSpace.ai Inc. His research focus is behavior prediction and planning for autonomous vehicles in road traffic environments. Some of his distinguished academic projects at Clemson University are Deep Orange 8, where he served as a software architect for reimagining a full-scale autonomous vehicle platform from ground up, and Advanced Robotics for Manufacturing based Smart Companion Robot, where he was involved in optimizing the navigation as well as the SLAM modules on various industry-grade robots for their operational design domains. In addition to the academic experience, Dr. Gill has over 8 years of industry based technical leadership experience with embedded software development. He received his BE in Instrumentation Engineering (2003) from Mumbai University and his PhD in Automotive Engineering (2019) from Clemson University International Center for Automotive Research.

Yi Chen

Yi Chen is currently pursuing a PhD with the Collaborative Robotics and Automation Laboratory, Department of Automotive Engineering, Clemson University, Greenville, SC, U.S. His research interests include collaborative robotics, machine intelligence, and autonomous driving.

Farbod Akhavan Niaki

Farbod Akhavan Niaki is Principal Process Technology Engineer at The Timken Company. His research focus is on digital transformation in manufacturing processes, process monitoring and machining aerospace and advanced steel alloys. Prior to joining the Timken company, Dr. Niaki was a Research Assistant Professor at Clemson University International Center for Automotive Research (CU-ICAR). The research results of Dr. Niaki's work have been published in different peer-reviewed international journals and conference proceedings including ASME, and SME journals and IEEE proceeding. Dr. Niaki is also recipient of awards such as "2017 Reviewer of the Year" from *ASME Journal of Manufacturing Science and Engineering* and National Science Foundation (NSF) grant on interaction of wear and subsurface damage in machining nickel-based superalloys. Dr. Niaki received his BS and MS in Mechanical Engineering from Sharif University of Technology, Iran, and his PhD from Clemson University Department of Automotive Engineering in 2016.

Mark Tomaszewski

Mark Tomaszewski is a System Engineer for Moog Inc., a global leader in advanced motion control products. In his current role, he leads test equipment system development from requirements elicitation to deployment for commercial and military aircraft actuation and control systems. In his previous role, Mark was a Research Engineer in the Vehicle Automation group at Clemson University's International Center for Automotive Research where he provided technical leadership, training, and development support to multiple research teams. In this role, he was a key contributor to projects based in autonomous robot technology spanning application domains from advanced manufacturing to on-road vehicle autonomy. Mark holds both BS and MS degrees in Mechanical Engineering with a focus on dynamics, control, and mechatronics from University at Buffalo, The State University of New York.

Weitian Wang

Dr. Weitian Wang is currently a tenure-track assistant professor in the Department of Computer Science at Montclair State University. His research focuses on collaborative robotics and smart systems, including collaborative robotics, smart manufacturing, human-robot interaction, advanced sensing technology, and machine learning. The results of Dr. Wang's work have been published in multiple peer-reviewed international journals and conference proceedings. He received several awards in his research activities such as ASME Dynamic Systems and Control Conference Robotics TC Best Paper Award (DSCC 2018). Dr. Wang is enthusiastic about STEM education and participates in numerous education and outreach programs for K-12, undergraduate, and graduate students

Laine Mears

Laine Mears is the BMW SmartState Endowed Chair of Automotive Manufacturing, Professor and founding faculty member in the Automotive Engineering department at Clemson University. He teaches and conducts research in manufacturing quality estimation, Intelligent Machining Systems, manufacturing process design and control, and manufacturing equipment diagnostics, at the Clemson University International Center for Automotive Research. He has published over 160 peer-reviewed articles, and is the recipient of the NSF CAREER award, SAE Ralph Teetor Educational Award, the South Carolina Governor's Young Researcher Award for Excellence in Scientific Research, and the IMECHE George Stephenson Gold Medal and Thatcher Bros. Prize. He currently directs the Clemson Vehicle Assembly Center and the NSF THINKER Research Traineeship Program. In addition to academic experience, Dr. Mears has over 10 years in industry, holding positions with Hitachi Automotive and SKF Bearings as both Manufacturing Engineer and Engineering Manager in high-volume precision manufacturing environments. Applicable work in industry includes leading quality implementation teams for QS-9000 and IATF-16949 quality systems, power optimization of hard machining processes, and startup of a new bulk deformation rolling process. Dr. Mears has a BS in mechanical engineering from Virginia Tech (1993) and MS (2001) and PhD (2006) in mechanical engineering from Georgia Tech. He is a Fellow of both the American Society of Mechanical Engineers and SME, and a Senior Member of the American Society for Quality. He is a Certified Manufacturing Engineer, ASQ Certified Quality Engineer (CQE), BMW Lean Six Sigma Black Belt, and licensed Professional Engineer.

Pierluigi Pisu

Dr. Pierluigi Pisu is an Associate Professor of Automotive Engineering at the Clemson University International Center for Automotive Research with a joint appointment in the Holcombe Department of Electrical and Computer Engineering, Clemson University. He is the Leader of the Deep Orange 10 Project. He has a PhD in Electrical Engineering from The Ohio State University and a M.S. in Computer Engineering from the University of Genoa, Italy. He is an Associate Editor of the IEEE Transactions on Intelligent Transportation Systems and the IEEE Conference on Control Technology and Applications (CCTA). His research interests lie in functional safety, security, control and optimization of Cyber-Physical Systems for next generation of high performance and resilient connected and automated systems with emphasis in both theoretical formulation and virtual/hardware-in-the-loop validation. He is a recipient of the 2016 IBM Faculty Award and member of IEEE, SAE, and ASME.

Yunyi Jia

Dr. Yunyi Jia is the McQueen Quattlebaum assistant professor in the Department of Automotive Engineering at Clemson University. He directs the Collaborative Robotics and Automation (CRA) Lab and his research focuses on robotics, autonomous vehicles, and advanced sensing systems. He has been the recipient of the 2020 SAE Ralph R. Teetor Educational Award, 2019 NSF CAREER Award, 2018 NSF CPS CRII Award, and 2017 SAE Trevor O. Jones Outstanding Paper Award. He received his PhD in Electrical Engineering from Michigan State University in 2014, MS in Control Theory and Control Engineering from South China University of Technology in 2008, and BS in Automation from National University of Defense Technology in 2005. He is a member of the IEEE, ASME, and SAE.

Venkat Krovi

Prof. Venkat N. Krovi is currently the Michelin Endowed SmartState Chair Professor of Vehicle Automation at Clemson University – International Center for Automotive Research. His research focuses on intelligent modulation of distributed physical-power-interactions (motions/forces) between humans and autonomous-systems to unlock the "power of the many". Research activities focus on the life-cycle treatment (design, modeling, analysis, control, implementation and verification) of a new generation of systems for realizing Human-Autonomy synergy with applications in vehicle automation, plant-automation, and defense arenas. He currently serves as the Editor-in-Chief of the *ASME Journal of Mechanisms and Robotics* and was the Founding EiC of the SAE *Journal of Connected and Automated Vehicles*. He has also taken significant leadership roles within multiple professional societies (ASME, IEEE) and currently serves on the Executive Committee of the IEEE Robotics and Automation Society.

10. *Collaborative Robotics for Deformable Object Manipulation with Use Cases from Food Processing Industry*

Philip Long

Philip Long is a Senior Robotics Researcher at Irish Manufacturing Research (IMR), Ireland. He received a PhD in robotics from Ecole Centrale de Nantes France, his MS in advanced robotics from the University of Genova and Ecole Centrale de Nantes, and a Bachelor of Engineering from National University of Ireland Galway (NUIG). From 2014 to 2017, he was a robotics researcher at the Jules Verne Institute of Technological Research (IRT JV). From 2017 to 2019 he worked as an associate research scientist in the Electrical and Computer Engineering Department at Northeastern University. His research interests include modeling of robotic systems, sensor based control laws, closed chain kinematic systems and human robot collaboration.

Philippe Martinet

Philippe Martinet received his PhD in 1985 from the Blaise Pascal University, France. From 1990 until 2000, he was an assistant Professor with CUST in the Electrical Engineering Department, Clermont-Ferrand. From 2000 until 2011, he was Professor at the Institut Français de Mécanique Avancée (IFMA), Clermont-Ferrand. He was performing research at the Robotics and Vision Group of

LASMEA-CNRS, Clermont-Ferrand. In 2006, he spent one year as a visiting professor in ISRC at the Sungkyunkwan university in Suwon, South Korea. He was the leader of the group GRAVIR (over 74 persons) from 2001 to 2006. to From 1997 to 2011, he led the Robotic and Autonomous Complex System team (over 20 persons). From 2008 until 2011, he co-led a Joint Unit of Technology called Robotization in meat Industry, and the Korea France Joint Research Center on Cognitive Personal Transport Service Robot in Suwon (South Korea). From 2011 to 2017, he was a professor at IRCCyN. He was global coordinator of the ERASMUS MUNDUS Master program EMARO+. Since 2017, he is Research Director at INRIA. His activities span robot visual servoing, control of autonomous guided vehicles, and the modelling/identification/control of redundant and parallel robot.

Taskin Padir

Dr. Taskin Padir is an Associate Professor of Robotics, and the Founding Director of the Institute for Experiential Robotics at Northeastern University. Dr. Padir obtained his PhD and MS in electrical and computer engineering from Purdue University. He holds a BS in electrical and electronics engineering from the Middle East Technical University in Turkey. His expertise is in design and control of robot systems, supervised autonomy in human-robot systems, shared autonomy for intelligent vehicles, and human-in-the-loop control systems. His projects have been sponsored by NSF, NASA, DOE-EM, DARPA, DoD, Commonwealth of Massachusetts, and many industry partners. Professor Padir led project teams for the NASA Sample Return Robot Centennial Challenge, SmartAmerica Challenge and the DARPA Robotics Challenge. He also leads one of two research groups selected by NASA to develop autonomy for humanoid robot Valkyrie. Dr. Padir is an Editor for the International Conference for Robotics and Automation.

11. *Collaborative Robots for Assembly of Large-scale Structures*

Ashis G. Banerjee

Dr. Ashis G. Banerjee is an Assistant Professor of Industrial & Systems Engineering and Mechanical Engineering at the University of Washington. Prior to his current appointment, he was a Research Scientist at General Electric Global Research. Before that, he was a Research Scientist and Postdoctoral Associate at the Massachusetts Institute of Technology. He obtained his PhD and MS in

Mechanical Engineering from the University of Maryland, College Park, and BTech in Manufacturing Science and Engineering from the Indian Institute of Technology, Kharagpur. Dr. Banerjee has published more than 50 articles in peer-reviewed journals and conference proceedings. His research interests include digital manufacturing, predictive and prescriptive analytics, and autonomous robotics. He serves as an Associate Editor for *the Journal of Micro-Bio Robotics*, *IEEE Robotics and Automation Letters*, and on the Conference Editorial Board of the IEEE International Conference on Robotics and Automation, IEEE International Conference on Automation Science and Engineering, and IEEE/RSJ International Conference on Intelligent Robots and Systems. Dr. Banerjee has received several honors including the 2019 Amazon Research Award, the 2012 Most Cited Paper Award from the Computer-Aided Design journal, the 2009 Best Dissertation Award from the Department of Mechanical Engineering, and the 2009 George Harhalakis Outstanding Systems Engineering Graduate Student Award from the Institute for Systems Research at the University of Maryland. He was also nominated for the Big-on-Small Award at the 2019 International Conference on Manipulation, Automation and Robotics at Small Scales.

12. *Robotic Finishing of Geometrically Complex Parts*

Ariyan M. Kabir

Dr. Ariyan Kabir is the co-founder and CEO of GrayMatter Robotics. Before that, he was a Postdoctoral Researcher at the University of Southern California (USC). He completed his PhD from USC with a research focus on artificial intelligence for robotics. His interests are in planning and learning algorithms for high degrees of freedom robotic systems. He is developing algorithmic foundations to find near-optimal solutions for computationally hard problems in real-time. He led the USC team to the finals of the 2017 KUKA Innovation Award and showcased robotic finishing technology at the Hannover Messe. Ariyan has won one best paper award and two best poster awards.

Prahar M. Bhatt

Prahar M. Bhatt is a PhD student at the Aerospace and Mechanical Engineering Department at the University of Southern California (USC). He is currently working at the USC Center for Advanced Manufacturing. Prahar's interests include artificial intelligence, motion planning, machine learning, non-linear optimization, robotics, and system design. He has obtained his master's degree focused in Aerospace Engineering from the University of Illinois at Urbana-Champaign and his bachelor's degree in Mechanical Engineering from Nirma University, India.

Brual C. Shah

Dr. Brual C. Shah is Research Scientist in the Department of Aerospace and Mechanical Engineering in Viterbi School of Engineering at the University of Southern California. He received his Ph.D. in Mechanical Engineering from the University of Maryland, College Park. Dr. Shah has published five journal articles and conference papers, and one patent. He has also received a best paper award for one of his conference papers. Dr. Shah has received 1st Prize in Agile Robotics for Industrial Automation Competition (ARIAC) competition organized by National Institute of Science and Technology (NIST). Dr. Shah's interests are in making Intelligent decision-making algorithms for realizing operations of autonomous systems. His current research includes developing Motion Planning, Optimization, and Machine Learning algorithms for Mobile Robots and Industrial manipulators. He is a member of the American Society of Mechanical Engineers (ASME) and Institute of Electrical and Electronics Engineers (IEEE).

Satyandra K. Gupta

Dr. Satyandra K. Gupta is Smith International Professor in the Department of Aerospace and Mechanical Engineering and Department of Computer Science in Viterbi School of Engineering at the University of Southern California. He served as a program director for the National Robotics Initiative at the National Science Foundation from September 2012 to September 2014. Dr. Gupta's interests are in the area of physics-aware decision making to facilitate and advance the state of automation. He has published more than three hundred fifty technical articles. He is a fellow of the American Society of Mechanical Engineers (ASME), Institute of Electrical and Electronics Engineers (IEEE), and Society of Manufacturing Engineers (SME). He serves as editor of the *ASME Journal of Computing and Information Science in Engineering*. Dr. Gupta has received numerous honors and awards for his scholarly contributions. Representative examples include a Young Investigator Award from the Office of Naval Research in 2000, Robert W. Galvin Outstanding Young Manufacturing Engineer Award from the Society of Manufacturing Engineers in 2001, CAREER Award from the National Science Foundation in 2001, Presidential Early Career Award for Scientists and Engineers in 2001, Invention of the Year Award at the University of Maryland in 2007, Kos

Ishii-Toshiba Award from ASME in 2011, Excellence in Research Award from ASME Computers and Information in Engineering Division in 2013, and Distinguished Alumnus Award from Indian Institute of Technology, Roorkee in 2014. He has also received ten best paper awards at international conferences.

13. *Advancing Capabilities of Industrial Robots Through Evaluation, Benchmarking, and Characterization*

Adam Norton

Adam Norton is the Associate Director of the New England Robotics Validation and Experimentation (NERVE) Center at the University of Massachusetts Lowell. His research interests include the design of robot control interfaces, evaluation methods for robots and end users, and using robotics for outreach with students. Adam has developed metrics and evaluation methods for autonomous industrial vehicles, robotic manipulators, exoskeletons, response robots, and human-robot interaction through funded research projects by the Advanced Robotics for Manufacturing (ARM) Institute, the U.S. Army Combat Capabilities Development Command Soldier Center (CCDC-SC), DARPA, the National Institute of Standards and Technology (NIST), the National Science Foundation, and the Office of Naval Research. Adam is an active voting member and developer of test methods on three standards committees: ASTM E54.09 Committee on Homeland Security Applications, Subcommittee on Response Robots, ASTM F45 Committee on Driverless Automatic Guided Industrial Vehicles, and ASTM F48 Committee on Exoskeletons and Exosuits.

Elena Messina

Elena Messina leads the Manipulation & Mobility Systems Group of the Intelligent Systems Division at the U.S. National Institute of Standards and Technology (NIST). Her current responsibilities include managing the Measurement Science for Manufacturing Program, which is focused on advancing the capabilities of agile and autonomous collaborative robots through the definition of performance requirements, metrics, test methods, tools, and testbeds. She is internationally recognized for her work in the development of performance metrics and evaluation methodologies for robotic and autonomous systems. Elena founded key efforts to develop test methodologies for measuring performance of robots, which range from long-term use of robotic competitions to drive innovation to consensus standards for evaluating robotic components and systems. Elena has over 165 publications and is co-editor of several books, including "Intelligent Vehicle Systems: A 4D/RCS Approach," "Performance Evaluation and Benchmarking of Intelligent Systems," and "Autonomous Industrial Vehicles: From the Laboratory to the Factory Floor." Her awards and recognition include three Department of Commerce Bronze Medals for Superior Performance and Technical Leadership, the Edward Bennet Rosa Award for research and development leading to standardized test methods for emergency response robots, and IEEE Robotics & Automation Society Distinguished Lecturer. Prior to joining NIST in 1994, Elena held engineering and management positions in private industry, developing solid modeling products at the Structural Dynamics Research Corporation and advancing industrial robot capabilities at Cincinnati Milacron. She received a degree in Engineering Science from the University of Cincinnati.

Holly Yanco

Dr. Holly Yanco is a Distinguished University Professor, Professor of Computer Science, and Director of the New England Robotics Validation and Experimentation (NERVE) Center at the University of Massachusetts Lowell. Her research interests include human-robot interaction, robot autonomy, fostering trust of autonomous systems, evaluation metrics and methods for robot systems, and the use of robots in K-12 education to broaden participation in computer science. Application domains for her research include assistive technology, urban search and rescue, manufacturing, exoskeletons, and robot manipulation. Yanco's research has been funded by the National Science Foundation, including a CAREER Award, the Army Research Office, the Advanced Robotics for Manufacturing (ARM) Institute, DARPA, DOE-EM, NASA, NIST, Google, Microsoft, and Verizon. Yanco is Co-Chair of the Massachusetts Technology Leadership Council's Robotics Cluster, served as Co-Chair of the Steering Committee for the ACM/IEEE Conference on Human-Robot Interaction and Journal of Human-Robot Interaction from 2013-2016, and was a member of the Executive Council of the Association for the Advancement of Artificial Intelligence (AAAI) from 2006 to 2009. Her awards include a Commonwealth of Massachusetts Citation for Outstanding Performance, Mass High Tech's Women to Watch Award, and a Premier Courseware Award from the National Engineering Education Delivery System (NEEDS). Yanco has a PhD and MS in Computer Science from the Massachusetts Institute of Technology and a BA in Computer Science and Philosophy from Wellesley College.

© 2020 World Scientific Publishing Company
https://doi.org/10.1142/9789811222849_0001

Chapter 1

Introduction

Satyandra K. Gupta, Venkat Krovi, and Craig Schlenoff

Manufacturing is the staged transformation of raw materials into finished goods (using human-labor, machines, tools, mechanical, chemical, or biological processing) on a large scale. The production-line represents a key innovation of the industrial revolution. The principal mass-manufacturing modality of the 20th century robotics and automation technologies are critical to various manufacturing industries by virtue of their ability to dramatically increase precision, relieve boredom, and increase throughput and productivity.

Worthy of note, manufacturing operations are increasingly becoming lean with just-in-time supply-chain and logistics operations in order to keep them economically feasible. Autonomous transportation for "last-mile logistics" — to-and-from the loading-dock to local-inventory-holds to the production-line — promises revolutionary improvements in speed, efficiency, safety, and reliability. Success and productivity depend upon synchronized orchestration of humans and automation which can occur at various spatio-temporal scales. There is a significant need for movement of people and materials between multiple physical locations — with enormous value unlocked by overcoming the high-cost and inflexible fixed-automation (conveyor-belts, etc.) and the engendered implicit lock-in.

The recent megatrends of reshoring of U.S. manufacturing and securing the supply chain, coupled with the shortage of skilled-labor have created a renewed interest in automating the dull-dumb-dirty-dangerous tasks while retaining flexibility to adjust. While monolithic fenced robots or even roboticized production lines may have helped kick off the process, the 4th Industrial Revolution (networked cyber-physical robotic systems) has supercharged the diversity of opportunities, implementations, and realized-value.

Current megatrends in the manufacturing arena include: "mass production while permitting customization in lot-sizes-of-one", "digitalization to gain digitally-enabled insight into a traditionally opaque analog world", "cloud-manufacturing systems", "scaling-up the production of smart intelligent systems". Even when workers are affordable, the next generation of miniaturized, complex products with short life-cycles requires assembly adaptability, precision, and reliability beyond the skills of human workers.

Advances in automation have provided for sustained productivity increases and manufacturing growth over the past decade. Sustaining this growth will require automation to become more flexible, enabling the automation of tasks that require a high degree of human dexterity and the ability to react to unforeseen circumstances. Applying robots is a promising approach, but their traditional program-by-teaching model takes considerable time, requires extensive expertise, and does not lend itself to tasks that require adaptability. This has kept robots in high-volume, repetitive operations. Historically, industrial robot use was limited to mass production applications in automotive and electronics applications. In these applications, robots are placed in carefully designed cells and robots repeat preprogrammed motions. Often very limited number of simple sensors are integrated in robotic cells. Humans cannot enter the robotic cells while the cell is in operation. Robotic cells in traditional applications also utilize custom designed fixtures and tools. These methods increase the upfront cost of a robotic system and they can only be useful in mass production applications.

Another way to describe this is that robots are not considered agile. But, in order for them to be useful to small manufacturers and to also allow larger manufacturers to offer more automated customization of high-volume parts, they need to be. Humans are generally agile, but there is a lot that goes into allowing them to be so. They need to 1) understand what they are capable of doing (e.g., how much they can lift, how far they can reach), 2) understand characteristics of objects in the environment (e.g., how much they weigh, where they can be grasped, what function they can provide), 3) be able to reason over information (e.g., that an object is too heavy to lift, but they can push it to the correct location), and 4) be able to develop a plan, often on the fly, with respect to how they can use this information to accomplish their goal (e.g., move a part from the parts bin to the work area). Robots must be programmed to have these same capabilities.

Robots have been precluded from low-volume, time-critical, and flexible projects. Off-line programming of robots is possible, similar to the computer-aided manufacturing (CAM) method widely used for machine tools. However, the poor accuracy of robots compared with machine tools limits them to jobs with low tolerance requirements, or requires additional methods such as calibration, modeling, and external sensing to improve their accuracy.

Over the past decades, fixed infrastructure deployments (robots in cages) have made way for emerging classes of robots (e.g., mobile manipulators) and human-robot collaboration in shared spaces. In as much, the modern production-floor now offers an interesting sandbox to examine: alternate methods of realizing production (flexible automation) coupled with alternate provisioning of ancillary support between fixed (production-line), flexible (mobile robotic agents), and built infrastructure (WIFI, localization beacons).

Industrial robotics grew in deployments building upon a *general-purpose manipulator* capable of being *reprogrammed flexibly for multiple tasks*. While the former aspect is well-exercised, current deployments do not fully exploit the reprogrammability (due to a variety of reasons including complexity). Growth of collaborative robots (designed to work together with humans) has been stymied by the lack-of-awareness, change-management, and lack of effective technology use-case performance or business ROI evaluations.

However, advances and cost reduction in sensing technologies (especially laser scanning) have brought robot systems into the price range of even small-to-medium enterprises. In addition, the use of end-of-arm-tooling (EOAT) has given integrators the ability to provide faster turnaround time and utilize the same infrastructure in a high-mix, low-volume environment.

The robotic systems of tomorrow must be capable, and flexible. These systems need the capacity to perform their duties at least as well as their human counterparts, be quickly re-tasked to other operations, and cope with a wide variety of unexpected environmental and operational changes. To be successful at these tasks, these systems need to incorporate domain expertise, knowledge of their own skills and limitations, and both semantic and geometric information.

Hence, there is both considerable excitement and trepidation about the latent potential of next-generation robotics (which will enable shorter production runs, smaller factories, and higher productivity) to transform production-systems and its ability to power growth around the world. AI-enhanced robotics (e.g., with better machine vision) with other technological advances (better sensors/compute/actuation), promises to see significantly improved pricing and performance over the next decade.

New advances in the field of robotics are opening new applications for robots in manufacturing. The following is a list of notable developments in the field of robotics:

- **3D Vision**: Affordable 3D vision sensors enable robots to build internal models of the workspace. Parts in the robot can be scanned and obstacles can be detected. This enables robots to generate and update trajectories in real time and avoid obstacles. This capability enables robots to handle multiple different types of parts in the cell without requiring manual programming.
- **Force Sensing**: Integration of force sensors on robots enables them to handle uncertainty in the workspace. Cells with force sensors can be used to prevent damage to parts and tools and also be used to ensure process quality in applications such as robotic sanding.
- **Artificial Intelligence**: Recent advances in artificial intelligence can be used to automatically generate robot instructions from high level task descriptions. This also enables robots to handle complex workspaces with static and dynamic obstacles.
- **Knowledge Representation** — New and improved ways of formally representing knowledge are allowing robots to reason over the information and infer additional information that is not explicit. This helps enable areas such as dynamic replanning and error detection and recovery.
- **Deep Learning for Object Recognition**: The use of deep learning is enabling robots to identify objects in the cell and interact with them in meaningful ways. For example, recent work shows that deep learning can be used to enable robots to grasp previously unseen objects.
- **New Control Strategies**: Traditionally position and velocity control has been used to follow programmed trajectories for robots. Impendence control and visual servo are emerging as useful control strategies for robots to exhibit intelligent behaviors. Visual servo allows robots to align parts based on features without relying on customized fixtures. Impedance control enables robots to manipulate compliant and flexible parts.
- **New Gripper Technologies**: Several new grasping technologies have emerged that range from grippers based on jamming to gecko-inspired adhesives. This is enabling robots to pick up complex and delicate parts.
- **Collaborative Robots**: The advent of human-safe robots is enabling robots and humans to work in close physical proximity. This is enabling use of robots on applications where human and robot collaboration is needed. Human and robots can work on different aspects of tasks in a shared workspace. For example, humans can perform the assembly, while robots bring parts to the cell. Human and robot can also physically

collaborate on a task. For example, robots can hold a heavy part in place while a human operator performs the fastening task.

- **Mobile Manipulation**: Mobile manipulators combine a mobile base with a manipulator. They enable robots to manipulate and transport parts. This enables robots to be utilized on material handling and machine tending applications.
- **Augmented-Reality Based Robot Programming**: Augmented reality interfaces allow human operators to program robots using gestures. Planned robot motion can be first seen on the virtual models before they are executed on the physical robots.
- **Robot Operating System (ROS)**: The advent of ROS has significantly simplified the software integration. A number of libraries are available within the ROS framework for performing basic functions such as motion planning and SLAM. A new application can be built by selecting the appropriate libraries and using ROS framework to integrate them.

Traditionally, robots have been popular in applications such as welding, painting, assembly, and material handling. The above described advances are creating opportunities for deploying robots in new applications such as:

- **Bin Picking:** In many manufacturing operations parts arrive randomly oriented in a container. This application requires picking up parts presented in a random orientation in a container. The container can contain only one type of part or multiple different types of parts. This technology is emerging as an alternative to bowl feeders.
- **Kitting:** This application requires placing the desired parts on a kit tray or pallet so that assembly station can have the parts ready for the assembly operation.
- **Machine Tending**: Manufacturing operations require parts to be placed or removed from the machine. Mobile manipulators can be used for machine tending.
- **Composite Fabrication:** Composites are increasingly getting popular. Robots are being used to manipulate composite fibers, tapes, and sheets during composite fabrication.
- **Additive Manufacturing:** Robots offer additional degrees of freedom compared to traditional additive manufacturing machines. Performing additive manufacturing with robots enables use of non-planar layers. It can be used to create parts with improved mechanical properties and improve the surface finish.

- **Inspection**: Inspecting a complex part requires moving a sensor around the part to image the part from many different viewing directions. Sensors are being mounted on robots to perform inspection.
- **Assembly of Compliant Parts:** Robots are being utilized to assemble compliant parts. Examples include wire-harness assembly.
- **Material Handling in Textile Fabrication:** Textile fabrication requires positioning the material into machines. Textiles are highly flexible material. Robots are being considered as an option for performing material handling in this application.
- **Drilling:** Many aerospace applications require drilling of a large number of holes. Robots are emerging as an attractive solution for drilling holes on large structures.
- **Sanding**: Many ceramic and composite parts require sanding operation before painting. Robots are being used in sanding applications.
- **Grinding**: Many metal parts require grinding to improve surface finish. This application requires monitoring of force and surface quality. Robots are being considered for both edge chamfering and surface grinding.

© 2020 World Scientific Publishing Company
https://doi.org/10.1142/9789811222849_0002

Chapter 2

Agile Industrial Robots

Craig Schlenoff, Zeid Kootbally, William Shackleford, Fred Proctor,
Brian Antonishek, William Harrison, and Anthony Downs

2.1 Introduction

Advances in automation have provided for sustained productivity increases and manufacturing growth over the past decade. Sustaining this growth will require automation to become more agile and flexible, enabling the automation of tasks that require a high degree of human dexterity and the ability to react to unforeseen circumstances. Applying robots is one promising approach, but their traditional program-by-teaching model takes considerable time, requires extensive expertise, and does not lend itself to tasks that require adaptability. This has limited robots to high-volume, repetitive operations and precluded them from low-volume, time-critical, and flexible projects. Off-line programming of robots is possible, similar to the computer-aided manufacturing (CAM) method widely used for machine tools. However, the poor accuracy of robots compared with machine tools limits them to jobs with low tolerance requirements, or requires additional methods such as calibration, modeling, and external sensing to improve their accuracy. These methods increase the upfront cost of a robotic system. However, advances and cost reduction in sensing technologies (especially laser scanning) have brought robot systems into the price range of even small-to-medium enterprises. In addition, use of end-of-arm-tools (EOAT) has given integrators the ability to provide faster turnaround time and utilize the same infrastructure in a high-mix, low-volume environment.

The robotic systems of tomorrow must be capable and flexible. These systems need the capacity to perform their duties at least as well as their human counterparts, be quickly re-tasked to other operations, and cope with a wide variety of unexpected environmental and operational changes. For the purpose of this chapter, we refer to this as agility. The authors acknowledge that the term "agility" is used in other contexts in the robotics field, but we feel that this is the best term to represent the above concepts.

To be successful at these tasks, these systems need to incorporate domain expertise, knowledge of their own skills and limitations, and both semantic and geometric information. Key areas of robot agility include:

(1) The ability of a robot to be rapidly retasked without the need to shut down the robot for an extended period of time when a new operation needs to be performed.
(2) The ability of a robot to recover from errors, so that when a part is dropped, for example, the robot can assess the situation and determine the best way to proceed to accomplish the goal.
(3) The ability to quickly swap in and out robots from different manufacturers so that a company is not tied to a single robot brand.
(4) The ability for a robot to respond to changing environmental conditions, for example, when a part is not in the precise location the robot anticipated.

Humans are generally agile, but there is a lot that goes into allowing them to be so. They need to 1) understand what they are capable of doing (e.g., how much they can lift, how far they can reach), 2) understand characteristics of objects in the environment (e.g., how much they weigh), 3) be able to reason over information (e.g., that an object is too heavy to lift, but they can push it to the right location), and 4) be able to develop a plan, often on the fly, with respect to how they can use this information to accomplish their goal (e.g., move a part from the parts tray to the assembly).

A lot is needed to provide the infrastructure for a robot to be agile. At the lowest levels, a robot needs a way to internally represent information about itself, its capabilities, and attributes of objects in the environment. An IEEE Working Group, which has published the IEEE 1872 Standard (Core Ontology for Robotics and Automation),[1] is addressing this challenge. This standard provides a starting point for representing characteristics of objects in the environment and the capabilities of the robot.

Also needed is a way to neutrally represent tasks and plans so that they can be easily understood and shared among different robot systems. This is addressed through the Canonical Robot Command Language (CRCL),[2] which is a low-level messaging language for sending commands to, and receiving status from, a robot. CRCL is intended primarily to provide commands that are independent of the kinematics of the robot that executes the commands. This allows robots to be more easily swapped in and out since the robot commands are represented in a robot-agnostic format.

Equally as important, one needs a way to measure how agile a robot is. Test methods are needed to assess how well a robot can adapt to a changing environment, in which parts are dropped or are in wrong locations or when tasks suddenly change. In addition, metrics are needed to capture the key attributes to assess agility, whether it be time, accuracy, cost, or some combination of factors.

In this chapter, we will explore existing robot agility research efforts while focusing on key technologies that help to enable agility, such as the ones mentioned in the preceding paragraphs. In particular, we will look at perception, knowledge representation, task planning, motion planning, and various artificial intelligence (AI) approaches. We will then show an example of how these technologies can be put together into an overall architecture that enables robot agility in a small set of sample implementations, focusing on task failure (dropped part) and robot failure (robot breaking down). Lastly, we will describe initial efforts in developing test methods to assess robot agility, which will explore sample agility challenges and associated metrics in a robot kitting operation. We will show how these test methods are being validated via the Agile Robotics for Industrial Automation Competition (ARIAC)[a], which is a simulation-based competition. ARIAC allows teams to develop agile AI-based systems that will control robots in a simulated manufacturing factory floor. Agility challenges are introduced to the system during the production operations to see how well the systems respond.

2.2   Robot Agility and Approaches

Many definitions of agile manufacturing have emerged during the last 30 years without being opposed or contradictory to each other.[3] DeVor et al.[4] define agility as the capability of managing a turbulent environment and uncertain changes. This definition is consistent with the interpretation of various authors who define an agile company as being a business which remains competitive and stable, while both the competition and the consumer demand is changing unexpectedly.[5,6]

As a result of the multiple interpretations of the concept of agility with respect to a company, different strategies were adopted. Studies found in the literature show that agile robots for manufacturing consist of hardware and software components. One of the earliest efforts on agile manufacturing work cells was proposed by Newman et al.[7] who describe agility as a design philosophy that promotes hardware and software reuse to enable redesign for entirely new applications. The agile

---

[a](http://www.nist.gov/ariac/)

system designed by the authors is intended to achieve responsive and economical automation of batch production by reusing generic production software and equipment. Components such as flexible part feeders, fabrication of custom grippers and fixtures, and low-cost vision sensors are recommended as agile hardware components for the design of agile manufacturing systems. Software recommendations include, at least, object-oriented programming, concurrent tasks within a real-time operating system, and agile sensing. It is interesting to note agile sensing as a common component with the one described in our chapter. In this context, agile sensing refers to automated error detection and correction to achieve robust and dependable automation. Other authors paid particular attention to the introduction of new parts to the system. Quinn et al.[8] describe different well-defined tasks when new parts are added into production. A vision routine determines the pose of the part via a vision routine library and new routines for the part may need to be added if the characteristics of the part are not present in the library. Adjustments to the part feeder such as a belt change or a change in the angle of inclination may be needed to address new parts. Finally, grippers may be customized to be able to grasp new parts, thus minimizing the use of specialized hardware and tool changes during assembly.

The reduction of time and expertise to program robots is essential for agile industrial robotic systems. The predominant method of planning motion for robots is via teach programming, where an operator guides the robot through a sequence of moves using a teach pendant, recording locations at points of interest, and adding instructions for tooling. This method relies on the good repeatability of robots, which is their ability to return to a location with very small deviations, typically smaller than a millimeter. The accuracy, or the degree to which the robot's coordinates coincide with the nominal ideal coordinates of the workcell, is usually much worse, typically on the order of millimeters. While accuracy is not important for taught programs, it is essential if programs are to be computed offline using ideal workcell coordinates.

Offline programming can be combined with teach programming to combine the best features of each. In this method, a set of taught locations is made throughout the work volume at points of interest, such as the centers of delivery trays and fixtures. Small offsets to these taught locations are computed just prior to the operations, perhaps using Computer-Aided Design (CAD) information about the actual geometry of parts, or information from cameras on the actual location of objects. These computed offsets will be smaller than the computed value of the full location that would result from full offline programming, and sources of robot inaccuracy will have a correspondingly small effect.

Full offline programming requires good calibration of the robot, models of how the robot may deflect or deform under acceleration while moving or loading by the end effector, and sensors to compensate for errors that cannot be calibrated or effects that cannot be modeled. This is the case for fully agile robot systems, where teach programming is eliminated and all robot motion planning is done automatically with minimal guidance from people.

While online programming is an efficient and cost effective solution for a simple robotic system, as the process becomes more complex, the suitability of online programming decreases. On the other hand, offline programming is more suitable to manufacturers, as robots are more likely to be reconfigured multiple times to adapt to changes in production. Offline programming methods are often used in industry to reduce downtime and improve efficiency.[9] In offline programming, individual simulation components should be easy to integrate in the overall system without external help. Moreover, physics-based system-level simulations are seen as a key component to reduce the time needed to validate and verify robotic work cells. An example of such effort is the use of real-time feedback in a virtual environment to understand and process the action and reaction relationships of complex systems such as robot kinematics.[10] As we can see, a common aspect to both online and offline programming methods is the need for experts in the field. Many research efforts state that it will be more efficient to have the user use his own "language" to teach the robot a task. Learning from Demonstration (LfD) is one of these methods and refers to a task solution where the task is demonstrated by a human operator and mapped to native robot commands. Potential users of this technique are not required to be experts in the field of robotics or machine learning. In a general setting, an LfD environment consists of a robot manipulator and a motion capturing system. The demonstration can be performed in several ways. In kinesthetic teaching mode,[11] the user physically maneuvers the robot. An advantage of this method is that it helps avoid the correspondence problem, induced by the human to robot mapping function. In teleoperation mode,[12] the user manipulates the robot using software and the joints of the robot arm are appropriately translated and rotated. In motion capture mode,[13] a demonstrator performs the task without any interaction with the robot by using a motion capturing system.

2.3   Components of an Agile Industrial Robot

In this section, we explore some of the key components that are needed to make an industrial robot agile, and provide examples of what those components may look like and how they help with robot agility.

2.3.1 *Using Perception for Agility*

2.3.1.1 *What does perception mean for robots?*

For a robotic system to be able to perform agile tasks, it must first "understand" the locations and types of objects that are available for it to interact with in its workspace. That's where a perception system comes in. A perception system is the "eyes and ears" of the robot system and is used to find out exactly where objects are positioned, how they are rotated, and possibly what they are made of.

The positions and rotations of objects are calculated using various sensing devices including: visible light cameras, depth cameras, infrared cameras, and laser scanners.

Material properties can be estimated by using techniques such as spectral analysis with visible light cameras, touch sensing, or acoustic sensing. Different materials emit different acoustic signatures when tapped lightly by a probe. Clues such as these can make it possible to guess the material properties of an object and thus enable an estimation of an object's weight and/or how fragile that object might be.

2.3.1.2 *Perception devices*

There are many different types of perception devices available and they all have their advantages and disadvantages. The best choice in perception hardware comes down to exactly how much precision is needed for the perception task and which hardware will work best in the specific operating environment.

Visible light sensors, or video cameras, are well-researched perception devices and have well-established routines for getting the most from them. Image segmentation and analysis can be used to separate and locate parts in a scene[14] and calibration routines can establish where the camera is located in reference to the parts.[15]

A more recent perception device is that which uses a standard light sensing camera along with a projected matrix onto the scene which allows for the calculation of depth values for objects in the scene. These devices return corresponding point cloud data that can establish the relationship between visible light point values and their sensed depth values.

Another device that is used to measure the depth of objects in a scene is that of a laser range finding scanner, or Light Detection and Ranging (LIDAR). This device also returns point clouds that can be processed and associated with objects in a scene.

Infrared (IR) cameras can be used to measure differences in heat signatures emitted from objects which can then be used to determine the locations of objects of interest.

Motion-capture type sensing setups can also be used for perception but can be cost prohibitive and time-consuming to set up. But, the position data that they return can be extremely precise.

Another method that is not currently widely adopted but is making advances is that of touch or pressure related sensor devices. These devices can help the perception system "feel" an object in the robot's workspace. This data can give an indication of successful part grasps or even material types based on surface texture and pressure resistance of the object.

2.3.1.3   *A typical perception scenerio*

An example of a robot using a perception system to accomplish a goal is that of a robotic manufacturing part inspection station. The scene in Fig. 2.1 shows a layout of such an inspection station. It consists of a conveyor belt of newly created parts which are passing through the quality inspection station before they move on to the next manufacturing area. There is a visible light camera stationed directly above the conveyor belt which inspects the parts as they pass by. If a part fails the quality inspection, then the robot immediately removes the part from the production line.

Figure 2.2 shows a view of exactly what the vision system's camera is able to see in the robot workspace. The names and numbers at the top of the figure represent the physical X and Y position locations of the parts in the workspace along with a confidence factor that ranges from 0 to 1.0 with 1.0 being 100% confidence that a part is in the exact location that is reported. To be most helpful for the agility system to act on this reported information, the accuracy of these reported positions and object parts should be as high as possible.

2.3.2   *Knowledge Representation*

As described in Section 2.1, to be agile, a robotic system needs to understand the capabilities of its robot and the relevant objects in the work area, gather and store sensory information, make and optimize plans, execute plans, and exchange messages among its subsystems. Each of those activities requires an appropriate representation of the information involved. In addition, a robotic system needs to provide feedback to human developers or operators.

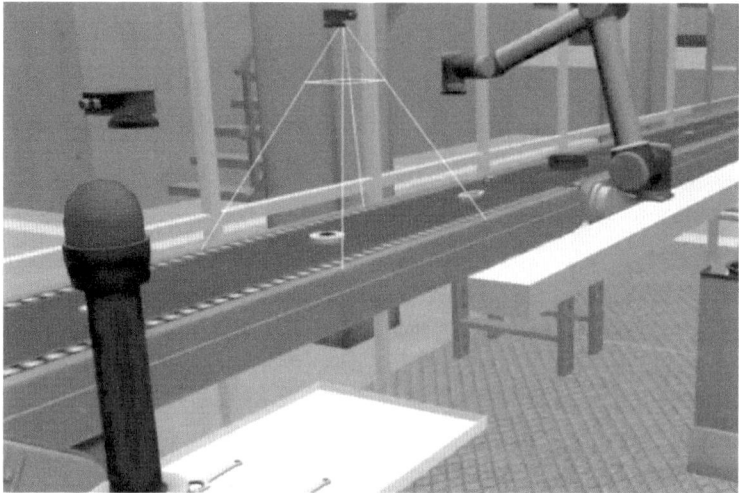

Fig. 2.1. A simulation of a part inspection robot workspace.

As described in Rowley,[16] data, information, and knowledge are often considered to form a layered pyramid with data at the bottom and knowledge at the top;
higher layers such as wisdom are sometimes added. Rowley's succinct summary
of the layers as described in two other papers is:

- data = know nothing / symbols
- information = know what / data processed to be useful
- knowledge = know how / application of data and information

Subsystems of a robotic system are computer-controlled, consume information,
and generate information. Where two or more subsystems deal with the same information, the representation of the information must be suitable for each of them, and
they must share a common understanding of the meaning of the representation. If a
subsystem requires a specialized representation of shared information, a translator
that preserves meaning while changing representation is required.

2.3.2.1 *Approaches to knowledge representation*

The first requirement of building a suitable knowledge representation for a robotic
system is to know what information is needed to carry out the system's activities.
Once components of a robotic system have been selected and scenarios for system activities have been developed, the information requirements may be obvious.
Frequently, however, it will be helpful at that stage to use a more formal method
such as activity modeling (e.g., Icam DEFinition for function modeling IDEFO[17])

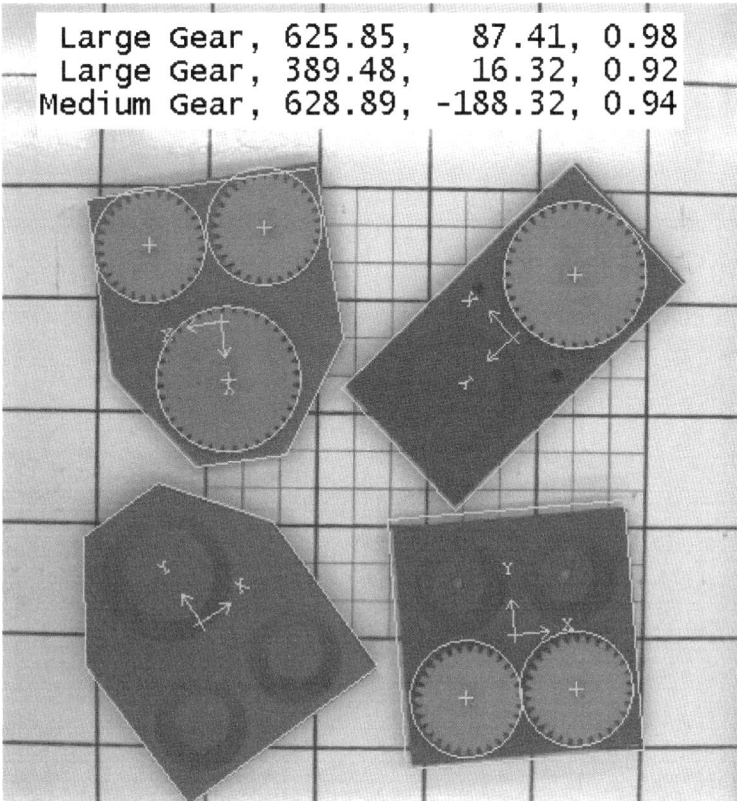

```
 Large Gear, 625.85,   87.41, 0.98
 Large Gear, 389.48,   16.32, 0.92
Medium Gear, 628.89, -188.32, 0.94
```

Fig. 2.2. View from perception system.

or data flow diagramming. Inevitably, as a robotic system is developed, it will be discovered that additional information is required. Whatever representation method is chosen, it must be amenable to changes in the model of the information during development.

The major difficulty of knowledge representation in computer-controlled systems is that only data can be stored. Information may be extracted from the data by a computer routine that understands the structure of the data. Knowledge requires "understanding" what the information means. For a human to acquire knowledge from a model of information, the model must be accompanied by a natural language description of its meaning. Often, the names used in a model provide much of the meaning to a human, but names are usually no help to a computer. A computer system might be said to have acquired knowledge if it contains a program that does something useful with the information. Some information modeling languages help the modeler by enabling natural language to be inserted in many places as part of the formal model (not as comments that might be stripped out).

Some modeling languages include methods of specifying constraints on the data beyond its structure. Languages such as Web Ontology Language (OWL)[18,19] take a small step beyond that by being logic-based, so that automatic reasoners can check for logical inconsistencies in the model and/or instances and can make inferences that are not obvious.

Widely used information modeling languages include eXtensible Markup Language (XML) Schema Definition Language (XSDL),[20–22] IDEF1X,[23] Unified Modeling Language (UML),[24] and EXPRESS[25] among others. For some languages (e.g., XSDL and EXPRESS), there are precise rules for how files of instance data must be constructed in order to be valid against the model. Also for some, there are software tools that will generate computer code in languages such as C++, Java, and Python. The code automatically builds data structures in the language, provides access functions for setting and getting the data, and provides for automatically serializing and deserializing (i.e., writing and reading) instance files. Thus, by using an appropriate modeling language, a large part of the work of building a computer program that does something useful with information can be done automatically.

Information can be stored in a file system or in a database system. It is often useful to have a mix of the two. For some information modeling languages (e.g., XSDL) and database systems, there are software tools that will automatically build a database structure from an information model and will populate the database automatically from instance files. Note that in the effort presented in this chapter, the authors translated OWL information to a graph database. The decision to map the ontology to a database was made for multiple reasons. An efficient approach was needed to store the ontology document for the ease of querying while at the same time having crucial information available for multiple robots performing pick and place operations. Moreover, during these operations, the system reads sensor data at a very high frequency rate and requires a dynamic structure that can hold data that needs to be modified and made available to other modules of the system.

In the robotics work, the authors have used XSDL and OWL for information modeling and programmed primarily in C++ and Java. We have used several automated tools for building computer code, structuring database systems, and translating between XSDL and OWL.[26] As described in Section 2.4 we have also used the Process Domain Definition Language (PDDL)[27] for expressing planning problems and plans.

2.3.2.2 *Sample knowledge representation*

A set of related information follows showing how a Cartesian point has been modeled, instantiated, and coded in our work. Some documentation and white space have been removed. The hand written XSDL model of

Listing 2.1. XSDL Model of Point — hand written.

```
<xs:complexType name="PointType">
    <xs:annotation>
      <xs:documentation>
         X, Y, and Z are the Cartesian coordinates of the Point.
      </xs:documentation>
    </xs:annotation>
    <xs:complexContent>
      <xs:extension base="DataThingType">
       <xs:sequence>
         <xs:element name="X" type="xs:decimal"/>
         <xs:element name="Y" type="xs:decimal"/>
         <xs:element name="Z" type="xs:decimal"/>
       </xs:sequence>
      </xs:extension>
    </xs:complexContent>
  </xs:complexType>
```

Listing 2.2. OWL Model of Point - generated automatically.

```
Declaration(Class(prim:Point))
AnnotationAssertion(rdfs:comment prim:Point
  "X, Y, and Z are the Cartesian coordinates of the Point.")
Declaration(DataProperty(prim:hasPoint_X))
DataPropertyDomain(prim:hasPoint_X prim:Point)
DataPropertyRange(prim:hasPoint_X xsd:decimal)
FunctionalDataProperty(prim:hasPoint_X)
EquivalentClasses(prim:Point ObjectIntersectionOf(
  DataSomeValuesFrom(prim:hasPoint_X xsd:decimal)
  DataAllValuesFrom (prim:hasPoint_X xsd:decimal)))
Declaration(DataProperty(prim:hasPoint_Y))
DataPropertyDomain(prim:hasPoint_Y prim:Point)
DataPropertyRange(prim:hasPoint_Y xsd:decimal)
FunctionalDataProperty(prim:hasPoint_Y)
EquivalentClasses(prim:Point ObjectIntersectionOf(
  DataSomeValuesFrom(prim:hasPoint_Y xsd:decimal)
  DataAllValuesFrom (prim:hasPoint_Y xsd:decimal)))
Declaration(DataProperty(prim:hasPoint_Z))
DataPropertyDomain(prim:hasPoint_Z prim:Point)
DataPropertyRange(prim:hasPoint_Z xsd:decimal)
FunctionalDataProperty(prim:hasPoint_Z)
EquivalentClasses(prim:Point ObjectIntersectionOf(
  DataSomeValuesFrom(prim:hasPoint_Z xsd:decimal)
  DataAllValuesFrom (prim:hasPoint_Z xsd:decimal)))
```

a point shown in Listing 2.1 is converted into the OWL point model shown in Listing 2.2 by our XSDL to OWL generator. The C++ Header code in Listing 2.3 is generated automatically by our XSDL to C++ generator (which also generates the class implementations). The manually generated XML point instance of Listing 2.4 could have been generated programmatically in C++ using the class implementation code. The OWL point instance in Listing 2.5 was generated automatically by our automatically generated XML to OWL translator generator.

Listing 2.3. C++ Header File Code - generated automatically.

```
class  PointType  :
  public  DataThingType
{
public :
  PointType (
    bool  printTyppIn  =  false );
  PointType (
    XmlID  *  NameIn,
    XmlDecimal  *  XIn,
    XmlDecimal  *  YIn,
    XmlDecimal  *  ZIn,
    bool  printTyppIn  =  false );
  ~PointType ();
  void  PRINTSELFDECL;
  XmlDecimal  *  X;
  XmlDecimal  *  Y;
  XmlDecimal  *  Z;
};
```

Listing 2.4. XML Point Instance - hand written.

```
<Point >
  <Name>Point1 </Name>
  <X>2.5 </X>  <Y>1 </Y>  <Z>1 </Z>
</Point >
```

Listing 2.5. OWL Point Instance - generated automatically.

```
Declaration ( NamedIndividual (: Point1 ))
ClassAssertion ( prim : Point  : Point1 )
DataProperty Assertion ( prim : hasPoint_X  : Point1   "2.500000"^^ xsd : decimal )
DataProperty Assertion ( prim : hasPoint_Y  : Point1   "1.000000"^^ xsd : decimal )
DataProperty Assertion ( prim : hasPoint_Z  : Point1   "1.000000"^^ xsd : decimal )
```

2.3.3 *Task Planning*

Task-level planning is a classical AI problem which is used to find a sequence of actions (a plan) to reach a desired goal state.[28] More particularly, the aim of research in task-level planning is to develop algorithms for specifying the robot commands required to achieve high-level goals such as "Grasp part P" and "Place part P inside tray T". This type of specification is different from the ones required for industrial robot systems, which insist on a complete specification of each motion of the robot and not simply a description of a desired goal. The task-level planning problem is commonly formalized using a suitable language, such as propositional or first-order logic, to represent task relevant actions, states, and constraints. The automation of planning in a computer program involves representing the world, actions, their effects on the world, the effects of sequences of such actions, the interaction of actions that are taking place concurrently, and controlling the search so that plans can be found with reasonable efficiency. Classical planning is a particular type of planning, which relies on the assumption that execution of the actions is the only source of change in the environment, the preconditions and effects of all actions are known, and the state of the environment is fully observable. In classical planning, actions and their preconditions and effects are presented in a planning domain while the planning problem describes the initial world model and the goal(s) to reach. Therefore, the domain is usually given as part of the system and the initial state of the planning problem is generated during runtime from sensor data to represent the current world.

An important characteristic of task-level specifications is that they are independent of the robot performing the task. This characteristic is tightly related to the agile concept, which promotes rapid and cost-efficient reuse of software and hardware components. For the automation of industrial robots, robot retasking and task allocation for new robots can really benefit from the agile approach of task-level planning. Robot retasking in manufacturing assembly may be described as the same robot building different models of a product using only one single planning domain, as long as the same robot actions are required to build the different models. In this case, the only component that changes between the assembly of these different models is the description of the current world as well as the goal(s) to reach (described in the problem), while the domain stays unchanged. Robot task allocation may occur when a robot fails and needs to be swapped out. The operations that were being carried out by the original robot need to be allocated to the new functioning robot. Since the goal to reach stays unchanged for the new robot, only the current state of the environment needs to be updated via sensor data and a new plan may be generated.

Models for classical planning do not take into account exogenous events when the only changes allowed to occur in the environment are due to actions performed by the agent.[29] Obviously, these constraints are unrealistic and unpractical when it comes to modeling an environment for an industrial robotic system. To implement an agile and robust robotic system that deals with unpredicted situations in real environments, some of the classical-planning assumptions can be relaxed to obtain more interesting non-classical models. A fundamental assumption made in classical planning is that the planner has full knowledge of the conditions under which the plan will be executed and the outcome of every action is fully predictable (no uncertainty). Contingency and probabilistic planning approaches address this issue by generating conditional plans and policies, respectively. Continuous planning has been proposed as an alternative approach to the aforementioned two approaches to deal with imperfect information about the environment, non deterministic changes, or exogenous events.[30] In this approach, a continuous loop between planning, plan execution, and execution monitoring is performed. Classical planning uses a trivial model of time that consists of a linear sequence of instantaneous states. In many real-world planning domains, the execution of certain actions can only occur during some predefined time windows where one or more necessary conditions hold. For instance, a robot can grasp an object only when the object has been placed on the table by another agent. The truth of these conditions is determined by some exogenous events that happen at known times, and that cannot be influenced by the actions available to the robot. Other robotic applications require time durations for actions, overlapping actions, and actions whose durations depend on the conditions under which they are executed. Action durations and time windows can be described with temporal planning.[31] Temporal planning can be solved with methods similar to classical planning. The main difference is that the definition of a state has to include information about the current absolute time and how far the execution of each active action has proceeded. As can be seen, task-level planning may be represented with different planning models where the choice of the model is driven by the constraints relevant to the domain.

2.3.3.1 *Robot planning task for kit building*

This section provides a complete example for a robotic kit building planning task in the Planning Domain Definition Language (PDDL). PDDL was first developed by McDermott et al.[32] in 1998 mainly to make the 1998/2000 International Planning Competition (IPC) possible, and then evolved with each competition. In order to operate, the PDDL planners require a PDDL file-set that consists of two files that specify the domain and the problem. From these files, a planner creates a plan that will take the robot from its initial state to a goal state or set of goal states. The version of PDDL used in this example is based on version 2.2.[27] For the sake of simplicity, we restrict the domain to non-concurrent actions since executing multiple robot skills at the same time is not possible without affecting each other. In this example, we model manipulation skills, such as pick and place, for an industrial robotic arm performing kit building.

Listing 2.6. PDDL preamble.

```
(define (domain kit-building-domain)
  (:requirements :strips :fluents :typing)
  (:types
     EndEffector
     Slot
     StockKeepingUnit)
```

The preamble (Listing 2.6) of a PDDL domain first states a name for the domain. This can be any name but will be needed later for the preamble of the problem file. Because PDDL is a very general language and most planners support only a subset, domains may declare requirements to inform a planner which subset are necessary to build a plan. In this example, the requirements used are :strips, :fluents, and :typing. The :strips requirement informs a planner that only the STRIPS (Stanford Research Institute Problem Solver) subset is used in the domain description. The :fluents declares the use of numeric-value fluents in the domain. A numeric-value fluent is a term with time-varying value, that is, a value that can change as a result of performing an action. The :typing requirement restricts the grounding to use only objects of a certain type for variables. The :types section inform on the type of the variables used in predicates and actions.

Listing 2.7. PDDL predicates.

```
(:predicates
  (gripper-for-sku ?gripper - EndEffector ?sku - StockKeepingUnit)
  (gripper-empty ?gripper - EndEffector)
  (slot-in-kittray ?slot - Slot ?kittray - KitTray)
  (slot-empty ?slot - Slot))
(:functions
  (current-nb-parts-in-kittray ?kittray - KitTray)
  (capacity-nb-parts-in-kittray ?kittray - KitTray))
```

Next, predicate and fluent symbols along with arities are provided (Listing 2.7). This is an important part of any domain formalization as it defines what constitutes the initial state and thus describes the model of the current world, as we will see in the problem description.

Listing 2.8. PDDL actions take-part and place-part.

```
(:action take-part
  :parameters (
    ?sku - StockKeepingUnit
    ?gripper - EndEffector)
  :precondition (and
    (gripper-for-sku ?gripper ?sku)
    (gripper-empty ?gripper))
  :effect (and
    (not(gripper-empty ?gripper))))

(:action place-part
  :parameters (
    ?slot - Slot
    ?kittray - KitTray
    ?gripper - EndEffector)
  :precondition (and
    (slot-empty ?slot)
    (slot-in-kittray ?slot ?kittray)
    (< (current-nb-parts-in-kittray ?kittray)
       (capacity-nb-parts-in-kittray ?kittray)))
  :effect (and
    (increase (current-nb-parts-in-kittray ?kittray) 1)
    (not (slot-empty ?slot))
    (gripper-empty ?gripper)))
```

PDDL actions are then defined for the current domain (Listing 2.8). To take place, predicates in the :precondition section need to be true. For the action take-part, the gripper needs to be empty and able to grasp any object of a certain type, identified by the stock keeping unit. The action place-part places the part held by the gripper inside a slot within a kit tray. For place-part to be used by the planner, the destination slot must be empty. The consequences of performing an action are denoted in the :effect section. The effects of an action are not explicitly divided into "adds" and "deletes". Instead, negative effects (deletes) are denoted by negation. For instance, after performing the action take-part, the gripper is holding an object and is described as the gripper "not" being empty. The effects for performing the action place-part include a filled slot (not empty) and an empty gripper (the object previously held has been released).

Listing 2.9. PDDL problem.

```
(define (problem kit-building-problem)
  (:domain kit-building-domain)

  (:objects
    parallel_gripper - EndEffector
    slot_1 slot_2 slot_3 - Slot
    kit_tray_1 - KitTray
    small_gear_sku - StockKeepingUnit)

  (:init
    (gripper-for-sku parallel_gripper small_gear_sku)
    (gripper-empty parallel_gripper)
    (slot-empty slot_1)
    (slot-empty slot_2)
    (slot-empty slot_3)
    (slot-in-kittray slot_1 kit_tray_1)
    (slot-in-kittray slot_2 kit_tray_1)
    (slot-in-kittray slot_3 kit_tray_1)
    (=(current-nb-parts-in-kittray kit_tray_1) 0)
    (=(capacity-nb-parts-in-kittray kit_tray_1) 3))

  (:goal (and
    (=(current-nb-parts-in-kittray kit_tray_1)
      (capacity-nb-parts-in-kittray kit_tray_1))))
)
```

A PDDL problem preamble (Listing 2.9) consists of a unique name and a reference to a domain. The reference to a domain ensures that all predicates used in the initial state and goal description are declared in the corresponding domain. In this example, the problem refers to the domain that was developed earlier in this section. The :objects section consists of objects present in the problem instance and may be automatically generated from vision data and data from the knowledge representation. The initial state description (:init section) consists of a list of all the ground atoms that are true in the initial state and initialized values for fluents. Note that all other atoms are by definition false (closed-world assumption). In this example, the initial state describes the type of objects that parallel_gripper can hold, the emptiness for the gripper and the slot, and the kit trays in which each slot is located. Values for PDDL fluents are also initialized in this section. These values come from both vision data and information from the knowledge representation. The current number of parts in kit_tray_1 is retrieved from scans performed by the vision system while the number of parts that kit_tray_1 is expected to hold is retrieved from the knowledge representation. The goal description (:goal section) is a formula of the same form as an action precondition. The provided goal state in this example is reached when the number of parts that is expected to be in kit_tray_1 matches the current number of parts in kit_tray_1, thus describing a complete kit.

Listing 2.10. Plan.

```
(take-part small_gear_sku parallel_gripper)
(place-part slot_1 parallel_gripper)
```

A plan such as the one presented in Listing 2.10 is generated from a PDDL planner that took the aforementioned domain and problem descriptions as inputs.

2.3.4 *Motion Planning*

When task planning has determined a sequence of operations, specific robot paths must be determined that carry out the operations while taking into account current conditions in the workcell, such as the actual location of parts, tooling, fixturing, and obstacles. In general, these will not be known at the time task planning is done, and they may be updated continually from sensor information. Motion planning is followed by execution of the planned paths. This execution may further refine the motion planning, possibly in several more steps, until the final output signals effect motion of the actuators. Planning of moves to target locations may take place off the robot controller, with plans consisting of a sequence of motion types (straight line motion or smooth joint motion) and associated parameters (speed or time) that are provided to the robot controller for immediate or later execution. Motion that is affected by sensor feedback, such as from cameras or force sensors, requires support within the robot controller, as the feedback conditions cannot be predicted ahead of time by external planning software.

Brady et al.[33] described the basis for the trajectory planning of motion for industrial robot applications, where a sequence of target locations is generated at points around a work volume assumed to be free of obstacles between the points. If the geometry of the path between points is not critical, motion of the individual joints from their starting to ending values can be done independently, possibly coordinating them so that they arrive at the goal location at the same time. When the geometry of the path is important, such as when moving a tool along a feature as in welding or applying adhesives, motion of the robot joints must be coordinated. This manner of control is more computationally complex, and relies on the kinematic equations of the robot structure that relate joint positions to the resulting Cartesian location and orientation. Craig[34] provides an introduction to this topic of robot kinematics. All modern industrial robots support these types of motion, and many provide more sophisticated control of path geometry, such as smooth polynomial splines.

The drawback of this common approach is that the target path points, intermediate points, and the type of path between these points must be generated before motion takes place. Once motion is initiated, it will proceed until complete or is aborted due to an exception or emergency. In an agile robot system, changes to the environment are expected, and robot motion must be robust against the intrusion of obstacles or unexpected changes in the locations of parts or other resources. This type of continually-updated motion planning was the rule rather than the exception for mobile robot and autonomous driving applications. Early work by Thrun[35] described the basis for search-based planning of robotic trajectories in this domain, which relies heavily on sensors to determine the state of the environment at every instant and plan acceptable alternatives to motion when assumptions change.

The authors have defined a robot-independent representation of motion planning and associated status, CRCL,[2] CRCL is defined in XML schema, and includes generic command and status definitions for typical industrial robots. Command messages include:

- Cartesian motions
- joint-level motions

Listing 2.11. Sample CRCL program.

```
<CRCLProgram
  <InitCanon> <CommandID>1</CommandID> </InitCanon>
  <MiddleCommand xsi:type="SetTransSpeedType">
    <CommandID>3</CommandID>
    <TransSpeed xsi:type="TransSpeedAbsoluteType">
      <Setting>1.0</Setting>
    </TransSpeed>
  </MiddleCommand>
  <MiddleCommand xsi:type="MoveThroughToType">
    <CommandID>8</CommandID>
    <MoveStraight>false</MoveStraight>
    <Waypoint>
      <Point> <X>1.5</X> <Y>1</Y> <Z>1</Z> </Point>
      <XAxis> <I>1</I> <J>0</J> <K>0</K> </XAxis>
      <ZAxis> <I>0</I> <J>0</J> <K>-1</K> </ZAxis>
    </Waypoint>
    <Waypoint>
      <Point> <X>1.5</X> <Y>1</Y> <Z>0.0001</Z> </Point>
      <XAxis> <I>1</I> <J>0</J> <K>0</K> </XAxis>
      <ZAxis> <I>0</I> <J>0</J> <K>-1</K> </ZAxis>
    </Waypoint>
    <NumPositions>2</NumPositions>
  </MiddleCommand>
  <EndCanon>
    <CommandID>41</CommandID>
  </EndCanon>
</CRCLProgram>
```

- actuating grippers and other tooling
- setting units, speeds, accelerations, and tolerances
- configuring status reports
- displaying messages

Status information includes static configuration information for the robot, and dynamic information about its current operating status and the execution of any CRCL commands. A sample CRCL program is shown in Listing 2.11, and sample status is shown in Listing 2.12.

Listing 2.12. Sample CRCL status.

```
<CRCLStatus
  <CommandStatus>
    <CommandID>1</CommandID>
    <StatusID >1</StatusID >
    <CommandState >CRCL_Working </CommandState >
  </CommandStatus>
  <JointStatuses >
    <JointStatus >
      <JointNumber >1</JointNumber>
      <JointPosition >30.0</JointPosition >
      <JointTorqueOrForce >3.7</JointTorqueOrForce >
    </JointStatus >
    <JointStatus >
      <JointNumber >3</JointNumber>
      <JointPosition >90.0</JointPosition >
      <JointVelocity >0.87</JointVelocity >
    </JointStatus >
  </JointStatuses >
  <PoseStatus >
    <Pose >
      <Point > <X>1.5</X> <Y>1</Y> <Z>1</Z> </Point>
      <XAxis> <I >1</I > <J >0</J> <K>0</K> </XAxis>
      <ZAxis> <I >0</I > <J >0</J> <K>−1</K> </ZAxis>
    </Pose >
  </PoseStatus >
  <GripperStatus  xsi:type="ParallelGripperStatusType">
    <GripperName >jaws </GripperName >
    <Separation >0.44</Separation >
  </GripperStatus >
</CRCLStatus>
```

Motion planning has been studied for 30 years, and recent advances have managed to bring the time required to find a plan for a sophisticated robot down to a few seconds. This outcome is quite promising especially for multi-jointed arms that take too long to simply pick an object up in an environment that has not been pre-engineered for the robots. With advances in computer processors in particular, research efforts are now allowing real-time planning and operations, even in large-scale manufacturing environments. With few exceptions, these approaches rely on general-purpose central processing units (CPUs) or computationally faster graphic processing units (GPUs). A relevant effort using CPUs for real-time motion planning is described by Murray et al.[36] The authors designed their new processor to perform collision detection such that the processor performs thousands of collision checks in parallel.

Another research effort was proposed by Wei et al.[37] to perform real-time motion planning. The authors proposed a real-time Robot Operating System (ROS)[b] architecture, called RT-ROS, on multi-core processors. RT-ROS provides an "integrated real-time/non-real-time task execution environment so real-time and non-real-time ROS nodes can be separately run on a real-time OS and Linux, respectively, with different processor cores". RT-ROS was implemented on a dual-core processor and experimented with real robot applications. The authors demonstrated the ability of RT-ROS to provide real-time support for the ROS platform with high performance by exploring the multi-core architecture.

2.3.5   *A Look Ahead: Artificial Intelligence Approaches*

AI in industrial robotics is best approached by describing the ideal intelligent robotics system, and this is best done by first starting from the ideal intelligent manufacturing system. From there, we can deduce how artificial intelligence may best serve the manufacturing process as a whole.

2.3.5.1   *Ideal manufacturing process*

In the ideal case, only specified designs and production goals along with their associated constraints should be needed. With this information, a multilevel intelligent agent could potentially design and execute all of the intermediate steps resulting in a fully functional order fulfillment manufacturing process. Understanding that this is the ideal case for complete intelligent manufacturing, we can then determine how the ideal robotic system might fit into such an infrastructure at both an intermediate and a final form.

An intelligent robotic system that fits into the aforementioned ideal manufacturing system needs to both understand its surroundings and understand its goals and abilities in the context of those surroundings. The ideal case would mean turning a list of specifications over to your robot and having the robot figure out everything in between.

---

[b]http://www.ros.org/

Fig. 2.3. A truly intelligent robotic system completes the job without asking how it should be done.[38]

As shown in Fig. 2.3, a truly intelligent robotic system should:

- Recognize pertinent information and objects
- Require no programming by an operator
- Function in a dynamic environment

2.3.5.2   *Recognize pertinent information*

An intelligent robotic system must have adequate understanding of the environment in which it operates. At a minimum, it must be able to recognize the components that it is charged with working.[39] While this could be categorized chiefly as robot perception, looking at it through the lens of artificial intelligence yields the potential for increased functionality and manufacturing system intelligence.

A system's ability to understand the objects in its environment can be linked to artificial neural networks[40] within the categorization of machine learning. This is not the only artificial intelligence methodology that can be applied; however, it is one of the best suited for object identification.[41]

Deep learning is a sub-category of artificial neural networks. It is responsible for advances in speech and audio recognition, image and video recognition, as well as natural language processing.[42] Deep learning is also known to be robust to errors in training data.[40]

Deep learning techniques can allow a robot to recognize components needed for processing in its environment. Once successfully applied, this would include parts both by themselves as well as randomly placed bunches of parts in bins. Furthermore, once the robot has been sufficiently trained, the system as a whole becomes resistant to errors from other parts of the process. Building from a kit, for example, can potentially be continued even when the kit may have extraneous or missing parts.

2.3.5.3 *Programming*

Programming an industrial robot is one of the most critical tasks for building a manufacturing process. Less time spent programming would result in a decrease in the time needed to bring a manufacturing process online, potentially resulting in tremendous savings for the manufacturer. Teach pendant programming and even offline programming require a skilled operator to be successful. Techniques like learn from demonstration (LfD),[43] or programming via natural language processing provide alternatives that both decrease the expertise needed for programming as well as the required time.

Of particular interest is the mix of planning and machine learning.[44] In this case, the robot can be shipped with a base level of knowledge and then given the desired specific functionality through planning. A robot could then intelligently complete operations in a very dynamic environment. Dropped parts and other errors could be solved by the robotic system without requiring any stoppage of the process.

2.3.5.4 *Functioning in a dynamic environment*

In the context of industrial robotics, a dynamic environment might include overcoming errors and adapting to order changes. The techniques discussed in Section 2.3.5.2 and Section 2.3.5.3 apply here as well. Regardless of the approach used, be it planning or machine learning, the goal is to have a system trained to a high enough level of agility such that erroneous events or planned changes do not require outside intervention.

Deep Reinforcement Learning (DRL) combined with simulation could greatly increase a robot's ability to function in a dynamic environment. DRL is a process by which an agent acts in an environment and is rewarded by taking actions that result in a desired goal.[45] DRL based methods have the potential to exceed the capabilities of a human created controller.[46] AlphaGo Zero, a model created by Google, was able to exceed human level intelligence through self play and a combination of techniques including DRL.

Though DRL is famous for its applications in games, it has also been success-fully applied to robotics. The authors of Ref. 47 were able to train a robot to insert a block into a shape sorting cube, and screw a cap onto a bottle using DRL. Additionally, the authors of Ref. 48 take this even further by using an approach that can perform more than 20 different actions. The author's models are able to do tasks including dexterous manipulation, legged locomotion and car driving.

Simulation can be used to enable DRL for robotics. The authors of Ref. 49 use simulation during the initial stages of DRL when learning attempts are likely to be the most unpredictable. After this stage DRL can then be performed on real robots where failed attempts will not result in damaged equipment.

The use of DRL with simulation means that models can experience and solve large numbers of possible challenging scenarios. The experienced scenarios could theoretically encompass a large fraction of the possible scenarios the model will face during deployment. AlphaGo Zero for example, experienced 4.9 million games during its' training. Large numbers of experienced scenarios could lead to very agile robots successfully functioning in dynamic environments.

2.3.5.5   *Enabling robot AI through training data*

All of the above possibilities presuppose that machine learning approaches can be applied. With the exception of DRL, this in turn means that there must be enough training data for the desired performance in the specified application. This is highly dependent on the application, however, given the highly controlled nature of industrial environments and the very similar pick and place tasks applied by different users. The same data sets may be useful in training similar applications.

Being that AI methodologies have not widely been applied to industrial plant robotic applications, the questions of training data and how much a challenge train-ing data will present have yet to be answered. Only with the approaching ubiquity of AI will this question be answered.

2.4   Implementing Agility

In this section, as shown in Fig. 2.4, we describe a series of small demonstra-tions that were run on real robots.[c]   The software implementing these demos is available at https://github.com/wshackle/aprs-framework (or https://github.com/

---

[c]See https://www.nist.gov/programs-projects/agility-performance-robotic-systems for videos of these demos.

wshackle/aprs-framework/archive/master.zip for a more direct download). Installation instructions are included in the README.md file. Test routines are also
included that do not require real robots nor the installation of the database to make
it easier to experiment with on any computer. There are many challenges to dealing
with large unfamiliar code bases. Hopefully working with this moderately sized
code base will be valuable practice. Students are encouraged to experiment with
modifying the code and/or changing the inputs to determine what kinds of inputs
does the system handle well and what inputs would cause it to fail. Inputs include
both data sensed from the environment and the desires of users. How does that
compare with the likelihood of receiving those inputs in the real world?

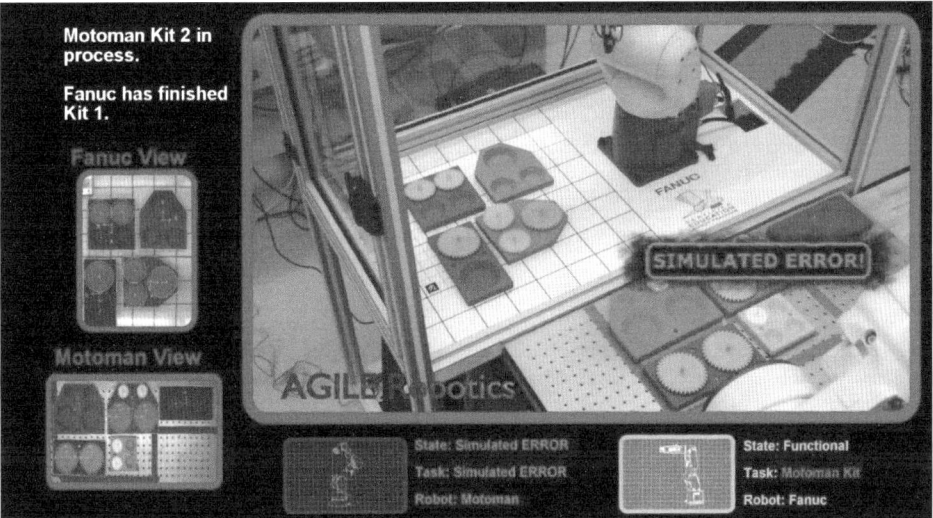

Fig. 2.4. Agility laboratory work area shared by two robots.

2.4.1 *Learning Users Intentions*

The traditional way for users to express their intentions to robots was to drive the
robot manually to perform the task while recording the low-level motions needed
to accomplish the task. Then the task can be repeated automatically as many times
as desired by replaying those low-level motions. While it might sound simple, in
practice it can be quite tedious and error prone. It often requires specialized training
for each user to operate the robot safely and efficiently. The low-level motions will
not be appropriate to be reused if the parts are in different starting positions or for
another robot to perform the same task. The problem is that users are providing far

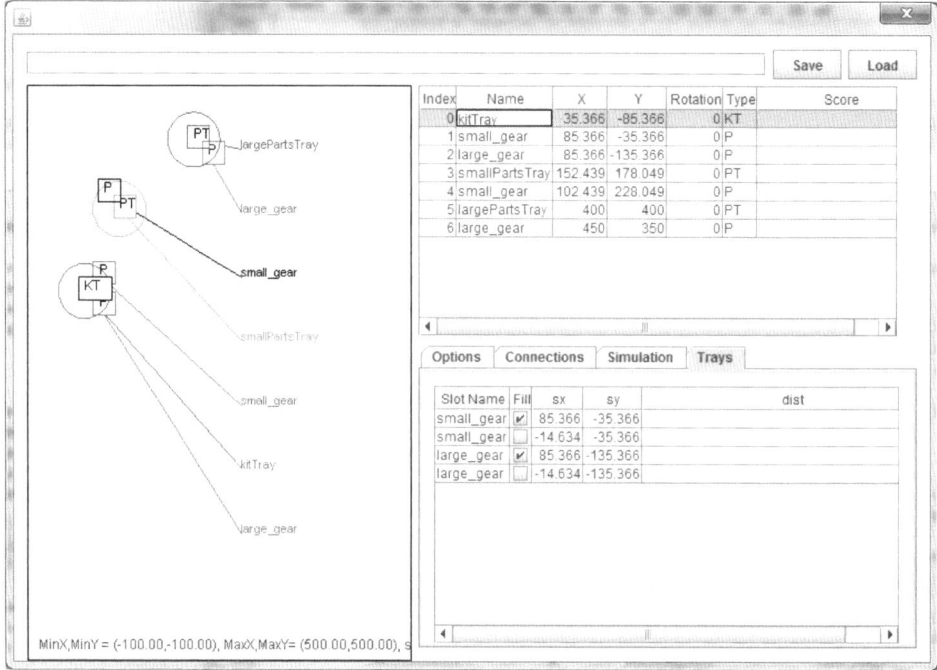

Fig. 2.5. Kitting demonstration launcher.

too many details on how the task is to be performed and not clearly indicating what the task should achieve. In this demo, we use sensor data that provides the position and orientation of parts and trays using camera(s) and computer vision algorithms previously described to determine the desired configuration to create and execute a plan to recreate that configuration. The user moves the parts by hand, presses a button to indicate the kit is in the desired configuration, and an image is captured. The image is converted to a list of parts and trays and their positions. The database is consulted to determine where the slots are relative to each tray position. The slot positions are matched with the part positions so that the full list of parts is reduced to a pairing of which parts are in which slots and which slots are empty. To see this in action, one can run the main function in the GoalLearnerTest class in the aprs.framework.learninggoals package or the "Goal Learning Test" button from the main launcher.

For the test, the user can add or subtract parts from the kit using the checkboxes in the fill column of the table in the bottom right, or move parts by dragging them in the left panel (see Fig. 2.5). The list at the top right provides the raw data that will be passed to the next stage which is just a list of parts and their positions on the real system. This is exactly the type of data provided by the computer vision and the user places real parts rather than clicking checkboxes. By editing the test class, one can change the initial positions of the parts, add or subtract parts or add or subtract slots from the trays. On the real system, rather than having any of this compiled into the program, this is retrieved from a database.

When the desired configuration is achieved and the window closed, the goal learner is passed the list of part positions. It will create a list of PDDL actions that when taken will fill a kit with a similar configuration and be repeatedly automatically executed as many times as desired (see Table 2.1). The check kits at the end can be exercised by selecting "Execute"→"Force Fake Take" from the menu during the simulation run to prevent the next part from being picked up. This will mean that the kit will be missing a part at the end and additional moves will be executed to replace it.

2.4.2   *Optimizing Plans*

In the previous demonstration, the plan was created that would take any part of the appropriate type in a parts tray. Using any part will work but it may be that some parts are closer and would result in a slightly faster time than others. The order the parts were moved was also chosen arbitrarily. There may be a slight improvement in the speed by ordering the moves such that parts that can be picked up close to where the previous part was dropped off. This demo can be executed by running the main function in the OptaplannerTest class in the aprs.framework.optaplanner package or by choosing "Optaplanner Test" from the main launcher. This will randomly generate an initial plan to pickup and place a series of parts at the drop off location. It would then display it in one window (Fig. 2.6) and then run the planner to produce a hopefully better plan (Fig. 2.7) that moves the same types of parts to the same drop off locations but with a shorter overall path.

To do this, we used OptaPlanner.[d]   In order to use OptaPlanner, one needs to provide a solution class, a planning entity class with at least one planning variable, and a scoring class (or DROOLS file).   Our solutions class is OpActionPlan in the aprs.framework.optaplanner.actionmodel package.   Our entity class is OpAction in the same package.   For scoring, we elected to implement an EasyScoreCalculator in EasyOpActionPlanScoreCalculator in the aprs.framework.optaplanner.actionmodel.score package.   The solutions class defines the domain of both the problems and solution. One instance of it is created to store the initial plan.   The plan instance contains a reference to a collection

---

[d]https://www.optaplanner.org/

Table 2.1. PDDL actions generated from the goal learner.

PDDL Action	Comment
(look-for-parts 0 largePartsTray=1 smallPartsTray=1 large_gear=2 small_gear=2 kitTray=1)	Move the robot to a position that will not occlude the camera. Wait until the database is updated from the vision system. Try up to 5 times and then fail if the vision system did not see at least the number of parts listed for each part type. (In the future a higher level system may respond to this error.)
(take-part small_gear_in_pt_1)	Take a small gear from a part tray. (Small gears in kit trays can not be used.)
(place-part empty_slot_1_for_small_gear_in_kitTray_1)	Place the part currently in the gripper in an empty slot 1 for small gears in a kit tray
(take-part sku_large_gear gripper_1)	Take a large gear from a part tray. (Large gears in kit trays can not be used.)
(place-part empty_slot_1_for_large_gear kitTray_1 gripper_1)	Place the part currently in the gripper in an empty slot 1 for large gears in a kit tray.
(look-for-parts 2)	Move the robot to a position that will not occlude the camera. Wait until the database is updated from the vision system. The data received here will be used in the check kits action later.
(clear-kits-to-check)	Clear a list of kits to check. The robot takes no action now but this may affect a later action.
(add-kit-to-check kitTray slot_2_for_small_gear=empty slot_1_for_small_gear=small_gear slot_1_for_large_gear=large_gear slot_2_for_large_gear=empty)	Add information on a kit that should have been seen. For each slot should it be empty or full and if full what kind of part should it contain.
(check-kits)	If all of the kitTrays expected with add-kit-to-check are found in the current data do nothing, otherwise such as when we failed to pickup a part issue additional take-part and place-part actions to repair/complete the kit.

of the planning entity class. As the planner runs, it changes the value of planning variables in the planning entity collection, and evaluates the resulting solution against the provided scoring method until it finds the best solution it can in the time allowed. Finally, it returns a new instance of the solution class with a reference to that collection of planning entities. In our case, the calculated score will contain two parts; the number of hard-constraints violated multiplied by -1 and the length of the resulting path using Cartesian distance multiplied by -1. We multiply by -1 to indicate violating a hard constraint or having a longer path are both bad things so higher scores mean less of them. The hard score is always considered first so plans that violate constraints are always worse than plans that do not violate constraints regardless of the length of the path. The planning variable in OpAction is indicated by the PlanningVariable annotation.

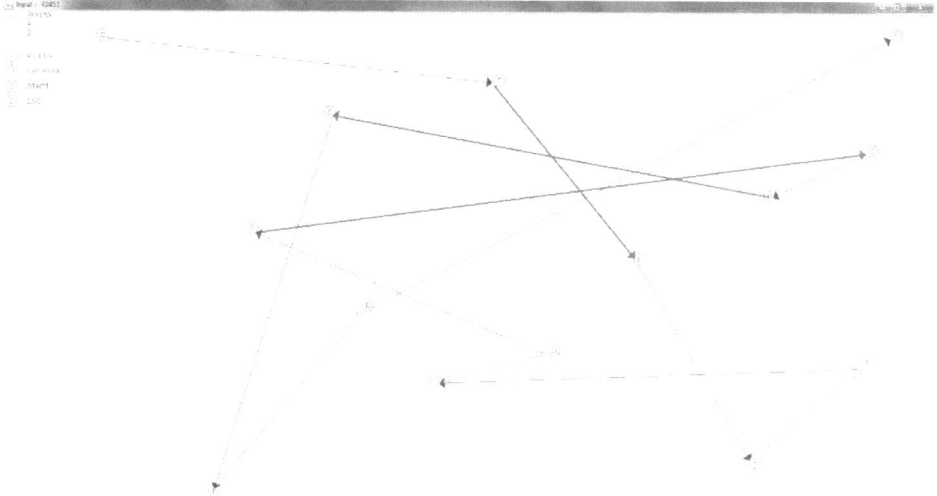

Fig. 2.6. Suboptimal plan for shared robot kitting actions.

@PlanningVariable(graphType = PlanningVariableGraphType.CHAINED,
    valueRangeProviderRefs = "possibleNextActions", "endActions")
private OpActionInterface next;

Setting the graphType to CHAINED indicates that we are not interested in exploring plans that contain loops. While such plans would clearly be scored poorly, letting the planner explore them would take much longer to find a solution. The range of the variable is indicated by the setting for valueRangeProviderRefs and correspond to annotated methods in either the entity or solutions classes. In both

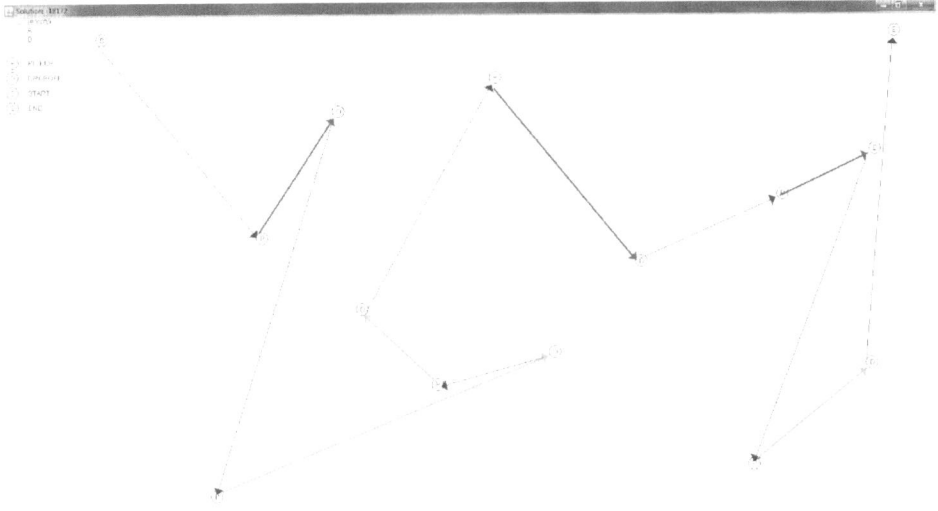

Fig. 2.7. Optimal plan.

cases, they correspond to fixed finite lists of possible values for that variable that are initialized when the initial plan is created.

```
@ValueRangeProvider(id = "possibleNextActions")
   public List⟨OpActionInterface⟩ getPossibleNextActions() {
      return possibleNextActions;
   }
```

2.5   Evaluating Industrial Robot Agility

2.5.1   *Test Methods*

The National Institute of Standards and Technology (NIST) is developing draft test methods for evaluating agility for industrial robots. These test methods are being refined by using them as the basis for ARIAC.[50] The idea was to use the iterative nature of a competition to move these agility metrics toward a state where they would be ready to go through the standardization process, while also building up interest in them in order to have a larger number of interested parties available for joining in the standards process when that time comes.

Three test methods were developed and then used as the basis for ARIAC: Baseline Kit Building, Dropped Part, and In-Process Kit Change. The Baseline Kit Building test method is the simplest of the test methods, as it has no externally applied agility challenges. The goal for the test method is to build a kit using the parts and kit tray provided in as efficient and accurate a method as possible. The other two test methods add in external agility challenges to the process. The Dropped Part test method has a goal of building the same type of kit, but at some point, while the system is moving the parts to the kit tray, a part is forced to drop, and the system is observed to see how it handles the dropped part. Does/Can it pick up the dropped part or does it need to find a duplicate part and use that to complete the kit? For the In Process Kit Change test method, the added agility challenge is that a High Priority order for a new kit comes into the system while it is building the original kit. The system must decide how to handle the higher priority kit given the current state of the workspace. Does it set aside the original kit or re-use parts from the original kit to complete the higher priority kit?

For the purposes of the competition, quantitative metrics were time and position based, and qualitative metrics included how and if the task was completed. A more detailed description and discussion of the test methods can be found in.[51]

2.5.2   *ARIAC*

NIST has conducted research in the field of robot agility and particularly robot task planning enabled through robot ontologies for quite some time. Unlike direct research, a competition provides an opportunity to address and promote a research topic. For this reason, NIST worked with the Open Source Robotics Foundation (OSRF) in creating ARIAC. The competition organizers used ARIAC as a tool to promote the concept of robot agility from a software perspective, as well as pushing the state of the art further. Additionally, ARIAC provided a testing opportunity for the agility metrics developed at NIST.

ARIAC was conducted completely in simulation using Gazebo, a Linux-based robot simulator. Teams submitted their code to OSRF where it was run and scored using an automated system. Teams from all over the world participated, most of which were from research groups.

The organizers of ARIAC had three key objectives:

(1) Promoting the idea of robot agility through task planning as a well-defined concept distinct and separate from agile manufacturing and hardware robot agility.
(2) Fostering a working relationship between industry and academia to ensure that robot agility research topics are relevant and that the findings are applied.
(3) Applying the robot agility metrics developed by NIST on manufacturing systems with different design approaches.

2.5.2.1   *Competition simulation environment*

ARIAC was conducted using an open source robot simulation program called Gazebo.[52] The organizers of ARIAC elected to conduct the competition in simulation using Gazebo for a few key reasons. The first is that using an open source robot simulation engine significantly lowers the barrier to entry for all interested parties. Potential participants are not required to purchase anything as long as they have a sufficiently powerful computer. Secondly, a simulation-based competition allowed teams to compete without requiring travel. This helps to reduce the inherent advantage teams might have when they are located close to the organizers. Finally, the ROS was used as a communication infrastructure which allowed for a clear separation between robot control code and hardware and physics simulation. This allowed for a clear evaluation of robot software agility and not perception or hardware agility.

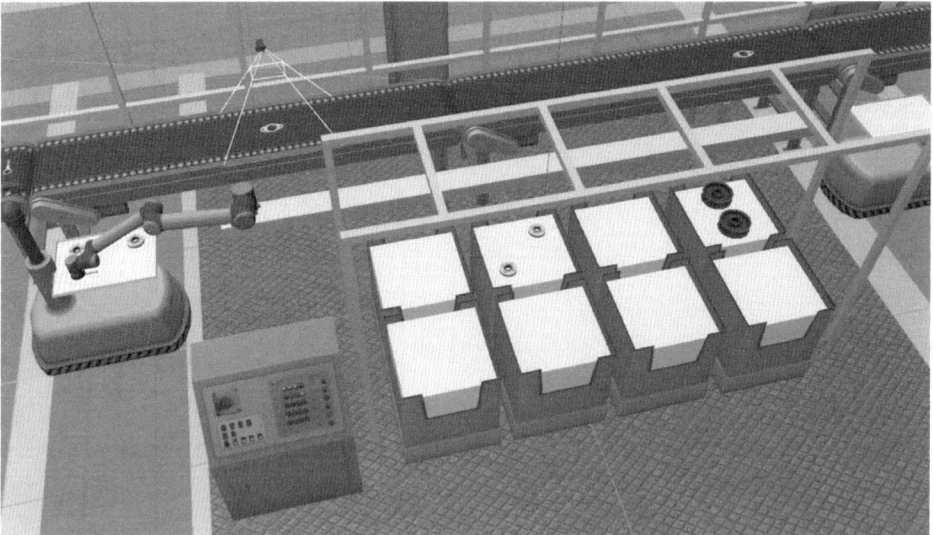

Fig. 2.8. Ideal intelligent manufacturing process.

In Fig. 2.8, the simulated environment included a single five degree of freedom robot on a rail, a conveyor for part introduction, and stationary bins which also held parts. The robot was tasked with building a kit and placing the ordered parts on an autonomous guided vehicle that would then take the finished kit away. The organizers decided on a kitting operation because it had many of the complexities of assembly without the requirement of high fidelity contact dynamics.

2.5.2.2 *The competition*

The ARIAC finals were held after a qualification phase where teams had to complete specific tasks using a simulation interface provided by the organizers. This allowed the participants to understand what would be asked of them for the competition, while also allowing the organizers to test the final competition structure. Ten teams from around the world were able to successfully complete the qualification phase.

The final competition was held remotely. Teams submitted their code to the organizers, at which point the organizers ran their code on a local system ensuring identical environments for all participants. Teams faced challenges such as forced dropped parts and changes in order requests midway through their order fulfillment. Ten teams qualified and the top three finishers presented at a conference workshop.

All of the teams who participated were able to complete all of the tasks, however, no team completed all tasks perfectly. The point spread between the top teams was distinct, implying that the challenges were neither too hard nor too easy.

Overall, ARIAC was successful in promoting robot agility; however, more will be done in coming years to help push the state of the art further. Making task challenges more difficult and including other aspects such as higher fidelity grasping will help in this regard.

2.6 Conclusion

In this chapter, we have defined what is meant by an agile industrial robot, explored various approaches to enabling robot agility, and described some of the key components needed to help make a robot agile. These components include perception, knowledge representation, task planning, and motion planning. For each of these, we provided an example of how these components can help to enable robot agility. We also explored the area of artificial intelligence and described the value that it can provide to robot agility. Lastly, we provided a web site where the reader can download some code, adjust variables, and experiment with some of the technologies described in this chapter to see how they can all come together to realize a simulated agile robot.

References

1. IEEE, IEEE Standard Ontologies for Robotics and Automation, *IEEE Std 1872-2015* , pp. 1–60 (2015), doi:10.1109/IEEESTD.2015.7084073.

2. F. Proctor, S. Balakirsky, Z. Kootbally, T. Kramer, C. Schlenoff and W. Shackleford, The Canonical Robot Command Language (CRCL), *Industrial Robot: An International Journal* **43**(5), 495–502 (2016), doi:10.1108/IR-01-2016-0037.

3. N. Dahmardeh and S. Banihashemi, Organizational Agility and Agile Manufacturing, *European Journal of Economics, Finance and Administrative Sciences* **27**, 178–184 (2010).

4. R. DeVor, R. Graves and J. Mills, Agile Manufacturing Research: Accomplishments and Opportunities, *IIE Transactions* **29**(10), 813–823 (1997).

5. S. Goldman, R. Nagel and K. Preiss, *Agile Competitors and Virtual Organizations: Strategies for Enriching the Customer*, Industrial Engineering. Van Nostrand Reinhold (1994).

6. E. Bottani, Profile and enablers of agile companies: An empirical investigation, *International Journal of Production Economics* **125**(2), 251–261 (2010).

7. W. Newman, A. Podgurski, R. D. Quinn, F. Merat, M. Branicky, N. Barendt, G. Causey, E. Haaser, Y. Kim, J. Swaminathan and V. Velasco, Design lessons for building agile manufacturing systems, *IEEE Transactions on Robotics and Automation* **16**(3), 228–238 (2000), doi:10.1109/70.850641.

8. R. Quinn, G. Causey, F. Merat, D. Sargent, DAVIDM., N. B. W. Newman, V. V. Jr, A. PODGURSKI, J.-Y. JO, L. Sterling and Y. KIM, An Agile Manufacturing Workcell Design, *IEEE Transactions* **29**(10), 901–909 (1997).

9. S. Mitsi, K.-D. Bouzakis, G. Mansour, D. Sagris and G. Maliaris, Off-line programming of an industrial robot for manufacturing, *The International Journal of Advanced Manufacturing Technology* **26**(3), 262–267 (2005).

10. J. Braumann and S. Brell-Cokcan, Real-time robot simulation and control for architectural design. In *Physical Digitality: Proceedings of the 30th eCAADe Conference, eCAADe: Conferences*, vol. 2, pp. 479–486, Prague, Czech Republic (2012).

11. S. Calinon, F. Guenter and A. Billard, On Learning, Representing, and Generalizing a Task in a Humanoid Robot, *IEEE Transactions on Systems, Man, and Cybernetics, Part B (Cybernetics)* **37**(2), 286–298 (2007), doi:10.1109/TSMCB.2006.886952.

12. A. Jha and S. S. Chiddarwar, Robot programming by demonstration using teleoperation through imitation, *Industrial Robot: An International Journal* **44**(2), 142–154 (2017), doi:10.1108/IR-03-2016-0114.

13. P. Azad, T. Asfour and R. Dillmann, Robust real-time stereo-based markerless human motion capture. In *Humanoids 2008 - 8th IEEE-RAS International Conference on Humanoid Robots*, pp. 700–707 (2008), doi:10.1109/ICHR.2008.4755975.

14. P. Wang, X. Shen, Z. Lin, S. Cohen, B. Price and A. L. Yuille, Joint object and part segmentation using deep learned potentials. In *Proceedings of the IEEE International Conference on Computer Vision*, pp. 1573–1581 (2015).

15. Z. Zhang, A flexible new technique for camera calibration, *IEEE Transactions on Pattern Analysis and Machine Intelligence* **22**(11), 1330–1334 (2000).

16. J. Rowley, The wisdom hierarchy: representations of the dikw hierarchy, *Journal of Information Science* **33**(2), 163–180 (2007), doi:10.1177/0165551506070706.

17. ISO, Syntax and semantics for idef0, *ISO 31320, Part 1* (2012).

18. World Wide Web Consortium, Owl 2 web ontology language primer (second edition), *W3C Standard* (2012a). Available at https://www.w3.org/TR/owl2-primer (Accessed November 18, 2020).

19. World Wide Web Consortium, Owl 2 web ontology language structural specification and functional-style syntax (second edition), *W3C Standard* (2012b). Available at https://www.w3.org/TR/owl2-syntax (Accessed November 18, 2020).

20. World Wide Web Consortium, Xml schema part 0: Primer second edition, *W3C Standard* (2004a). Available at https://www.w3.org/TR/xmlschema-0 (Accessed November 18, 2020).

21. World Wide Web Consortium, Xml schema part 1: Structures second edition, *W3C Standard* (2004b). Available at https://www.w3.org/TR/xmlschema-1 (Accessed November 18, 2020).

22. World Wide Web Consortium, Xml schema part 2: Datatypes second edition, *W3C Standard* (2004c). Available at https://www.w3.org/TR/xmlschema-2 (Accessed November 18, 2020).

23. ISO, Syntax and semantics for idef1x97, *ISO 31320, Part 2* (2012).

24. Object Management Group, Unified Modeling Language Version 2.5(2015). Available at http://www.omg.org/spec/UML (2015) (Accessed November 18, 2020).

25. ISO, The express language reference manual, *ISO 10303, Part 11* (1994).

26. T. Kramer, B. Marks, C. Schlenoff, S. Balakirsky, Z. Kootbally and A. Pietromartire, Software tools for xml to owl translation, *NISTIR 8068* (2014).

27. M. Fox and D. Long, PDDL2.1: An extension to PDDL for expressing temporal planning domains, *Journal of AI Research (JAIR)* **20**(1), 61–124 (2003).

28. S. Russell and P. Norvig, *Artificial Intelligence: A Modern Approach, 3rd Edition.* Pearson (2009).

29. D. Nau, M. Ghallab and P. Traverso, *Automated Planning: Theory & Practice.* Morgan Kaufmann Publishers (2004).

30. T. Keller, P. Eyerich and B. B. Nebel, Task Planning for an autonomous service robot. In R. Dillmann, J. Beyerer, U. Hanebeck and T. Schultz (eds.), *KI 2010: Advances in Artificial Intelligence.* In *KI 2010: Advances in Artificial Intelligence,* R. Dilmann, J. BEyerer, U. Hanebeck and T. Schultz (eds). Springer (2010).

31. A. Gerevini, A. Saetti and I. Serina, An Approach to Temporal Planning and Scheduling in Domains with Predictable Exogenous Events, *Journal of Artificial Intelligence Research* **25**(1), 187–231 (2006).

32. D. McDermott, M. Ghallab, A. Howe, C. Knoblock, A. Ram, M. Veloso, D. Weld and D. Wilkins, PDDL – The Planning Domain Definition Language, Tech. Rep. CVC TR-98-003/DCS TR-1165, AIPS-98 Planning Competition Committee, Yale Center for Computational Vision and Control (1998).

33. M. Brady, *Robot motion: Planning and control.* MIT Press (1982).

34. J. J. Craig, *Introduction to Robotics: Mechanics and Control*, vol. 3. Pearson Prentice Hall Upper Saddle River (2005).

35. S. Thrun, W. Burgard and D. Fox, *Probabilistic Robotics.* MIT Press (2005).

36. S. Murray, W. Floyd-Jones, Y. Qi, D. Sorin and G. Konidaris, Robot motion planning on a chip. In *Robotics: Science and Systems* (2016).

37. H. Wei, Z. Shao, Z. Huang, R. Chen, Y. Guan, J. Tan and Z. Shao, Rt-ros: A real-time ros architecture on multi-core processors, *Future Generation Computer Systems* **56** (2015), doi:10.1016/j.future.2015.05.008.

38. J. Viswanathan, Robots can do it all (2017), produced here with the expressed permission of the author.

39. C. Li, J. Bohren and G. D. Hager, Bridging the robot perception gap with mid-level vision. In *Robotics Research,* H.I. Christensen and O. Khatib (eds). Springer (2018).

40. T. M. Mitchell, *Machine Learning.* WCB (1997).

41. M. Oquab, L. Bottou, I. Laptev and J. Sivic, Is object localization for free?-weakly-supervised learning with convolutional neural networks. In *Proceedings of the IEEE Conference on Computer Vision and Pattern Recognition*, pp. 685–694 (2015).

42. L. Deng, A tutorial survey of architectures, algorithms, and applications for deep learning, *APSIPA Transactions on Signal and Information Processing* **3** (2014).

43. J. Zhang, Y. Wang and R. Xiong, Industrial robot programming by demonstration. In *International Conference on Advanced Robotics and Mechatronics (ICARM)*, pp. 300–305 (2016).

44. V. Mokhtari, L. S. Lopes and A. J. Pinho, Experience-based planning domains: An integrated learning and deliberation approach for intelligent robots, *Journal of Intelligent & Robotic Systems* **83**(3-4), 463–483 (2016).

45. Y. Li, Deep reinforcement learning: An overview, *arXiv preprint arXiv:1701.07274* (2017).

46. D. Silver, J. Schrittwieser, K. Simonyan, I. Antonoglou, A. Huang, A. Guez, T. Hubert, L. Baker, M. Lai, A. Bolton, Y. Chen, T. Lillicrap, F. Hui, L. Sifre, G. van den Driessche, T. Graepel and D. Hassabis, Mastering the game of go without human knowledge, *Nature* **550**(7676), 354 (2017).

47. S. Levine, C. Finn, T. Darrell and P. Abbeel, End-to-end training of deep visuomotor policies, *The Journal of Machine Learning Research* **17**(1), 1334–1373 (2016).

48. T. P. Lillicrap, J. J. Hunt, A. Pritzel, N. Heess, T. Erez, Y. Tassa, D. Silver and D. Wierstra, Continuous control with deep reinforcement learning, *arXiv preprint arXiv:1509.02971* (2015).

49. S. Gu, E. Holly, T. Lillicrap and S. Levine, Deep reinforcement learning for robotic manipulation with asynchronous off-policy updates. In *International Conference on Robotics and Automation (ICRA)* pp. 3389–3396 (2017).

50. N. ARIAC, Agile robotics for industrial automation competition (2017). Available at https://www.nist.gov/el/intelligent-systems-division-73500/agile-robotics-industrial-automation, (Accessed December 4, 2017).

51. A. Downs, W. Harrison and C. Schlenoff, Test Methods for Robot Agility in Manufacturing, *Industrial Robot: An International Journal* **43**(5), 563–572 (2016).

52. OSRF, Open Source Robotics Foundation - Gazebo (2014). Available at www.gazebosim.org (Accessed November 18, 2020).

© 2020 World Scientific Publishing Company
https://doi.org/10.1142/9789811210679_0003

Chapter 3

State-of-the-Art in Human-Robot Interaction

Jeremy A. Marvel, Megan Zimmerman, and Shelly Bagchi

3.1 Introduction

Popular culture has given numerous predictions regarding what the future of manufacturing will look like, and a predominant commonality between them is the focus on the relationship between human and machine. These predictions run the full gamut of human-robot interaction from benevolent to benign to malevolent. It is not without some sense of irony, however, that the general themes and proposed situations are often identical, but presented from the vantage points of different perspectives to elicit a desired response from the audience. On one extreme, the future is bright and full of chrome and translucent plastic. In stark contrast, however, other portrayals depict the future as a dystopian, smog-choked landscape. Humans and robot may be working together in either scenario (either as equals or as slaves), or the divide between human and machine may become indelibly wide (either as proof of the advancement of mankind beyond the need for laborious work, or as the depravity of existence in which the jobless masses look with envy at the robots that have stolen their means of earning a living).

Arguably, the differences in portrayal are largely philosophical, and serve merely as backdrops for a larger conflict irrelevant to the topic of manufacturing. In reality, however, it is generally accepted that the role of robots and automation will increase in the production of manufactured goods. Current trends already project the expansion of the robotics market, with significant advances in robot sensing, safety, and artificial intelligence (AI) blazing the path for exponential growth. Looking backward over the past two decades, this predicted growth seems well-founded given the significant leaps in industrial robot systems and ancillary technologies. Machine vision and robotic force control have enabled flexible factory automation. Integrated machine learning can be used to automatically adjust operational parameters to compensate for process uncertainties. There are even collaborative robot safety standards that are poised to drive the use of automation technologies in human-occupied work zones.

In traditional factory configurations, people and machines are both physically and procedurally separated. However, with the recent introduction of collaborative robots into the market, these once-rigid boundaries have started to dissolve. Robots are being freed from their cages, and the distances separating people and machine are slowly dissolving. Though their tasks on the factory floor remain largely discrete, further technological advancements are expected to promote human-robot collaboration in which the robots function as tools to enable people to be more effective at their jobs. The potential impacts of these shifts in thinking are not yet well-understood. Will they improve manufacturing quality and drive industrial innovation? Or will they result in the dehumanization of skilled labor by equating people with the machines with which they interact?

As the industry continues to evolve through the 21st century, manufacturing jobs and skill sets will grow increasingly high-tech in nature. This has the potential for redirecting the application of the unskilled labor market, and may simultaneously provide the impetus to elevate and grow the workforce toward more technical, diverse, and specialized trades. Which way the balance tilts is not necessarily foreseeable. What is clear, however, is that the practices of 50 years ago are no longer sufficient to sustain modern production and consumption of manufactured goods. Both humans and machines are integral to the future of manufacturing, and the interactions of the two are central to production success.

Evidence for a more restrained vision of the future is already witnessed in modern, non-industrial domains. The life-saving skills of physicians, pharmacists, and surgeons have been improved dramatically thanks to the introduction of robotic technologies in surgery, the treatment of cancer, and the handling of drugs. Fire fighters, police, and search-and-rescue professionals are more effective at serving and protecting the populace through the introduction of robotic platforms that enable faster responses and wider, more efficient coverage of disaster zones. The capabilities of the robots complement the skills of the human operators, and the interfaces both enable and empower situation awareness, safety, and speed of responses to issues as they occur.

The ability of a robot to effectively team and interact with human colleagues is ultimately bounded by the technological limits of the robot systems. Human-machine interfaces (HMI), system and process sensing and control, and modeling of the environment and the operational spaces all impact the effectiveness and efficiency of the human-robot team. The means and mechanisms through which people receive information about the robots' and tasks' status and performance embody the HMI. In contrast, the information and actions exchanged between people and robots by means of the user interface constitute the human-robot interaction (HRI). This chapter will present the current state-of-the-art in terms of both HMI and HRI, and the distinguishing characteristics of HMI and HRI are presented in more detail in Sections 3.3 and 3.4, respectively.

Measuring and characterizing these various elements and their impacts is a challenging endeavor, and is largely subjective with regard to the environment and application to which the robots are tasked. This, in turn, means that making intelligent decisions for optimization of the interfaces and interactions is difficult at best. As will be described later, the design choices vendors and integrators make for their systems' interfaces ultimately drive the means by which operators interact with the machines. Design decisions to push function over form are not without consequence, and it is clear that modern stereotypes of manufacturing equipment and environments are largely driven by the interface designs of the past. In all fairness, some of these stereotypes are well-founded, as equipment installed in the 1970s may still be in frequent use today. However, as older equipment is replaced or upgraded to meet modern manufacturing practices and production goals, the face of the machine is evolving.

As a developer and vendor of advanced automation, one is expected to provide a user experience that is indicative of the company's unique brand. This branding of the "feel" of the interface and interaction draws largely upon the company's legacy systems. Newer robot vendors, however, must develop their own distinct branding from scratch. These newer interfaces and interactions can introduce disruptive technologies into the market, effectively offering end-users with novel—if yet unproven—design alternatives. What looks new and innovative, however, is not always an improvement. This is a realization that is typically uncovered following the investment of capital and time into the technology. Therefore, what is needed is a set of objective metrics by which new interfaces and interactions can be assessed quickly and efficiently.

In this chapter, we will discuss the applications of HRI and HMI in industrial robotics, and will discuss topics such as collaborative robot safety, advances in HMI designs and development paradigms, and the current state of HRI. Throughout the following sections, we will present and discuss several metrics by which human-robot collaborations may be assessed, both quantitatively and qualitatively. Moreover, market and research trends will be presented to highlight the convergence (and lead time) of HRI theory with real-world application.

3.2   Humans and Robots in Industry

With the beginning of the Industrial Revolution in the late 1700s, manufacturing worldwide experienced a boom in production efficiency and output. New machines and processes, and the increased utilization of mechanical power were introduced. These gave birth to factories, accelerated technological innovations, and led to dramatic improvements in trade and economy. A century later, new innovations in chemical and metallurgical production gave rise to a second Industrial Revolution. These new manufacturing capabilities, in turn, would ultimately lead to the birth of the automotive and aerospace industries, which serves as the impetuses for future advancements in technology and production efficiency. Industry became a massive machine, churning out new goods and raw products to be distributed domestically and internationally. Within this machine, the human workers were the cogs that would endure the greatest stress.

Worldwide, worker rights and safety would also see improvements, but only as a result of large-scale organization efforts, legal battles, and numerous tragedies that would claim far too many lives. New standards for operator safety and environmental factors (such as noise and air quality) would be penned by standards bodies representing manufacturers, integrators, and end-users of factory equipment. Some of these standards would become regulatory, and be enforced by occupational health organizations and agencies in an effort to universally drive a culture of workplace safety and valuation of workforce wellbeing.

When a new technology called robotics was introduced, both employers and employees welcomed it with open arms. For the former, it was a new piece of equipment that could automate production tasks, work tirelessly day and night, and positively impact product quality and consistency. The latter group recognized that robots could assume the roles that were too dangerous or uncomfortable for laborers. This would offload the tasks likely to result in injury to the machines, and permit the skilled labor force to focus their abilities and efforts on safer and less menial tasks.

In 1961, the first industrial robot to be used in manufacturing was brought online in a General Motors die-casting plant in Trenton, New Jersey. From this point, the number and types of robots in manufacturing grew steadily. The United States and Japan were the largest consumers of robots, with the automotive industries effectively driving the development and improvement of robot hardware, control, and application technologies.

It should, therefore, be no surprise that the first robot-attributed fatalities occurred in vehicle manufacturing plants. 1979 saw the first person killed by a robot in a Ford plant in Flat Rock, Michigan. The first robot-attributed fatality in Japan would occur in 1981 in Akashi, Hyogo Prefecture. At the time, robot safety standards were nonexistent, and safe operational practices were implemented ad hoc, and were often insufficient to prevent access to hazards and operator injury. Robot safety standards would not be produced until several years later. The development of these standards will be discussed in greater detail in Section 3.2.2.

For the most part, industrial robots are large, heavy, strong, and completely unaware of their surroundings. Due to the inherently dangerous nature of robots and the applications to which they have been tasked, direct interactions between people and robots have essentially been nonexistent since robots were first introduced onto the factory floor. Indirect interactions have been accommodated by means of human-machine interfaces, the most common of which being the robot's teach pendant, ancillary graphical user interfaces through programmable logic controllers (PLCs), and simplified process interfaces such as buttons, switches, and joysticks. For the most part, robot interfaces have largely been utilitarian in nature, and designed with the process–not the user–in mind. However, in recent years, the designs and capabilities of user interfaces have changed to be more user-centric. The evolution of HMI for robotic applications is discussed in greater detail in Section 3.3.

Shortly after industrial robots were introduced to the manufacturing world, automated guided vehicles (AGVs) began appearing on factory floors. Used primarily for material handling applications, AGVs are typically classified as driverless, industrial trucks with both manual and automated functions. Historically, the control and functions of AGVs were predetermined, and their navigation determined by set guide paths. This automatic functionality and the usual lack of on-board intelligence have characteristically differentiated AGVs from mobile robots.

This distinction, however, does not necessarily reflect the current state of AGV technology. While some new AGV installations still use the archetypal set-paths model, the technological distinction between AGVs and mobile robots has been blurred due to the introduction of laser- and vision-based simultaneous localization and mapping (SLAM, e.g., Ref. 1), on-board navigation (e.g., Ref. 2), decentralized control (e.g., Ref. 3), and localized collision avoidance (e.g., Ref. 4) for AGV platforms.

Given the wide spectrum of robot capabilities, designs, and applications, what has driven the use of robots in specific industrial processes? Looking at the current market for industrial robots, it is clear that robotic manipulators can be any size, yet manufacturers have traditionally focused on the exceptionally large models. There are a number of reasons for this. First, larger robots can lift more mass.

Small robots cannot efficiently lift as much, and having human labor attempting to lift equivalent loads is both dangerous and could result in damage to parts and equipment. Larger robots also have longer reach. Although their loads may not be anywhere near the maximum capacity of the manipulator, larger robots can move tooling farther into a work zone than a person could, higher and more precisely into the air than human-operated equipment, and easily into restricted workspaces from above.

Despite the capabilities offered by robotics, human labor is still an absolute requirement for many manufacturing processes. Where robots offer repeatability and lift capacity, skilled workers provide adaptability, advanced sensing, intuition, and problem-solving skills. Though robots and humans working on the shop floor have historically been physically kept separate by means of barriers, fences, and protective sensing equipment, recent advancements in production styles, robot designs, and safety equipment haven opened the way for human-robot collaborations in the workspace. These will be discussed in greater detail in Sections 3.2.1 and 3.2.2.

3.2.1 *Human-Robot Collaboration*

When one considers the topic of human-robot collaboration, the image that comes to mind is often one of humans and robots working together to complete a common task. In reality, this is just one of four degrees of collaboration outlined by Helms, Schraft, and Hägele.[5] These four stages can be summarized as "separate," "sequential," "simultaneous," and "supportive."

Separate collaboration is, at its core, really no collaboration at all. The robots and humans are separated in time, space, and task. Their tasks are performed independently without any consideration of the efforts done by the other, which is in stark contrast with the interactions of the *sequential, simultaneous*, and *supportive* collaborative roles (as shown in Fig. 3.1).

In sequential collaborations, the human and robot tasks are performed consecutively. Although the spaces, tools, and work pieces may be shared, it is rarely done concurrently. Rather, there is a strict serialization of the tasks such that one collaborator does a task, then the other collaborator does a task, and so on. In contrast, simultaneous collaborations witness the human and robot performing tasks concurrently, often on the same workpiece. The tasks for each are usually different, but there is some commonality in terms of a shared workspace. In supportive collaborations, the human and the robot work as a cohesive team to complete a common task.

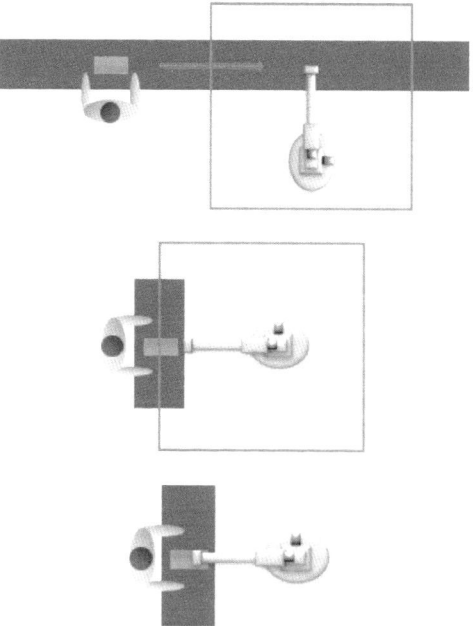

Fig. 3.1. In sequential collaborations (top) humans and robots are part of a serial process flow but are not co-located. Simultaneous collaborations (middle) see humans and robots working on different parts of the workpiece concurrently. Humans and robots in supportive collaborations (bottom) work together to complete shared task goals.

In the early years of industrial robots, *separate* collaborations were the norm. Then, as new manufacturing philosophies and capabilities were introduced to the factory, *sequential* collaborations slowly became more common. Today, sequential collaborations are still the de facto state-of-the-art, but, in recent years, a new class of industrial robot has dramatically changed the robotics market. These so-called "collaborative" robots are typically smaller, lighter, and safer (see Section 3.2.2), thus enabling the transition from sequential collaborations to simultaneous collaborations.

As a direct result of this new breed of robot, there has been a new trend in introducing robots into manual processes, or people into automated processes. Bringing robots into manual processes stands to improve quality control, improve ergonomics by removing the potential for repetitive strain injuries, and serve as a stop-gap for shortages of labor. Similarly, adding people to robotic processes adds flexibility and agility in unstructured environments or tasks, and improves reaction time to process uncertainty and errors.

In both cases, the utility of collaborative robots is currently targeted at improving the safety, efficiency, and capabilities of skilled labor. In these teams, the workers are benefited by the capabilities of the robots, whereas the robots' own limitations are merely being compensated for by the humans. As such, the robots, rather than being replacements for line workers, are more often being used as collaborative tools, and, in some instances are the mechanisms by which new manufacturing capabilities can be introduced into the workspace.

3.2.2 *Collaborative Robot Safety*

The topic of robot safety has been mentioned numerous times throughout this section. As industrial machines, robot are powerful, have a long reach, are unaware of their surroundings, and are thus very dangerous. As such, no discussion of human-robot interaction would be complete without a proper discussion about the topic of robot safety.

Long before the first industrial robot was even designed, the realization that protections against harm from robots was needed. In his 1921 play, *Rossum's Universal Robots*,[6] Karel Čapek introduced into the modern vernacular the term "robot" while spinning a tale of the use–and eventual uprising–of engineered slaves that results in the near extinction of the human race. In 1942, Isaac Asimov introduced his famous "Three Laws" in the short story, "Runaround",[7] as precautions against the slaves of humanity executing the genocide described by Čapek. Asimov's laws are as follows:

(1) A robot may not injure a human being or, through inaction, allow a human being to come to harm.
(2) A robot must obey orders given it by human beings except where such orders would conflict with the First Law.
(3) A robot must protect its own existence as long as such protection does not conflict with the First or Second Law.

While effective in science fiction, the real-world had no such precautionary laws to protect people from being injured by robots. Indeed, it was not until after a series of robot-attributed accidents and fatalities that development of robot safety standards began. The first of these standards was published in the United States in 1986 by the Robotics Industries Association (RIA) through the American National Standards Institute (ANSI).[8] After receiving industry feedback, this standard, *ANSI/RIA R15.06: American National Standard for Industrial Robots and Robot Systems - Safety Requirements*, was revised in 1992,[9] and again in 1999.[10]

After the 1999 revision of ANSI/RIA R15.06, the International Organization of Standardization (ISO) started work on ISO 10218, the international standard for industrial robot safety. ISO 10218 drew heavily from ANSI/RIA R15.06, and Part 1, which describes the safety requirements of the robot and its controller, was published in 2006. A revision of ISO 10218 was published in 2011.[11] Part 2 of ISO 10218, which outlines the safety requirements of a robot system (i.e., the robot, its controller, and any ancillary equipment or sensors required to accomplish the programmed task), was also published in 2011.[12]

In 2012, ISO 10218-1:2011 and ISO 10218-2:2011 were adopted by ANSI as the new ANSI/RIA R15.06.[13] Both parts of ISO 10218 also served as the basis for the Canadian CAN/CSA Z434 (adopted with minor deviations in 2014),[14] and the Japanese JIS B 8433 (adopted in 2015).[15, 16]

At the heart of ISO 10218-1 and ISO 10218-2 is the expectation of the physical separation between people and robots. Guidelines for physical safeguarding, ingress and egress zones, and safety equipment performance requirements and functions are detailed within these standards. However, in 2016 — ten years after the first publication of ISO 10218 — ISO published Technical Specification (TS) 15066, which outlines the safety requirements for collaborative industrial robot systems.[17]

ISO/TS 15066 presents requirements for four safety-related functions of collaborative robots, and enables robots to work near humans without the necessity for physical barriers. The two most notable of these safety-related functions are "speed and separation monitoring" (SSM; maintaining a safe separation distance between a human and an active robot), and "power and force limiting" (PFL; limiting the robot's transfer of pressures and forces onto the human body). These two concepts will be described in detail in Sections 3.2.2.1 and 3.2.2.2, respectively.

3.2.2.1 *SSM: Presence detection and localization*

The speed and separation collaborative safety function described in ISO/TS 15066:2016 focuses on providing a reasonable distance buffer between the active robot and a person. This separation distance is a mathematical function of 1) the robot's speed, 2) the time necessary for the robot to come to a controlled stop given its current load, 3) the distance traveled by the robot while it is stopping, 4) the person's speed and likely reach, and 5) the uncertainty associated with the robot's sensing and control (see Fig. 3.2).

A   B

Fig. 3.2. A sample encounter scenario involving a robot and a human. Based on the speeds of the robot and the person (A), the SSM system computes a minimum separation distance using estimates for sensor uncertainty and stopping times (B) to ensure the robot is inactive if and when the person contacts the robot.

When SSM is triggered, the robot must come to a controlled stop prior to making contact with a person by taking into account the total distance traveled by both. For the sake of simplicity, the SSM algorithm assumes the person will act in the absolute worst possible way, i.e., by walking quickly, directly toward the robot. Taking into account the statistically average brisk walking speed of a healthy adult male, the safety system is expected to calculate the distance the person can travel in the time necessary for the robot to come to a complete stop. If it is determined a minimum safety distance cannot be maintained in such a situation, the robot immediately slows or stops.

The SSM function also takes into account the realization that sensors are imperfect, and adds additional distance buffers based on the uncertainty of the robot's and person's positions in the event of sensor error. Generally speaking, safety-rated sensor systems commonly used for presence detection are either 1-dimensional (1D, e.g., pressure-sensitive mats[18] and light curtains[19]) or 2D (e.g., area scanners[20]). Camera-based systems[21] monitor a 3D volume, and trigger safety functions based on the observed intrusion into defined protective zones. The requirements for safety-rated sensor systems, however, are quite strict in terms of expected performance and reliability. Only safety-rated protective equipment can be used as a primary means of safeguarding a robot's work volume, though non-safety-rated sensor systems may be used as ancillary presence detectors.

Despite the provisions for human factors and system uncertainties, and having been standardized by an international body of technical experts, SSM is not yet considered a proven safety functionality. A number of limitations have been identified, including the facts that 1) robot speed is not universally defined nor consistently monitored, 2) the reporting of robot stopping behaviors does not take into account the robot's configuration, 3) safety systems are unaware of the shape of ancillary equipment (e.g., hoses, cables, grippers, and work pieces), 4) there is no standardized means for measuring the uncertainty of presence-detecting sensor systems, and 5) there are no safety-rated sensor systems that either uniquely identify or localize people in the workspace. As such, there are currently no standard test methods by which SSM functionality can be validated. A detailed analysis of the SSM function, the factors for assessing safety performance, and recommendations regarding its application are presented in.[22]

3.2.2.2   *PFL: Dynamic force metrology*

Though often the topic of discussion in the media, marketing, and research communities, from the safety perspective there is no such thing as a "collaborative" robot. Rather, there are collaborative safety functions, collaborative operations, and collaborative spaces involving robots reacting safely to the presence of human operators. When someone talks about collaborative robots, typically what they are referring to are actually "power and force limited robots."

In conditions where physical contact is expected between an active robot and a human, PFL is intended to ensure that the transfer of pressures and forces do not result in injury. For every region of the body (Fig. 3.3), ISO/TS 15066 specifies pressure and force limits at which the onset of pain is expected to begin. The technical specification also places limits on the shapes and minimum allowable surfaces areas of the robots, tooling, and work pieces to minimize risk of injury.

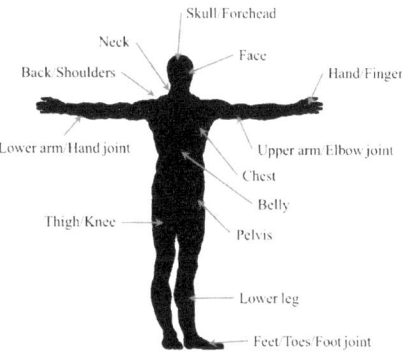

Fig. 3.3. Full body model of anticipated contact points for which pressure and force limits are established in ISO/TS 15066.

The basic premise of PFL is that, should contact occur, the robot is permitted to apply pressures and forces only up to the specified limits of the body model. Should those pressure or force limits be exceeded, the robot is expected to respond in a safe and reliable way–typically by means of a safety-rated monitored stop. Two different encounter scenarios are accounted for in PFL: 1) quasi-static encounters, in which a person is trapped between a robot and another surface, and 2) transient encounters, in which a robot strikes an unconstrained person who can recoil in free space.

In early drafts of the TS, specifications for a sensor system for the verification and validation of PFL were based on an earlier technical report.[23] The current values in ISO/TS 15066, however, are based on clinical studies evaluating the onset of pain.

A notable limitation of the PFL methodology is the assumption that the robot is aware of which part of the human body with which it is making contact. Similar to the issues with SSM, there are no sensor systems that can reliably provide accurate information regarding the location of different parts of the human body. Some body regions are capable of withstanding greater forces than others (e.g., the upper arm can absorb more force than the throat). As such, collaborative work cells and operations must be designed such that the robots have access to only certain parts of the body.

Additionally, most robot systems do not provide sufficient force sensing at the points of contact. For many robots, contact forces are inferred using joint-level current monitoring paired with gravity models. As the speed and mass of the robot increases, so too does the inherent noise in the force inference. Moreover, like the SSM functionality, there are currently no standardized test methods to validate PFL performance. Ongoing research efforts to develop test methods, measurement systems, and artifacts are expected to positively impact the quality and availability of validated PFL-enabled robots.

3.2.3 *Research Trends*

Human-robot collaboration is currently trending in the fields of research, and has attracted the attention of both academia and industry. With regards to industrial robots, however, the primary topic of active research pertains to the issue of collaborative safety. Although researchers are taking the safety issue seriously and their results demonstrate considerable promise, their approaches to the safety challenges often fall short of the robustness and reliability needed outside of the laboratory environment.

Many research projects utilize machine vision to monitor the robots' environments, with consumer-grade sensors often constituting the central basis of data collection. Such systems fall short of the requirements of being industry-hardened, let alone safety rated. As such, the results being achieved are inconsistent, and often demonstrate undesirable characteristics and behaviors while under test. Regardless, the approaches and algorithms being investigated have demonstrated that the desired performance is achievable at least some of the time.

Ultimately, the same limiting factor that impacts the reliability of SSM and PFL implementations also impacts the research community: there are no standardized test methods to validate functionality. In most demonstrations of safety functionality, researchers will put themselves (or others) into a hazardous situation and emerge unharmed. Such actions, however, expose people to hazards, and are therefore unacceptable test methods for safety verification and validation.

3.2.4 *Market Trends*

Given the popularity and projected growth of the collaborative robot system market, it is of no surprise that the number of companies producing "collaborative" robots is steadily growing. In many cases, the products offered by these new companies are remarkably similar to other robots on the market, but introduce a few new features in an effort to give them an edge.

A majority of these robots are small, lightweight, and operate with reduced speeds. Some will monitor forces and torques, but, again, do so by means of current monitoring. Others provide novel interfaces designed to make programming easier, or encourage regular interaction with the robot by means of graphical user interfaces. Currently, the "collaborative" label is not regulated, so buyers and integrators of these emerging robots must be dutiful in their research, and should be aware of the requirements outlined in ISO/TS 15066.

Another growing market trend focuses on the development of sensor systems to detect the presence of people within the safeguarded zone. Vision, laser, and capacitive sensor systems are being produced and marketed primarily for SSM implementations. While many of these new sensor systems are not yet safety-rated, manufacturers are often active within the standards communities to assist in the development of test methods to assess performance and reliability.

3.3 Human-Machine Interfaces

Within a typical robot work cell, there are a number of mechanisms through which people can command robot motions, issue process-related instructions, and receive useful feedback about the robot system or the status of the manufacturing process. Depending on the person's role within the work cell, however, the access to and utility of these interfaces may vary considerably. For example, as mentioned in Section 3.2, industrial robot controllers are typically equipped with teach pendants that serve as the primary interfaces for calibrating, moving, and programming the robots' motions. Such functions are critical for robot installation, process programming and tuning, and equipment maintenance, but may not be necessary for day-to-day production operations.

Some modern collaborative robot designs forgo the teach pendant entirely, and rely on advanced sensing, joint compliance, and AI to enable human-guided task learning. Ancillary equipment such as light towers (Fig. 3.4) and sirens may be connected to the robot to give quick visual and audible cues of robot state, but are otherwise limited in the amount of information they can provide. In work cells where the robot is the only complex machine, the robot's controller may also double as the controller for connected tools and feeder equipment (e.g., conveyors and loaders). However, if integrated into a larger system of interconnected, controlled tools, the controller may be configured to be slave to a master programmable logic control (PLC) used for controlling process flow and maintaining workplace safety.

Fig. 3.4. Light tower indicating the status of a robot. Here, the second light from bottom indicates that the robot's safety system is online and active, while the bottom light indicates perimeter safeguards have been silenced.

For programming and maintenance tasks, the teach pendant (Fig. 3.5) is typically the only means of interfacing with the robot. For single robot work cells, this is relatively straight-forward. In cells that contain multiple, coordinated robots, there are some instances where a single controller can coordinate multiple robots (specifically if all of the robots are from the same manufacturer). In other instances–and especially when the robots being coordinated are produced by different vendors–coordination must be accommodated through a PLC due to a lack of vendor support for integrating dissimilar operating systems and control interfaces.

Fig. 3.5. An example robot teach pendant.

In-process, operational feedback is more likely to come via an integrated PLC. The PLC will take sensor feedback and internal state information, combine it together, and provide a computational estimate of the overall health of the equipment and manufacturing process. While the PLC may offer some functional control for process optimization, its functionality is often too limited for real-time, human-robot collaborations. As such, when the PLC is the primary mechanism for interacting with the robots, the collaborative role of the human-robot team is limited to sequential or simultaneous tasks (per Section 3.2.1)

For several decades, the design of robot HMI has been a one-size-fits-all approach, largely due to technological limitations of interface components. So, depending on the role the human operator has, the interface may offer too many or too few control options. This is due principally to the fact that cost reduction, not the operator's needs, drive industry HMI designs.[24]

Several modern takes on collaborative robot interfaces, however, allow for the customization of functions, layouts, and information display based on the operator's role. For instance, programmers and maintenance personnel typically have access to more functionality and diagnostics information that is otherwise irrelevant for an average user's day-to-day operation of the equipment.

However, old practices are difficult to abandon. Rather than emphasizing human awareness by keeping operators informed, trained, or "in-the-loop," the traditional performance-based archetypes of basic programming, robot repeatability, and post-factor robot status warnings still drive HMI designs. It is expected that the HMI will provide contextual information regarding task and robot state, but not necessarily explicitly. For instance, a visual indicator may tell the operator where in the robot's program the controller is currently focusing its processor cycles.

From an HRI perspective, however, more should be expected of the HMI. In an ideal configuration, the HMI should accommodate operator situation awareness such that potential issues can be identified and dealt with quickly. The HMI should thus share visual information that supports and promotes the following:

- Establish a grounding of the robot/process state to facilitate human-robot coordination;
- Synchronize or schedule tasks;
- Improve clarity of information exchange; and
- Perform the task.

These functions are enabled in effective HRI via well-designed HMI and intelligent software. Human operators are more aware of potential issues if they play an active role within the process. Therefore, it is important that the HMI support operator engagement provided the operator's active participation in a human-robot team is expected.

3.3.1 *Research Trends*

Within the research communities, focal areas of innovative design are primarily targeted toward alternative and non-standard interfaces (i.e., not teach pendants or other hand-held graphical displays). Wearable technologies such as gloves, armbands, and helmets that track hand, arm, and head movements are being investigated as alternative mechanisms for controlling robots by means of tele-operation[25] and off-line training.[26] Head-mounted displays such as augmented reality headsets provide real-time information for operators regarding system and process diagnostics,[27] in-line error handling, and on-line training for novice users.[28] Similarly, head-mounted virtual reality headsets can be used for off-line training and validation of robot processes, effective interfaces for remote tele-operation by giving a robot-eye perspective of the world, and the instantaneous capability to interface with multiple robot systems that could be located miles apart.[29]

Fig. 3.6. Without contextual clues, even seemingly clear instructions may be misinterpreted.

Efforts to improve natural language processing for operator-generated commands and process feedback continue to make great strides, and the ability to uniquely recognize and parse voice commands in noisy manufacturing environments is improving at a steady rate. Current efforts are aimed at segmenting and removing background noise, parsing and comprehending colloquial speech patterns, and inferring intent from otherwise noisy or fragmented speech patterns common in daily speech. Additional efforts are working to establish context given the speech that is understood (Fig. 3.6). Other systems monitor stress patterns in speech patterns to identify strained efforts, frustration, or anxiety, enabling the robot to adapt to the perceived operator's moods or state of attention to support operator comfort and situation awareness.

Ultimately, these research trends are largely focused on making robot systems more accommodating of the human operators' inherent capabilities, activities, and speech patterns, rather than forcing people to adjust their way of doing things to compensate for the limitations of the robot interface.

3.3.2 *Market Trends*

From where technology exists today, it is clear that improvements in interfaces and interactive tools are required to advance the technology toward enabling supportive human-robot collaboration. What are needed are interfaces specifically designed to increase efficiency and productivity for both the robots and the operators. Such interfaces must enable increased productivity and support real-time feedback in situation awareness for improved prognostics and health monitoring of equipment and processes.

However, it is not the operator's needs, but rather cost reduction that continues to drive many HMI design decisions for larger, more established robot manufacturers. As such, the recommendations for stakeholder-influenced, iterative interface design improvements are not always heeded. Instead, innovations in HMI designs are being driven by smaller, often start-up robot manufacturers. Such companies are willing to take more risks and disrupt common design mindsets in an effort to make their mark on the market.[30] Such novel interface designs stand to significantly change the means by which people interact with robots by simplifying the processes of control and programming, but may ultimately lose functionality or safety as a consequence.

The modern workforce is increasingly technologically adept, and is expected to do so as manufacturing becomes smarter. As the technology and manufacturing processes evolve, so too will the skill sets needed to perform. As manufacturing technologies and processes become increasing dependent on software and inter-connective mechanisms, operator skills in software development and networking are expected to grow.[31] Even so, the opposite also holds true.

While they are clearly adaptive to older technologies, many modern workers have more modern tastes and are thus more discerning about the technologies with which they regularly interact.[32] In many ways, manufacturing technology has failed to keep pace with the ever-evolving consumer preferences, and it is not uncommon for generational differences to cause younger workers to forgo employment options in even modern manufacturing environments. While a large percentage of manufacturing interfaces are focused on productivity efficacy, current trends in consumer equipment are increasingly human-centric.

3.4 Human-Robot Interaction

Human robot interaction is the interdisciplinary field of study dedicated to evaluating the systems, interfaces, and design of interactions between humans and robots. HRI borrows concepts from human factors, Computer Science, Human Computer Interaction(HCI), psychology, and engineering. HRI is fundamentally different due to both the embodied nature of robots, and the potential for a robot to act as an intelligent agent in its environment. The underlying concept of HRI is largely centered on the exchange of information between people and machines through some form of interface. The nature of this information changes from task to task, but is ultimately focused on the following key factors:

(1) coordinating actions or the exchange of information,
(2) communicating task-relevant information,
(3) formatting information in a way that is specific to the operator or the role of the user, and

(4) enabling situation awareness by providing information and alerts in a timely and easily consumed way.

The many different domains of robotics take their own approaches towards HRI. Industrial robots provide information that is relevant to the manufacturing tasks they are assigned to. Medical robots track and report information pertinent to patients and medical practitioners. Service robots for residential applications often provide feedback regarding the status of their cleaning tasks or ask the operator for assistance with charging or navigation. Ultimately, the goal of these interactions is to establish common ground regarding the current state of the world, the tasks to be accomplished, and the roles to be taken. Breakdowns in communication or understandings of world state lead to bad interactions (Fig. 3.7);

Fig. 3.7. HRI is visualized as the mutual awareness and understanding of the environment, task, and people and machines involved.

Distinct from robot feedback is the way in which humans interact with these robot platforms. This can vary from direct control of the robot by a human operator, to a more hands-off approach where the robot is given a task. In industrial applications, however, there is very little direct interaction between the human workers and robots, even through non-contact methods. The robots are set to do a particular task, separate from any human workers, and generally only need intervention in the case of maintenance operations. Although these types of setups allow for the robot to work without as much safety limiting, this puts a limit on the complexity of the task an industrial robot can accomplish. Utilizing the flexibility of a human operator can assist the robot in tasks beyond its scope alone. Moreover, for smaller enterprises where the product may change frequently, human assistance can be invaluable for robot re-tasking.

The complexity of the human-robot interaction generally revolves around the uncertainty within the environment adding to the uncertainty of having human participants. As such, unstructured environments like search and rescue scenes and hospitals are more difficult environments for HRI than well-defined structured environments like manufacturing. This fact puts industrial and manufacturing environments in an interesting position. These structured domains can be used to provide more concrete and applicable examples for HRI, and allow research preformed in industrial HRI to be applied more readily in industry. Rather than approaching big picture questions in robotics that require lofty advances in AI, robotic platforms, and computer vision all at once, industrial HRI can answer questions applicable to the real world.

3.4.1 *Research Trends*

HRI trends in the research community are largely focused on assistive robots whose goals are to directly benefit the human in some way. Home robots make up a large part of research interest, and includes both socially assistive robots[33, 34] and medically or physically assistive robots.[35] Research in socially assistive robots is primarily directed towards areas such as engagement activities for adults with mental health disorders or "play therapy" for children with autism.[36] Physically assistive robots, on the other hand, can provide help to those with disabilities, ranging from smart wheelchairs to robotic feeders and shavers.[37]

Research into medical robots can be broken into two general types: surgical robots and hospital assistant robots. Surgical robots are somewhat of a special case, as most platforms are not truly autonomous but more of an intelligent tool to be used by a skilled physician.[38] However, these robots can be invaluable by giving a surgeon extra precision, haptic feedback, patient monitoring, and close-up camera feeds of the working area. This involves many HRI challenges, both on the side of the surgeon controlling the device as well as the surgical interaction with the patient. Other robotic assistants in medical areas are being developed to take over the more menial tasks such as autonomous food and medicine delivery, thus freeing up hospital personnel for patient care. These types of autonomous robots have less direct interactions, but must still take into account HRI principles so as not to cause hospital patients any undue distress.

Research is also being conducted into robotic platforms for military and emergency services purposes. Although these applications can vary from fire emergencies to collapsed buildings to army reconnaissance, the platforms are often similar in their HRI methods. Teleoperation is a commonly used form of control for military drones or first response robots, which can provide a live camera feed to the operator for scouting and navigation purposes. Research is being done to make these kinds of platforms more autonomous; however, for sensitive operations, it is often the user's preference to be in direct control of the robotic platform.

Human-robot collaboration (HRC) is a newer sub-area of HRI research. With the advent of contact-safe robot platforms, it has become feasible for humans and robots to collaborate on a task in the same workspace. Collaborative tasks with robots bring new challenges for teamwork, including communication, task planning, shared states, and human intention prediction - to mention only a few.[39] This type of HRI also relies on the human participant having some measure of trust in their robot partner,[40] while on the robot's side, it should perform actions with regard to the mental state of its human partner.[41] HRC is also a promising application area for robot learning-from-demonstration, allowing the human partner to teach parts of a task as needed.[42] Research in this area tends to be goal-focused rather than process-oriented, which means that interfaces and software for HRC are not yet readily available for commercial means.

3.4.2 *Market Trends*

Market trends in HRI are fairly different between western and eastern markets. In the western market, voice assistants like the Amazon Echo and Google Home are increasingly popular. These devices act as smart speakers compatible with other smart home technologies like lighting and thermostat controls. The lack of physical engagement with these assistive technologies limits their HRI capabilities, however. Other voice assistants, like the Jibo, seek to provide a level of personality to the experience through embodiment. Some of the more useful home assistants, such as robotic vacuums, unfortunately exhibit very few HRI capabilities. These platforms can be teleoperated as needed by the user, but their goals are generally not to interact with humans, and to accomplish service tasks unobtrusively.

In eastern markets, particularly Japan, the low birth rate and aging population has left a populace with very few unskilled workers, and a need for assistive robots for the elderly. This need leads to a spectrum of social robots, ranging from robotic animals like Aibo and Paro, to humanoid robots like Pepper.[a] Pepper in particular is not only for use in the home, but also provides services for retail applications as an informative kiosk or tour guide. These types of robots are slowly being seen in the west as well.

---

[a]Disclaimer: Commercial equipment and materials are identified in order to adequately specify certain procedures. In no case does such identification imply recommendation or endorsement by the National Institute of Standards and Technology, nor does it imply that the materials or equipment identified are necessarily the best available for the purpose.

Educational robots are becoming more prevalent as well. These robots generally have friendlier features in order to engage children. For example, the Nao robot is often used in research applications, but the small, humanoid design makes it ideal for interactions with younger children to whom it is similar in size. Less expensive models like Cozmo and Coji offer new types of interactions by teaching users how to create programs.

Industry has been a relatively late adopter of collaborative robot technology. However, in recent years, new types of industrial robots have become much more widely available as the technology has advanced. Industrial robot arms that are force-limited and thus safe for direct human interaction are now available from several companies, including Kuka, Universal Robotics, Rethink Robotics, Fanuc, and many others. Advances are still needed, however, in order to make these platforms truly collaborative; this includes human-friendly interfaces that are easy for non-technical users to understand and use.

3.5   Performance Metrics for HRI and HMI

What are the qualities of a good interface? Quite often, the answer is highly subjective, yet not entirely intuitive. The design of interfaces and engineering of interactions typically involve some level of compromise and balance.

Is simplicity of design the ideal to be achieved? Reducing complexity will make an interface easier to use, but typically comes at the cost of losing functionality. Some functions and processes may not even be able to be simplified due to their nature or intended use. For example, complex and sensitive chemical processing applications may involve so many parameters that simplifying a user interface (UIs) would interfere with the operator's job.

Would more options being available to the user be preferred to provide a more "rich" user experience? Adding features often makes an interface more useful or broad in applicability, but also increases the time necessary to find and use a specific function. Moreover, some features may see infrequent use. This could effectively lead to situations where options are more of a hindrance than an asset, especially if they take up valuable interface real estate or are difficult to find when needed.

How does a vendor design the interface to provide the ideal balance of ease-of-use and functionality? What trade-offs are made, and why? When the product goes to market, what is presented is the manufacturer's conscious design choices manifest as what is likely to be the only direct means of programming or interacting with robots that most end-users will ever see.

For the average robot system, interactions between humans and machine are relatively minimal. In applications involving continuous operations with little product turnover, it may be years before the controlling code is updated. As such, the robot's teach pendant may see little use beyond simply starting up the robot and performing the occasional preventative maintenance task.

Over the past decade, however, robot manufacturers have refocused their efforts to improving the user experience. Teach pendants have evolved from the single-line liquid crystal displays of yesteryear, and now incorporate touch-sensitive screens with full-feature graphical user interfaces that can be quickly changed based on the user's expertise level, the operator's purpose for interacting with the robot (e.g., programming versus simply running a program), or the application of the robot. Some of these interfaces can even be customized by the end-user for specific tasks.

As discussed in Section 3.3, designs of human-machine interfaces for robot applications are slowly becoming more user-centric. In this section, the metrics for assessing the quality and performance of HMI and HRI will be discussed. The metrics described in Section 3.5.1, although targeted at robots in particular, are broadly applicable to machines in general. Similarly, many of the metrics described in Section 3.5.2 can be broadly applied to any interactive equipment, but are specifically aimed at robots in this context. While many aspects are assessed *post facto* through operator surveys once the interactions have been completed, some metrics can be objectively assessed in real time using external sensors and monitoring systems.

3.5.1 *HMI Metrics*

Although robots are physical machines with monolithic boxes as controllers, the kinematics and dynamics are driven by software. Modern teach pendants are an extension of this software base, providing user interfaces for the operator with which the robot's motions, end-of-arm tooling actions, and responses to stimuli can be defined, controlled, and adjusted. As such, most of the metrics assessing the performance of HMI for robotics are, in reality, measuring the performance of the software. Software quality standards were originally introduced in ISO 9126-1:2001,[43] which has since been replaced by ISO/IEC 25010:2011.[44] ISO/IEC 25010 presents two models for evaluating quality: quality in use, and product quality. The quality in use model, shown in Table 3.1 evaluates the overall impacts and outcomes resulting from the use of a given system on different stakeholders. Such metrics include effectiveness, efficiency, overall satisfaction with the system, freedom from risk, and the level to which these metrics hold for specific contexts.

Table 3.1. Quality in use model for software assessments from Ref. 44.

Category	Metrics
Effectiveness	Accuracy
	Completeness
Efficiency	Resource utility
Satisfaction	Usefulness
	Trust
	Pleasure
	Comfort
Freedom from Risk	Economic
	Health and safety
	Environmental
Context coverage	Completeness
	Flexibility

The *product quality* model is used to characterize a given system based on its functional properties, including suitability for the task, performance efficiency, compatibility, usability, and reliability (Table 3.2). Each of these characteristic areas define sub-characteristics that are assessed as having their requirements met satisfactorily or unsatisfactorily along a Likert-like scale as experienced by primary, secondary, and indirect users. Given the diversity of the roles and experiences of the different users, evaluations from the various stakeholders are not easily combined or directly comparable due to their individual priorities and perspectives.

Modern trends in system marketing are prone to overuse terms such as "easy to use" or "intuitive," implying that the user will become intimately familiar with the functionality of the HMI with relatively little exposure. While there exists a number of best practices for guiding the development of such interfaces, there is not a universal metric by which one interface may be directly compared with another. Cultural differences, accessibility limitations, and simple lack of experience with similar interfaces or functions may impede the ease by which users acclimate to the HMI. As mentioned previously, there is frequently a trade-off between functionality and usability. Ultimately, the manufacturer or integrator is left to determine how to strike an acceptable balance between features and ease-of-use.

One of the earliest known HMI evaluation methodologies was proposed by Roberts and Moran to assess the impacts of the interface design of text editors.[45] The methodology breaks the evaluation into four metrics: learning time, expert

Table 3.2. Product quality model for software assessments from Ref. 44.

Category	Metrics
Functional suitability	Completeness
	Correctness
	Appropriateness
Performance efficiency	Time behavior
	Resource utilization
	Capacity
Compatibility	Coexistence
	Interoperability
Usability	Appropriateness recognition
	Learnability
	Operability
	User error protection
	UI aesthetics
	Accessibility
Reliability	Maturity
	Availability
	Fault tolerance
	Recoverability
Security	Confidentiality
	Integrity
	Non-repudiation
	Accountability
	Authenticity
Maintainability	Modularity
	Reusability
	Analyzability
	Modifiability
	Testability
Portability	Adapability
	Installability
	Replaceability

use time, error cost, and functionality (Table 3.3). Learning time reflects the time necessary to first learn how to use the system, while expert use time captures the amount of time to perform some task assuming mastery of the tool. Error cost measures the time penalty when errors are made, and functionality is measured as the ratio of the total number of functions supported by the system under test, to the larger set of all functions expected to be supported by the larger class of similar systems (Fig. 3.8). While somewhat incomplete, these metrics provide a quick and fair basis of comparison for systems and interfaces with similar goals. In the case of robot systems, however, the functional goals are broadly scoped, and are as varied as the number of unique designs, configurations, and applications of robots in industry.

Table 3.3. Interface evaluation metrics proposed for text editors from Ref. 45.

Metric	Measurement
Learning time	Time (in seconds) for novices to learn how to perform basic editing tasks using the system
Expert use time	Required time (in seconds) for an expert to perform the basic editing tasks using the system
Error cost	Time cost (in seconds) associated with making, discovering, and correcting for errors, and then resuming productive work
Functionality	Percentage of the complete taxonomy of tasks supported by the system

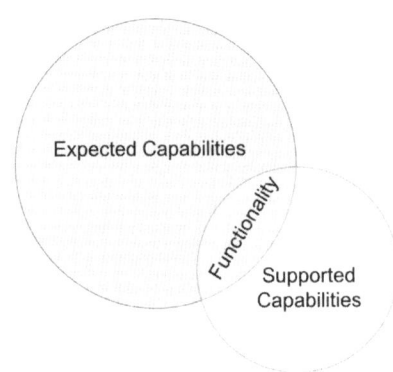

Fig. 3.8. The overlap between the expected capabilities and the presented capabilities defines the functionality of a given tool or system.

Such metrics are useful for capturing the overall effectiveness of the interface in that they determine how useful said interface typically is. However, these metrics do not address the aspects that contribute to the user's overall experience with using the HMI.

The principal functions of most industrial user interfaces are *information presentation* and *system/process control*. During day-to-day operations, information presentation will be the dominant function of the interface, but this information is provided ("presentation") with the assumption that it will be leveraged for doing something useful ("response").

There are two metrics associated with these presentation-response expectations. The first is whether the response was correct. The correctness value can be quantified in several ways, including 1) the number of erroneous responses, e; 2) the frequency of incorrect responses, $\frac{e}{\tau}$ over some time period, τ; 3) the mean time to an incorrect response, τ_{error}; 4) the measurable distance (if quantifiable), $\overline{\hat{r}r}$, from the given response, r, to the correct response, $\hat{r}$; or 5) some measurable consequence or cost, c, of an error. In some instances, all five of these measures may be reported, though using a subset is more common as not all metrics are applicable. Comparing two different HMI implementations as a function of the response correctness provides a quantifiable performance indicator of the interfaces.

The second metric is the amount of time lapsed between the initial display of information and the moment the operator confirms their response to the stimuli. These time-frames provide lower limits, $\tilde{t}$, to the amount of time required for a given stimulus-response cycle. Large deviations from $\tilde{t}$ indicate either the interface design is not optimal for the application, or the presentation of information is incorrect for the expected response.

There exist a number of timing indicators that may expose interface designs that are not optimized in terms of layout or the juxtaposition of information. For instance, if the layout of controls is broadly distributed, operators may require additional time to complete certain tasks to find and then actuate the necessary controls. Fitts' Law[46] states the time, t_{pos}, to move the hand to a target of size S that is a given distance, D, away is

$$t_{pos} = l_M \log_2 \left(\frac{D}{S} + 0.5 \right) \tag{3.1}$$

where $l_M = 100[70 \sim 120]$ msec/bit (Fig. 3.9). Farther distances result in longer hand traversal time, and more time searching for the appropriate control. In general, objects of interest should be placed prominently in the center of the field of view to minimize search time. Both data and control representations should therefore be compact and visual, with controls offering a select number of predefined potential responses rather than open-ended fields for text or variable manipulation.

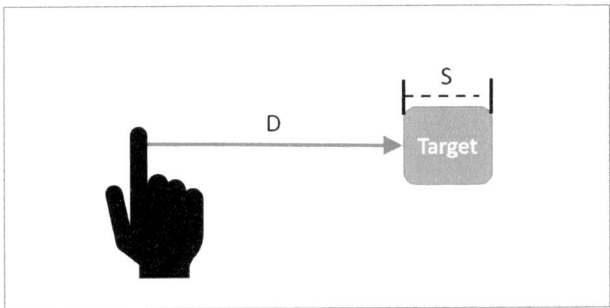

Fig. 3.9. Fitts' law states the distance between the user and the target(D) and the width of the target(S) impact the traversal time(T_{pos}).

Although not necessarily an indicator of "intuitive" usage, it has been noted that operator performance tends to improve as a function of repeated exposure and use of a given interface. The Power Law of Practice[47] effectively outlines that, as one becomes more accustomed to the interface, the time t_n to perform a task on the nth trial follows a power law

$$t_n = t_1 n^{-\alpha} \tag{3.2}$$

where $\alpha = 0.4\,(0.2 \sim 0.6)$. Repeated interaction with the interface for a given task is expected to take less time given practice and competence. If no such performance gains are observed, it is likely the HRI design or layout is interfering with the operator's performance.

3.5.2 *HRI Metrics*

In contrast to the HMI metrics, measurements for HRI efficacy are often measured as a function of the post facto impacts of the interactions between people and robots. In this section, a number of important factors impacting the quality of HRI will be discussed, and some of the metrics by which they can be assessed are presented.

3.5.2.1 *Communication efficacy*

In terms of whether or not communications between humans and robots are efficient, the principal means by which communication efficacy can be assessed is in terms of communication time, t_{comm}. This reflects the amount of time necessary for a message to be generated and transmitted, and its message understood by the target recipient. Such measures apply to text-based communications, verbal communications, and visual representations of information. However, measuring this timing is non-trivial, and is generally estimated as the difference between the initiation of the message and the subsequent action that results from the message.

Disruptions in communication adversely impact process (or work) performance, so the elements of communication delay, efficiency, and interruptions play an important factor in the measure of communication time. Communications must be received on time if they are to be effective. Delays in transmission or comprehension reduce the remaining time to address issues before the loss of parts (Fig. 3.10), equipment, or profit accrue. Technological factors that may negatively impact communication effectiveness include transmission delays, jitter, and bandwidth.[48] Such factors are relatively easy to isolate, characterize, and minimize.

Ultimately, when communicating critical information, messages must contain four principal components to optimize efficiency and utility:[49]

(1) a brief overview of the situation,
(2) the relevant background of the system or process,
(3) a diagnosis of the situation, and
(4) a recommendation of steps to move forward.

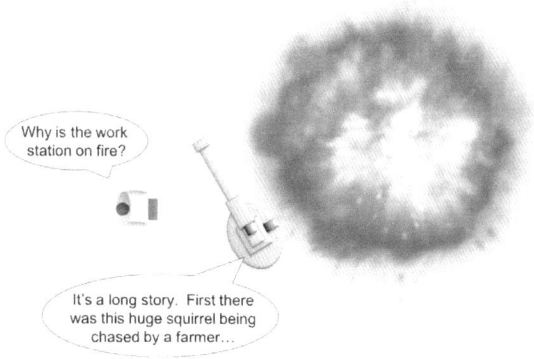

Fig. 3.10. Being given concise, clear information that contains only the relevant data leads to better efficiency in communications.

3.5.2.2 *Information quality*

It is expected that a robot system will be providing feedback regarding system and process state. While most of this feedback is of little use to the average user, when combined, it can provide highly insightful information about the system and process as a whole. For feedback from a robot system to be useful to an operator, it must consist of timely, actionable intelligence. Specifically, feedback must be given when it is most relevant to a desired response, and it must consist of enough information such that both the meaning and the expected response to the feedback are clearly understood. Good quality information from the robot to the operator enables the operator to make more informed decisions. Similarly, in situations where user input is required (e.g., Refs. 50 and 51), good quality feedback from the operator improves the robot's performance.

Arguably the largest contributing factor of the usefulness of the reported information is dependent on the quality of that information. High-quality information is relevant to the task at hand, and contributes to the operator's situation awareness (see Section 3.5.2.3). Low quality information, in contrast, may detract from situation awareness, and negatively impact the equipment or manufacturing process. The metrics for information quality vary somewhat according to application domain, but a generally agreed-upon model[52] consists of a number of principal attributes, a subset of which are shown in Table 3.4.

Table 3.4. Dimensions of information quality reported by Knight and Burn.[52] *Italicized* attributes indicate elements that are subjective in nature.[53] Equations for the measurement of certain factors are provided, when applicable, as are references to the sources of these equations.

Category	Description	Equation	References
Accuracy	Correctness of information	$\frac{|C|}{|N|}$	54–56
Believability	Credibility of information	$1 - \frac{|D|}{|N|}$	57
Completeness	Information required for a given task is not missing	$\frac{|N|}{|X|}$	57, 58
Relevancy	Applicability of information to the task	*(subjective)*	
Timeliness	Presentation of information in a favorable amount of time	$\frac{|A|}{|N|}$	59, 60
Value-Added	Benefit gained by the information's use, or the *usefulness*	$1 - \frac{|U|}{|N|}$	
Efficiency	Ease by which the task's information needs are met	$min\left(\frac{N}{R}, \frac{R}{N}\right)$	61
Understandability	Ease by which information is comprehended	*(subjective)*	
Accessibility	Ease of information retrieval	$max\left(0, 1 - \frac{t_{deliv} - t_{input}}{t_{dead} - t_{input}}\right)$	62

In general, the principal factors that contribute to information quality are accuracy, believability, completeness, relevancy, timeliness, value-added, efficiency, understandability, and accessibility[63] (see Table 3.4). Accuracy is most commonly measured in terms of *syntactic accuracy*,[54–56,59–61,64–66] which reflects the ratio of the size of the set of correct responses, C, to the size of all responses received, N. In contrast, believability is a subjective measure of the absence of information, but can be objectively measured by comparing the information received against a known baseline (i.e., a number of known default values, D). Similarly, completeness compares the amount of information received versus the amount of information needed to complete a given task, X. And whether or not information is provided in a useful amount of time is captured in the timeliness measure, where the time frame A is compared with the amount of information provided.[59,60] An alternative metric, similar to the measure of timeliness, evaluates accessibility in terms of time against a set deadline, t_{dead}, compared with the difference in time between information request t_{input} and final delivery t_{deliv}. Related to the concepts of accuracy and timeliness, the measure of HRI efficiency is a function of the amount of information required, R, versus the total amount of information received.

More subjective measures, such as relevancy and understandability, require the personal assessment of the individual users. Such assessments may be inconsistent over time as a function of personal mood, physical and mental wellness, level of attentiveness, and whether or not the operator is hungry. Regardless, such measures are worth capturing over time, and with enough samples a baseline average should emerge.

3.5.2.3 *Situation awareness*

The established literature of situation awareness largely adopts the widely-cited three-level situation awareness model presented by Endsley in 1995,[67] shown in Fig. 3.11. Level 1 situation awareness represents the capacity to perceive and measure objects and features within the operational environment. Level 2 situation awareness indicates the comprehension of the objects' significance within the operational context. And Level 3 situation awareness demonstrates the ability to predict with some level of accuracy the elements' states (e.g., location and orientation) in the future. The stacked nature of this model states that Level 3 situation awareness is impossible without also having Level 1 and Level 2 situation awareness.

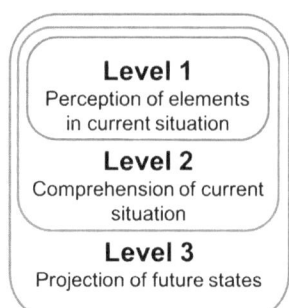

Fig. 3.11. The nested levels of situation awareness as described in Endsley.[67] Each successive layer extrapolates greater awareness based on the previous layer's understanding of the world.

HMI and HRI that fully support situation awareness are marked as having fewer errors, or requiring few corrective actions on the part of the operator. In contrast, the loss of situation awareness is associated with missing critical information,[68] and often leads to poor system performance.[69] Metrics for assessing the quality of situation awareness are typically represented by those established by Salerno et al., shown in Table 3.5.

Table 3.5. The SA system metrics from Ref. 70.

Dimension	Metric	Definition/Purpose
Confidence	Precision	Percentage of correct alerts
	Recall	Probability of detection
Purity	Misassignment	Percentage of evidence incorrectly associated
	Evidence recall	Percentage of detected events
Cost utility	Cost utility	Percentage of cost savings
Timeliness	Time	Time between event and alert

3.5.2.4 *Mental effort*

A significant measurement of the effectiveness of HRI is the amount of mental effort required to work collaboratively with a robot system (Fig. 3.12). Such measures are pseudo-quantitative in that a number of different factors are measured along a Likert scale, but are ultimately subjective in nature. Within the manufacturing context, the end goals of HRI design are targeted at reducing mental and physical fatigue, increasing sense of control or contribution to the task, and ultimately reducing any interaction dynamics that might negatively impact production goals.

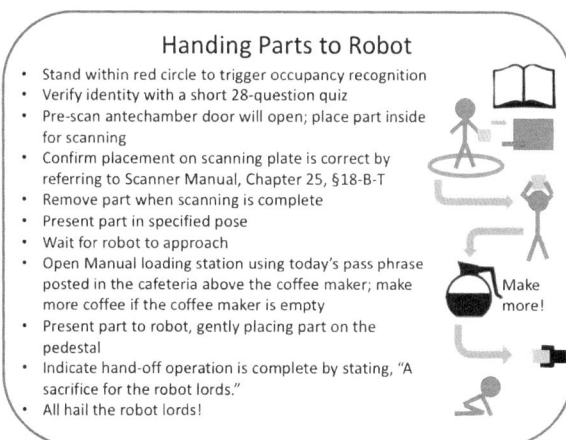

Fig. 3.12. The more complex a task is, or the number of specific steps that must be taken in order to complete a task, the more mental effort may be required to complete the task with the desired quality of results.

Arguably, the most widely-applied qualitative metric[71] is the National Aeronautics and Space Administration (NASA) Task Load Index (TLX).[72] The NASA-TLX performs a post facto rating of the levels of cognitive and physical demands placed on the participants during a given task. These demands (shown Table 3.6) are rated on different Likert scales and combined with "Source of Workload" weights. These measures are intended to characterize both the task and the level of personal effort exerted to complete the task.

Alternative metrics include the Workload Profile[73]) and the Subjective Workload Assessment Technique (SWAT,[74]). The Workload Profile evaluates multiple quality/demand elements of several mental dimensions on sliding scales in the range of 0 (no demand) to 1 (full effort), while the SWAT metric has participants select from among three possible responses for time, mental effort, and stress load dimensions. Based on a study by Rubio et al., the NASA-TLX is recommended for assessing impacts on individuals, while evaluations of cognitive demands are better evaluated using Workload Profile.[75]

3.5.3 *Research Trends*

A great amount of current HRI research is focused on intuitive interfacing, specifically with social robotics. Natural language processing, gesture recognition, body posture, facial expression identification, and emulation are all being pushed as next-generation interactive mechanisms through which robot systems can interact and

Table 3.6. The qualitative metrics of the NASA-TLX[72] ask participants to rank mental demands along multiple dimensions.

Title	Scale	Description
Mental Demand	Low-High	Level of mental and perceptual activity required to complete the task.
Physical Demand	Low-High	Level of physical activity required to complete the task.
Temporal Demand	Low-High	Amount of pressure felt as a result of the pace of the task.
Performance	Good-Poor	Assessment (either internal or external) of the quality of work performed toward the task goals.
Effort	Low-High	Amount of work exerted (mentally or physically) to achieve the level of performance.
Frustration	Low-High	Level of internal stress (insecurity, discouragement, irritation, stress, or annoyance) felt during the task.

communicate with people. Much of this research is particularly focused on rehabilitation and social interaction training for special needs children and adults, with metrics of success often being measured in terms of behavioral changes of clients and patients. Results along these lines demonstrate great promise, and it is expected that continued development of the current subjective metrics will ultimately lead to validated quantifiable test methods and metrics.

Within the "traditional" or industrial realms, however, research trends are moving away from physical interfaces, and are instead attempting to capture the nebulous "intuitiveness" metric. Clinical studies report results of post facto survey responses of trials consisting of small sample sizes. Levels of robot expertise are rarely quantified, and it is assumed that test subjects have at least some experience with similar robot systems. Along with these studies, the traditional teach pendant interface is being replaced by more sensor-based interfaces, including wearable devices, external camera systems, and neural activity monitors. To some extent, natural language processing and machine vision are employed in industrial robot interaction trials, but such interfaces are becoming less prevalent in favor of wearable and less intrusive interfaces such as directly moving robots to guide-teach applications and perform teach-by-example.

Regardless of the interfaces being evaluated, there are few repeatable metrics being developed or used for reporting purposes. Some reports will provide NASA-TLX responses, but little analysis is provided to identify what, in particular, influences mental effort or ease-of-use. Repeatability and replication of such studies, therefore, is difficult to ascertain.

3.5.4 *Market Trends*

In terms of the larger, more established manufacturers of robot systems, interface designs are demonstrating little, if any, change in design or functionality. Process performance clearly still drives interface design, though many manufacturers are now providing application-specific graphical interfaces (e.g., for guiding complex welds or performing surface finishing operations) on their teach pendants that are optimized for guiding the user through the programming process. While still ultimately demonstrating a process-focused design mentality, it is clear that human-centric design decisions are slowly manifesting in the design of process functionality.

Newer companies are looking to differentiate themselves through novel interfaces, largely centered around tablets or other mobile interfaces. Performance of these new robot systems has yet to be established, as does their compliance with robot safety standards, but the innovations of the interfaces does provide new mechanisms by which operators can interact with the robots. Whether or not these new interfaces follow any specific design guidelines, or if the design decisions prove to be influential or an improvement over the current state of the art, is yet to be determined.

3.6 Natural HRI

Natural HRI is the implementation of HRI with interfaces, controls, communication methods, and techniques designed to imitate how humans already interact within their environment with the goal of optimizing usability, understanding, efficiency, and situation awareness by reducing the amount of effort on the part of the human.

The inclination of designing interfaces based on the number of steps involved with a process is a natural one, but often leads to controls that, while they seem logical, are ultimately over-designed and not altogether helpful (e.g., see Fig. 3.13). Even more complicated is designing an interface for general-purpose machines like robots.

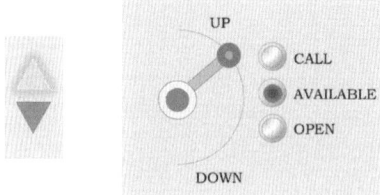

Fig. 3.13. Call buttons for elevators (left) are minimalist in design, indicating desired direction of travel, availability of a car, and the impending opening of the elevator door. A more function-oriented design (right) may focus more on providing inputs and outputs for more explicit information sharing.

The classical mindset for human-robot interaction is rooted in the expectation that interfaces dictate how one interacts with the system. A consequence of this mentality stems from the realization that most interfaces in industry are designed with the intent to train rather than the intent to be inherently usable.

Because, in general, humans accept that complex systems require training with the aid of manuals or personal instruction and, for the most part, humans consider modern robots complex systems, the industrial robot engineering community has largely neglected human centered design and usability in their robot interfaces. Additionally, industrial robots are typically viewed as merely additional machinery for accomplishing some additional task rather than individual agents that can be enabled with communication and decision making skills with artificial intelligence. When designing in robotics, you are not only designing for interactions between a human and an object, but also those between two agents capable of making their own decisions and carrying out their own actions in physical space. This means that designs for industrial robots are not often made with the full capabilities of modern technology in mind. Because of this neglect, it is difficult, in application, for modern industrial robots to be effectively used by and with a human, regardless of leaps in safety with the release of more collaborative robot systems.[76]

Because of the unique nature of the field, Natural HRI systems are composed of two subgroups:

(1) Interfaces for interacting with the robot as a tool, (i.e., control, reprogramming, and retasking)

(2) Interfaces and methods for interacting with the robot as another agent (i.e., Collaboration, Assistance, and Supervision)

Natural HRI systems of both types generally follow principles of human centered design to achieve interactions that are "natural" or are easily executed and do not require special help or training to be successful.

3.6.1 *Controller Design*

Interfaces for controlling, reprogramming, and retasking robots are of particular interest to the industrial robot community, as fully autonomous robots are not typically integrated into industrial workcells. This is true especially in cases where small or custom batches of product are produced, and robots need to be retasked quickly to keep up with demand. Enabling humans in the workcell to control, program, and teach robots in more intuitive ways stands to decrease the time for training of humans, and the time it takes for the human to reprogram the robot.[76]

When designing controllers for any system, engineers should consider the fundamental principles of interactions.[77]

- Affordances: Relationships between the capabilities of the agent (human or robot) and the properties of the object (robot) that determine how an object can be used.
- Signifiers: Any indicator that communicates appropriate behavior to the human.
- Mappings: Spatial and temporal relationship between controls and their action.
- Feedback: The communication of the results of an action.
- Constraints: Physical or social limitations of the system.

Of these, mappings pose particularly interesting questions in regard to robot control systems.

Humans are limited in their capabilities in terms of spatial orientation and motion planning for moving a body of non-human orientation through obstacles, and for accomplishing a task.[78] To compensate, "natural mappings", or mappings that take advantage of spatial analogies leading to immediate understanding, can be used.[77]

Teach by Demonstration (TbD) techniques are those where the human shows the robot how to accomplish the task, either by directly moving the robot by hand, or indirectly leveraging vision and machine learning. In both of these cases, the human can understand in their own physical space how the robot should be moving and how it can get there.

In the last few years, advanced virtual reality, augmented reality, and camera devices have become available to the consumer market, driven largely by the video game industry's desire for new peripherals. These new devices provide completely new ways for humans to interact with the physical and digital world. They have changed how we can interact with digital environments and allow for direct physical manipulation of digital objects. Using virtual reality, a human could embody a robot in some virtual space and train the robot using their own body to accomplish a task in real or virtual space in cases where the physicality, location, or nature of the robot is not conducive to direct manipulation.

These methods all seek to enable the human with spatial references that are immediately understandable to them. Alternative graphical user interfaces and 2D controls also stand to be usable though are less conducive to natural mappings.

3.6.2 *Communication and Collaboration*

Seamless and comprehensive communication is necessary to establish and maintain situation awareness and enable effective and natural collaboration with a robot co-worker. This can be done through a variety of mediums, with natural language communication, physical cues, or by leveraging real time augmented reality displays.

Natural language communications can be used between a robot and a human to establish their needs, next operations, and goals. Through new augmented reality technologies, robot systems can be enabled to explicitly show the human (either physically or digitally) potential issues and solutions, dramatically improving communication speed and efficiency.

Since the provision and maintenance of situation awareness is a motivating concern for these efforts, the presentation of reliable and understandable information is the primary focus. Emerging technology interfaces such as augmented and virtual reality displays paired with real-time digital models and 360° video naturally fit into this effort. These interfaces provide intuitive mechanisms for both feedback and control, enabling two-way communications regarding robot and operator performance, attention, and intent. This then propagates into state representations of the process and the human-robot team, in turn improving performance and safety.[79]

Small-scale and wearable technologies, in particular, are targeted as potential inputs to the human-robot-team observers. Wireless nine-degrees-of-freedom inertial measurement units, tilt sensors, light detectors, electromyographic inputs, and time-of-flight distance sensors are integrated into wearable sensor platforms (e.g., protective equipment), shared workpieces, and robot-mounted tools. Consumer products such as smart watches, head-mounted displays, and haptic gloves are also used as alternative interfaces to the robot systems. With the assumption of noisy or missing measurements, these ancillary platforms are then networked together, and the data fused to improve both the quality and the quantity of information to the collaborative team.

Considering all of the ways that autonomous robots can be utilized, enabling seamless interactions with both Natural HRI and good human-centered design techniques has the potential to change how robots are integrated and used in industry. Moreover, the quality of the interface has the potential to directly impact work-cell productivity, morale, and trust in human robot-teams. The effect that a good, well-informed design has on technologies in other fields is undeniable. Industrial robotics can learn from the mistakes of those who came before, and integrate designs with consideration for the human in the loop.

3.7 Conclusion

As the capabilities, design, and applications of industrial robots advance, the means by which human operators interact with the robots must necessarily evolve to keep pace. The environment and ethos of manufacturing are constantly changing, but the interfaces and interactions between humans and machines have stagnated. As the machines, themselves, evolve beyond the behemoths of repetition and strength, and become more adaptive and aware of their surroundings, the outdated archetypes of feedback and control ultimately fail in supporting future advancements.

Given that the designs of interfaces drive interactions between operators and machines, without adapting to changes in manufacturing paradigms, the interfaces themselves become the limiting factor in HRI. If the interfaces are ill-suited to meet the operators' experience, expertise, and role, the machine, itself, becomes obsolete. Similarly, if the interfaces cannot support the needs imposed by the environment and tasks for which the interactions with humans are intended, then, again, the machine is discarded.

Throughout the preceding sections, the state-of-the-art of human-robot interaction and interfaces has been presented. These sections highlighted the capabilities, requirements, performance metrics, and growing trends in HRI and HMI technologies. With the knowledge of how humans and robots currently interface with one another–and the expectations of future interactions—the metrics by which both HRI and HMI are evaluated are expected to help benchmark design paradigms, and drive innovation and performance into the next age of manufacturing robotics. As the technologies continue their trend of human-centric design, the blueprints of effective HRI and HMI pivot on both understanding how humans expect to interact with robots as collaborative teammates, and how these interactions impact the team's effectiveness in the manufacturing process.

References

1. Y. Chen, Y. Wu and H. Xing, A complete solution for agv slam integrated with navigation in modern warehouse environment, *Chinese Automation Congress (CAC), 2017,* pp. 6418–6423 (2017).
2. S. H. Lee and K. S. Chia, Auto guided vehicle control system using rotary encoders and proportional controller, *Int. J. Integ. Eng.* **9**, 2 (2017).
3. I. Draganjac, D. Miklić, Z. Kovačić, G. Vasiljević and S. Bogdan, Decentralized control of multi-agv systems in autonomous warehousing applications, *IEEE Transactions on Automation Science and Engineering* **13**(4), 1433–1447 (2016).
4. J. Verhaegh, J. Ploeg, E. van Nunen and A. Teerhuis, Integrated trajectory control and collision avoidance for automated driving. In *Proc. IEEE Int. Conf. Models Technol. Intell. Transport. Syst.,* pp. 116–121 (2017).
5. E. Helms, R. Schraft and M. Hägele, rob@work: Robot assistant in industrial environments. In *Proc. 11th IEEE Int. Workshop Rob. Human Interact. Commun.* , pp. 399–404 (2002).
6. K. Čapek, *RUR (Rossum's universal robots): a fantastic melodrama*. Doubleday, Page (1923).
7. I. Asimov, Runaround, *Astounding Science Fiction* **29**(1), 94–103 (1942).
8. ANSI/RIA R15.06, ANSI/RIA R15.06: American National Standard for Industrial Robots and Robot Systems - Safety Requirements, Standard, ANSI (1986a).
9. ANSI/RIA R15.06, ANSI/RIA R15.06: American National Standard for Industrial Robots and Robot Systems - Safety Requirements, Standard, ANSI (1992b).
10. ANSI/RIA R15.06, ANSI/RIA R15.06: American National Standard for Industrial Robots and Robot Systems - Safety Requirements, Standard, ANSI (1999c).
11. ISO 10218-1, 10218-1: Robots and robotic devices - Safety requirements for industrial robots - Part 1: Robots, Standard, ISO (2011).
12. ISO 10218-2, ISO 10218-2: Robots and robotic devices - Safety requirements for industrial robots - Part 2: Robot systems and integration, Standard, ISO (2011).
13. ANSI/RIA R15.06, ANSI/RIA R15.06: American National Standard for Industrial Robots and Robot Systems - Safety Requirements, Standard, ANSI (2012).
14. CAN/CSA-Z434-14, CAN/CSA-Z434-14: Industrial robots and robot systems, Standard, ANSI (2014).
15. JIS B 8433-1, JIS B 8433-1: Robots and robotic devices - Safety requirements for industrial robots - Part 1: Robots, Standard, JSA (2015).
16. JIS B 8433-2, JIS B 8433-2: Robots and robotic devices - Safety requirements for industrial robots - Part 2: Robot systems and integration, Standard, JSA (2015).
17. ISO/TS 15066:2016, ISO/TS 15066 - Robotics and robotic devices - Collaborative robots, Standard, International Organization for Standardization (ISO) (2016).

18. IEC 61496-1, IEC 61496-1: Functional safety of electrical/electronic/ programmable electronic safety-related systems - Part 1: General requirements, Standard, IEC (2010).

19. IEC 61496-2, IEC 61496-2: Safety of machinery - Electro-sensitive protective equipment - Part 2: Particular requirements for equipment using active opto-electronic protective devices (AOPDs), Standard, IEC (2013).

20. IEC 61496-3, IEC 61496-3: Safety of machinery - Electro-sensitive protective equipment - Part 3: Particular requirements for Active Opto-electronic Protective Devices responsive to Diffuse Reflection (AOPDDR), Standard, IEC (2008).

21. IEC 61496-4-3, IEC 61496-4-3: Safety of machinery - Electro-sensitive protective equipment - Part 4-3: Particular requirements for equipment using vision based protective devices (VBPD) - Additional requirements when using stereo vision techniques (VBPDST), Standard, IEC (2015).

22. J. A. Marvel and R. Norcross, Implementing speed and separation monitoring in collaborative robot workcells, *Rob. Comput.-Integ. Manuf.* **44**, 144–155 (2017).

23. D. G. Unfallversicherung, BG/BGIA risk assessment recommendations according to machinery directive, design of workplaces with collaborative robots, Tech. Rep. (2009).

24. B. Shneiderman, *Designing the User Interface: Strategies for Effective Human-Computer Interaction*. Pearson Education India (2010).

25. S. Park, Y. Jung and J. Bae, An interactive and intuitive control interface for a tele-operated robot (avatar) system, *Mechatronics* **55**, 54–62 (2018).

26. S. Stadler, K. Kain, M. Giuliani, N. Mirnig, G. Stollnberger and M. Tscheligi, Augmented reality for industrial robot programmers: Workload analysis for task-based, augmented reality-supported robot control. In *25th IEEE International Symposium on Robot and Human Interactive Communication (RO-MAN)*, pp. 179–184 (2016).

27. R. Behringer, S. Chen, V. Sundareswaran, K. Wang and M. Vassiliou, A distributed device diagnostics system utilizing augmented reality and 3D audio. In *Virtual Environments '99, Proceedings of the Eurographics Workshop,* pp. 105-114, Vienna, Austria (1999).

28. S. Webel, U. Bockholt, T. Engelke, N. Gavish, M. Olbrich and C. Preusche, An augmented reality training platform for assembly and maintenance skills, *Robotics and Autonomous Systems* **61**(4), 398–403 (2013).

29. M. Dahl, A. Albo, J. Eriksson, J. Pettersson and P. Falkman, Virtual reality commissioning in production systems preparation. In *2017 22nd IEEE International Conference on Emerging Technologies and Factory Automation (ETFA)*, pp. 1–7 (2017).

30. T. Weiblen and H. W. Chesbrough, Engaging with startups to enhance corporate innovation, *California Management Review* **57**(2), 66–90 (2015).

31. M. Rüßmann, M. Lorenz, P. Gerbert, M. Waldner, J. Justus, P. Engel and M. Harnisch, Industry 4.0: The future of productivity and growth in manufacturing industries, *Boston Consulting Group* **9**(1), 54–89 (2015).

32. J. C. Canedo, G. Graen, M. Grace and R. D. Johnson, Navigating the new workplace: Technology, millennials, and accelerating HR innovation, *AIS Transactions on Human-Computer Interaction* **9**(3), 243–260 (2017).

33. D. Feil-Seifer and M. J. Mataric, Defining socially assistive robotics. In *9th International Conference on Rehabilitation Robotics (ICORR 2005)* pp. 465–468 (2005).

34. A. Tapus, M. J. Mataric and B. Scassellati, Socially assistive robotics [grand challenges of robotics], *IEEE Robotics & Automation Magazine* **14**(1), 35–42 (2007).

35. S. W. Brose, D. J. Weber, B. A. Salatin, G. G. Grindle, H. Wang, J. J. Vazquez and R. A. Cooper, The role of assistive robotics in the lives of persons with disability, *American Journal of Physical Medicine & Rehabilitation* **89**(6), 509–521 (2010).

36. S. García-Vergara, L. Brown, H. W. Park and A. M. Howard, Engaging children in play therapy: The coupling of virtual reality games with social robotics. In *Technologies of Inclusive Wellbeing, A.L. Brooks, S. Brahnam and L.C. Jain (eds).* Springer (2014).

37. T. L. Chen, M. Ciocarlie, S. Cousins, P. M. Grice, K. Hawkins, K. Hsiao, C. C. Kemp, C.-H. King, D. A. Lazewatsky, A. E. Leeper, H. Nguyen, A. Paepcke, C. Pantofaru, W.D. Smart and L. Takayama, Robots for humanity: Using assistive robotics to empower people with disabilities, *IEEE Robotics & Automation Magazine* **20**(1), 30–39 (2013).

38. R. H. Taylor, A. Menciassi, G. Fichtinger, P. Fiorini and P. Dario, Medical robotics and computer-integrated surgery. In *Springer Handbook of Robotics, Bruno Siciliano and Oussama Khatib (eds).* Springer, (2016).

39. B. Scassellati and B. Hayes, Human-robot collaboration. *AI Matters* **1**(2), 22–23 (2014).

40. A. Freedy, E. DeVisser, G. Weltman and N. Coeyman, Measurement of trust in human-robot collaboration. In *International Symposium on Collaborative Technologies and Systems (CTS 2007)* pp. 106–114 (2007).

41. P. Rani, N. Sarkar, C. A. Smith and L. D. Kirby, Anxiety detecting robotic system–towards implicit human-robot collaboration, *Robotica* **22**(1), 85–95 (2004).

42. S. Nikolaidis, R. Ramakrishnan, K. Gu and J. Shah, Efficient model learning from joint-action demonstrations for human-robot collaborative tasks, in *Proceedings of the Tenth Annual ACM/IEEE International Conference on Human-Robot Interaction*. ACM, pp. 189–196 (2015).

43. ISO 9126:2001, ISO 9126-1 - Software engineering - Product quality - Part 1: Quality Model, Standard, International Organization for Standardization (2001).

44. ISO 25010:2011, ISO 25010 - Systems and software engineering - Systems and software quality requirements and evaluation (SQuaRE) - System and software quality models, Standard, International Organization for Standardization (2011).

45. T. L. Roberts and T. P. Moran, The evaluation of text editors: methodology and empirical results. *Commun. ACM* **26**(4), 265–283 (1983).

46. P. M. Fitts, The information capacity of the human motor system in controlling the amplitude of movement. *J. Exper. Psychol.* **47**(6), 381 (1954).

47. G. S. Snoddy, Learning and stability: a psychophysiological analysis of a case of motor learning with clinical applications. *J. Applied Psychol.* **10**(1), 1 (1926).

48. A. Steinfeld, T. Fong, D. Kaber, M. Lewis, J. Scholtz, A. Schultz and M. Goodrich, Common metrics for human-robot interaction. In *Proc. 1st ACM SIGCHI/SIGART Conf. on Human-Rob. Interact*, pp. 33–40 (2006).

49. M. Leonard, S. Graham and D. Bonacum, The human factor: the critical importance of effective teamwork and communication in providing safe care, *Quality and Safety in Health Care* **13**(suppl 1), i85–i90 (2004).

50. T. Fong, C. Thorpe and C. Baur, Collaboration, dialogue, human-robot interaction. In *Robotics Research*. Springer (2003).

51. K. N. Kaipa, A. S. Kankanhalli-Nagendra, N. B. Kumbla, S. Shriyam, S. S. Thevendria-Karthic, J. A. Marvel and S. K. Gupta, Addressing perception uncertainty induced failure modes in robotic bin-picking, *Rob. Comput.-Integ. Manuf.* **42**, 17–38 (2016).

52. S.-a. Knight and J. Burn, Developing a framework for assessing information quality on the world wide web. *Informing Science* **8** (2005).

53. C. Batini, C. Cappiello, C. Francalanci and A. Maurino, Methodologies for data quality assessment and improvement, *ACM Comput. Surveys (CSUR)* **41**(3), 16 (2009).

54. R. Y. Wang, A product perspective on total data quality management, *Comm. ACM* **41**(2), 58–65 (1998).

55. Y. Su and Z. Jin, A methodology for information quality assessment in the designing and manufacturing process of mechanical products. In *Information Quality Management: Theory and Application.* IGI Global (2006).

56. C. Batini and M. Scannapieco, Data quality concepts, methodologies and techniques, (2006).

57. M. A. Jeusfeld, C. Quix and M. Jarke, Design and analysis of quality information for data warehouses. In *Int. Conf. Concept. Model.,* pp. 349–362 (1998).

58. Y. W. Lee, D. M. Strong, B. K. Kahn and R. Y. Wang, Aimq: a methodology for information quality assessment, *Info. & Manage.* **40**(2), 133–146 (2002).

59. L. P. English, *Improving Data Warehouse and Business Information Quality.* J. Wiley & Sons (1999).

60. D. Loshin, *Enterprise Knowledge Management: The Data Quality Approach.* Morgan Kaufmann (2001).

61. L. L. Pipino, Y. W. Lee and R. Y. Wang, Data quality assessment, *Commun. ACM* **45**(4), 211–218 (2002).

62. M. J. Eppler and P. Muenzenmayer, Measuring information quality in the web context: A survey of state-of-the-art instruments and an application methodology. In *Proceedings of the Seventh International Conference on Information Quality (ICIQ-02),* pp. 187–196 (2002).

63. R. Y. Wang and D. M. Strong, Beyond accuracy: What data quality means to data consumers, *J. Manag. Info. Syst.* **12**(4), 5–33 (1996).

64. P. Falorsi, S. Pallara, A. Pavone, A. Alessandroni, E. Massella and M. Scannapieco, Improving the quality of toponymic data in the Italian public administration, *Proc. ICDT* **3** (2003).

65. M. Scannapieco, A. Virgillito, C. Marchetti, M. Mecella and R. Baldoni, The daquincis architecture: a platform for exchanging and improving data quality in cooperative information systems, *Info. Syst.* **29**(7), 551–582 (2004).

66. F. De Amicis and C. Batini, A methodology for data quality assessment on financial data, *Studies Comm. Sci.* **4**(2), 115–137 (2004).

67. M. R. Endsley, Towards a theory of situational awareness in dynamic systems, *Human Factors* **37**(1), 32–64 (1995).

68. D. G. Jones and M. R. Endsley, Sources of situation awareness errors in aviation, *Aviat Space Environ Med.* **67**(6), 507-512 (1996).

69. N. A. Stanton, P. R. Chambers and J. Piggott, Situational awareness and safety, *Safety Science* **39**, 3, pp. 189–204 (2001).

70. J. J. Salerno, E. P. Blasch, M. Hinman and D. M. Boulware, Evaluating algorithmic techniques in supporting situation awareness. In *Proceedings Volume 5813 Defense and Security. Multisensor, Multisource Information Fusion: Architectures,* pp. 96–104, Orlando, Florida (2005).

71. S. G. Hart, NASA-task load index (NASA-TLX): 20 years later, *Proc. Human Factors and Erg. Soc. Annual Meeting* **50**(9), 904–908 (2006).

72. S. G. Hart and L. E. Staveland, Development of NASA-TLX (Task Load Index): Results of empirical and theoretical research, *Adv. Psychol.* **52**, 139–183 (1988).

73. P. S. Tsang and V. L. Velazquez, Diagnosticity and multidimensional subjective workload ratings, *Erg.* **39**(3), 358–381 (1996).

74. G. B. Reid and T. E. Nygren, The subjective workload assessment technique: A scaling proce-
    dure for measuring mental workload, *Adv. Psychol.* **52**, 185–218 (1988).
75. S. Rubio, E. Díaz, J. Martín and J. M. Puente, Evaluation of subjective mental workload: A
    comparison of swat, nasa-tlx, and workload profile methods, *Appl. Psychol.* **53**(1), 61–86 (2004).
76. M. Zimmerman and J. Marvel, Smart manufacturing and the promotion of artificially-intelligent
    human-robot collaborations in small- and medium-sized enterprises, *AAAI Fall Symposium Se-
    ries: Symposium on Natural Communication for Human-Robot Collaboration* (2017).
77. D. Norman, *The Design of Everyday Things*. Basic Books (2013).
78. V. Lumelsky, On human performance in telerobotics, *IEEE Transactions on Systems, Man, and
    Cybernetics* **21**(5), 971–982 (1991).
79. J. A. Marvel, J. Falco and I. Marstio, Characterizing task-based human–robot collaboration
    safety in manufacturing, *IEEE Trans. Syst., Man, and Cybern.: Syst.* **45**(2), 260–275 (2015).

© 2020 World Scientific Publishing Company
https://doi.org/10.1142/9789811222849_0004

Chapter 4

Human-Robot Collaboration for Advanced Manufacturing by Learning from Multi-Modal Human Demonstrations

Weitian Wang, Yi Chen, Rui Li, Zhujun Zhang, Venkat Krovi, and Yunyi Jia

4.1 Introduction

Robots have been widely employed in a variety of applications in manufacturing for several decades[1,2] to perform industrial tasks such as painting, packaging, polishing, welding, etc.[3,4] In recent years, technological advancements and global competition have resulted in great challenges and more complicated working surroundings for manufacturing. The applications of robots are increasingly limited when manufacturing tasks become more flexible and more complex. For example, vehicle manufacturing is where most industrial robots are applied. Almost all automotive welding and painting jobs are currently being performed by robots. However, there is only a small proportion of robot applications in vehicle assembly tasks. Therefore, with regard to the increasing needs for flexibility, adaptability and complexity of assembly lines, a robot assisted system working with the human worker for the assembly tasks has numerous vital and outstanding advantages compared to traditional fully automatic machines.[5]

The emergence of collaborative robots[6] provides a great and promising solution to these complex hybrid assembly tasks.[7] Flexibility and diversity of the hybrid assembly process requires a close linkage between the collaborative robot and its human teammate. Human-robot collaboration has become a popular research topic in recent years due to the difficulty of automating the tasks. By taking advantage of human-robot collaboration, the tasks can be assigned to humans or robots based on their capabilities so as to leverage both of their unique expertise. Generally, robots can provide numerous merits such as working without fatigue and high productivity for huge and heavy assembly subtasks.[8] On the other hand, more intelligent and dexterous capacities can be supported by humans.[9]

4.2 Related Work and Motivation

Many studies have been conducted on human-robot collaboration in shared tasks.[10-14] For instance, in order to help human workers in fetch tasks and participate in manual arc welding, Schraft et al. presented a robot assistant system by combining human teammates' sensory skills and knowledge with the robot.[15] Shah et al. proposed a human-inspired execution system for human-robot collaborative tasks. They utilized insights from human-human teaming to make human-robot collaboration more natural and even reduce the human partner's idle time by 85%.[16]

Currently, in human-robot collaboration, the robots are mainly programmed and controlled by well-trained experts through off-line coding devices such as teaching pendants.[17] Meanwhile, the collaborative tasks are usually predefined to have the robot work with its human partner to perform repetitive tasks. Following this, the collaborative manipulations are typically triggered by human operators. However, these trigger mechanisms lead to inconvenient or even unsafe operations in some situations (e.g., human operators sometimes need to press a button to trigger robots when they are handling different tools or components in both hands). It is very challenging to apply these techniques to human-robot collaborative cases because of the extensive uncertainties generated by both task flexibility and human operations. For instance, different human operators may prefer to assemble the same product with different gestures, different tools and/or different sequences of operations.

More importantly, the human-robot collaboration process will be in disorder and may even be shut down if the task is changed. Modern manufacturing is seeing quick product updates with shorter life cycles and more customization[18] to meet the market needs. For example, automotive assembly lines have started to evolve to support flexible and reconfigurable product platforming approaches that are able to produce multiple vehicle variants on the same production line. The variability manifests itself in the form of multiple options for the sub-assemblies that need to be integrated. It will cost much human effort and time to recode the corresponding new task, which decreases the collaboration efficiency and task quality.

The challenges above have stimulated a variety of research in the community on lessening robot reprogramming time. One of such contemporary topic involves the robot executing tasks by learning from human demonstrations. By taking advantage of this approach, humans can pass knowledge to robots via demonstrated actions/behaviors without mastering considerable coding skills to have robots understand how to accomplish tasks.[19] The interaction in human-robot teams can be categorized as physical touch approaches and non-physical touch approaches. For the physical touch approaches, the human usually employs joystick teaching[20] and kinesthetic teaching[21] to show the demonstration information to the robot. The non-physical touch approaches provide more intuitive human-robot interaction means through more advanced equipment, e.g., robot learning from human demonstrations by vision systems[22,23] and wearable sensors,[24,25] which enhance the robot's ability to take more intuitive inputs.

However, these studies including teaching approaches and learning algorithms mostly attempt to have the robot exactly repeat human demonstrations, which are usually impractical in many dexterous tasks, such as vehicle assembly, due to the limitations of robot sensing and controls, as well as uncertainties in working environments. Instead, we need human and robot to collaboratively accomplish the task. To be more specific, we need robot to learn how to assist human to accomplish the task instead of replacing the human.

Therefore, considering the challenges of large growing needs of task flexibility, product customization, and human working preference, we propose a R^4 principle for human-robot teams in advanced manufacturing contexts. That is to say: robots should collaborate with humans actively to deliver/pick up the Right parts to/from the Right person at the Right time in the Right way under the shared working settings. It implies that the robot not only needs to master high-level cognitive abilities to understand human behaviors, but also should be aware of what next steps to do in the human-robot collaboration process.

It is in this context that we conduct our research on facilitating human-robot collaborative tasks, especially collaborative tasks in advanced manufacturing contexts, by learning from multi-modal human demonstrations.[26] In our studies, we propose a teaching-learning-collaboration (TLC) framework to make the human-robot team be increasingly productive and ubiquitous. For this purpose, we focus on investigating solutions for the robot to understand the ongoing humans' actions by learning from human demonstrations during human-robot collaboration processes. More importantly, the proposed approaches can also make the robot infer and plan the upcoming assembly steps using its learned strategies to assist its human partner to accomplish the shared tasks.

4.3 Overview of the TLC Framework

In this chapter, we introduce and discuss the results and findings of our recent studies—human-robot collaboration for advanced manufacturing by learning from multi-modal human demonstrations. We also derive several new results from human-robot collaborative tasks in manufacturing contexts. As shown in Fig. 4.1, the TLC framework includes three sections: human teaching, robot learning, and human-robot collaboration. In the human teaching process, human demonstrations can be acquired and parameterized by multiple approaches, such as natural language based approach, vision based approach, and wearable-sensing based approach. Using the extracted features of human demonstrations, we develop several robot learning algorithms for the robot to build its cognitive capability for the ongoing human-robot collaborative tasks. Following this, based on the learned knowledge, several human-robot collaboration models are designed for the robot to assist its human partner in collaborative tasks.

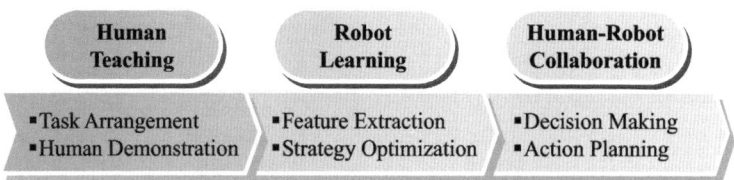

Fig. 4.1. Overview of the TLC framework.

The rest of this chapter is organized as follows. Section 4.2 describes how humans teach robots in collaborative tasks using multi-modal demonstrations, which contain natural language based demonstrations, vision based demonstrations, wearable-sensing based demonstrations, etc. The robot learning algorithms in our recent studies, including the maximum entropy inverse reinforcement learning (MaxEnt-IRL)[26,27] based learning algorithm, the convolutional neural network (CNN)[28] based learning algorithm, and the extreme learning machine (ELM)[29,30] based learning algorithm, are presented with their corresponding applications under manufacturing scenarios in Section 4.3. Section 4.4 describes the details about how robots assist human partners using their learned knowledge from human demonstrations. The proposed approaches are experimentally implemented in realistic human-robot collaborative scenarios, and the results are analyzed and discussed in Section 4.5. Finally, conclusions are drawn in Section 4.6.

4.4 Teaching Robots Using Multi-Modal Demonstrations

In this section, we introduce several approaches which are employed by humans to teach robots via multi-modal demonstrations in collaboration contexts. These approaches include teaching robots using natural language based demonstrations, teaching robots using vision based demonstrations, and teaching robots using wearable-sensing based demonstrations.

4.4.1 *Teaching Robots Using Natural Language Based Demonstrations*

4.4.1.1 *Representation of human-robot collaborative tasks*

In human-robot teams, the collaborative task and executors (human and robot) are able to be regarded as an integrated system. Considering product customization and human assembly preference, we assume that human actions which are used to teach the robot are stochastic and uncontrollable. In the collaboration process, the product parts must be manipulated by the human or the robot at any assembly step. The next operation of the parts by the executor is usually determined by the last operation. That is to say, the future state of the collaboration system is based solely on its present state. Therefore, the human-robot collaborative course is able to be represented by a finite-state Markov decision process (MDP),[31] which can be described by a tuple as

$$M = (S, A, T, \gamma, R), \tag{4.1}$$

where, $S = \{s_1, s_2, \cdots, s_K\}$ is the state space with a finite set of K states in the human-robot collaboration system, $A = \{a_1, a_2, \cdots, a_N\}$ is the action space with a finite set of N action of the human and robot in the human-robot collaboration system, $T = P(s'|s,a)$ is state transition probability from $s \in S$ to $s' \in S$ when the action $a \in A$ is taken in the collaborative task, $\gamma \in [0,1)$ is the discount factor, and $R = \{r_1, r_2, \cdots, r_K\}$ is the reward function which assigns a real-valued reward for taking the action $a \in A$ in the state $s \in S$.

In human teaching process, we denote the human demonstrations by

$$D = \{\zeta_1, \zeta_2, \cdots, \zeta_I\}, \tag{4.2}$$

where $\zeta_i, i \in I$ denotes one of the assembly policies that the human demonstrates to the robot. Additionally, each demonstration ζ_i can be depicted by system states and executors' actions as

$$\zeta_i = \{(s_i(0), a_i(0)), (s_i(1), a_i(1)), \cdots, (s_i(K), a_i(K))\}. \tag{4.3}$$

Therefore, the human-robot collaborative task can be characterized by the Markov decision process M with a set of given demonstrations D.

4.4.1.2 *Teaching robots using natural language*

In this work, human demonstrations D are performed by natural language instructions, which are processed from speech to text by the Google cloud speech recognition platform[32] and then transferred to formal representations for our robot learning algorithms based on our previous works.[26,33,34] Figure 4.2 illustrates the teaching process in human-robot collaboration.

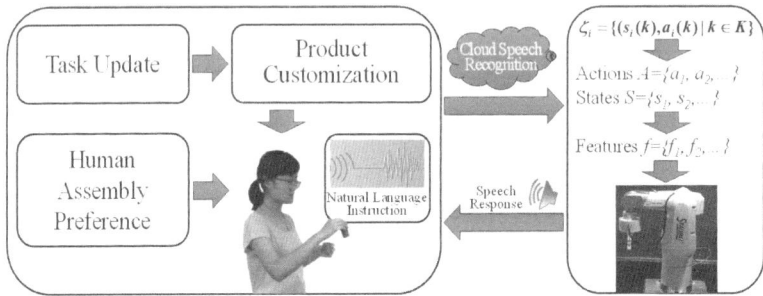

Fig. 4.2. Teaching robot via natural language based demonstrations. Human speech instructions are are processed from speech to text by the Google cloud speech recognition platform. After learning from human for each assembly step, the robot will rely human by speech via the voice synthesis system in the control system.

The human will perform the assembly sequence with speech instructions for the robot once the collaborative task is changed. Meanwhile, for a given product, different human partners may present diverse assembly preferences, which result in the product assembly sequence being uncertain. Therefore, the human actions and task states are detected dynamically by the feature extraction algorithm. For each assembly strategy ζ_i from human demonstrations D, we employ a feature function to characterize the internal state variation of the collaboration system. The feature function can be described as

$$f(\zeta_i) = \sum_{k=1}^{K} f(s_i(k), a_i(k)), \qquad (4.4)$$

where $f(s_i(k), a_i(k))$ denotes the feature activated by the action $a_i(k)$ applying to the state $s_i(k)$ in the assembly demonstration ζ_i.

4.4.2 Teaching Robots Using Vision Based Demonstrations

4.4.2.1 Formulation of collaborative tasks

In this approach, we propose a framework to model the typical process of human-robot collaborative mechanical assembly tasks as a time series, which include plentiful flexible manipulations (e.g. personalized preference in the sequence of object manipulating), massive strict constraints (e.g. force and tolerance), and dynamic environments. These features give rise to challenges to predefine and program each possible status or events that may happen in the collaborative assembly. However, any specific mechanical assembly process must follow a certain sequence of requirements to achieve a successful assembly which ensures that the assembled machine to work as it should be.

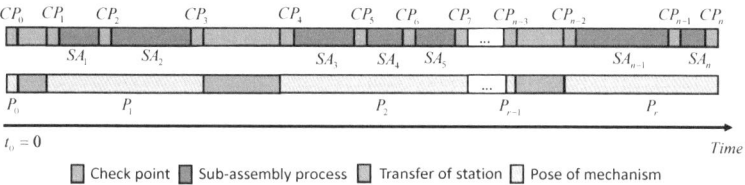

Fig. 4.3. Time series of collaborative assembly task.

Figure 4.3 illustrates the time series of a mechanical assembly task. From the mechanical perspective, *check points* CP_i represent a series of discrete states which are necessary and order-sensitive for the mechanism to ensure a successful assembly. A *sub-assembly* SA_i is defined as a set of maneuvers which make the state of mechanism transfer from current check point to next check point. The sub-assembly processes usually contain multiple flexible operations accomplished by human operators which are not order-sensitive and highly dependent upon the humans' personal preferences. A *pose* P_i represents a position and orientation of the semi-assembled machine that leads to comfortable and convenient installation of new parts for human operators corresponding to the current sub-assembly section. Therefore, an entire assembly task can be regarde as a time series consisti of check points, sub-assembly processes, hold and transfer of poses of semi-assembled machine.

For an arbitrary human-robot collaborative assembly task, the configurations of poses are always discrete and finite though their values are unknown in advance. The configurations of poses are mainly determined by the design of the mechanism and humans' personal performances. Therefore, the problem can be formulated as two steps. First, robots learn the applicable pose set $\{P\}$ for the co-assembly. In this process, the information of the tasks, such as operations of humans, status of semi-assembled mechanism in the process, are obtained through sequences of camera frames. Meanwhile, the applicable pose set $\{P\}$ are abstracted from the position feedback based on robot speed. Second, robots make a choice on the potential behaviors: either keep holding at the current pose or move to the next applicable pose based on given real-time images of the current situation in the shared workspace.

4.4.2.2 *Vision based teaching approach*

The system configuration for human teaching is illustrated in Fig. 4.4. In the human demonstration process, humans finish the assembly task by one-man operations based on personal performances in using hand tools and sequence of assembly. A typical one-round human-demonstration of the assembly task can be described as: (1) The human guides the end-effector of the robot to move the semi-assembled chassis to the pose P_1 which is comfortable and convenient for him/her to install the wheels on the driver side; (2) the human operator naturally installs the two wheels on the passenger side with hand tools. The maneuvers in this sub-assembly process are flexible. For example, which wheel is firstly installed is purely based on the human operator's personal preference; and (3) the human operator chooses the poses which are comfortable and convenient for him/her and repeats the previous two steps to install the front bumper, two wheels on the passenger side and the rear bumper.

For each round of demonstration, we can obtain four datasets of time series data: (1) The image time series which include the information of the mechanism status and human operations; (2) the time points when the robot speed turns to zero which indicate the human intends to hold the position of the end-effecter; (3) the time points when the robot, with zero-speed status, receives a non-zero speed command, which indicate the human wants to move the robot to next pose for further assembly; and (4) the positions of the end-effector when the robot speed turns to zero which indicate the pose set of the assembly task. Based on these four datasets, the images can be automatically and effectively labeled according to the time points.

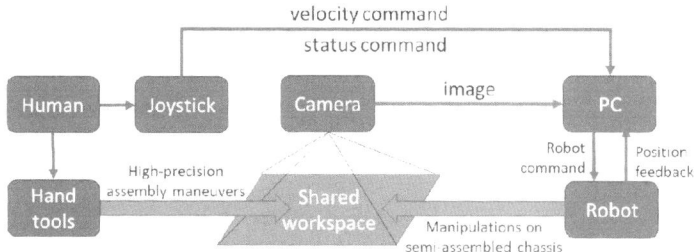

Fig. 4.4. System setup for human demonstration.

4.4.3 *Teaching Robots Using Wearable-sensing Based Demonstrations*

4.4.3.1 *Detection of human assembly intention*

We employ a wearable-sensing system for the human-robot team to acquire the human forearm postures and muscle activity information in human-robot collaboration process. The sensor system that we chose is Myo,[35] which can be worn at the driver's forearm and integrates with an inertial measurement unit (IMU)[36-38] and eight Electromyography (EMG) sensors.[39-41] The IMU chip contains an onboard digital motion processor (DMP) and a MPU-9150 module which consists of a 3 axis accelerometer, a 3 axis gyroscope and a 3 axis magnetometer. The detected information from the IMU and EMG sensors is preprocessed by a microcontroller unit (MCU) with a 32 bit Advanced RISC Machines (ARM) architecture 72MHz Cortex M4 CPU core. All the raw and calculated data are made available through a first-in-first-out (FIFO) buffer that is read by the MCU over the communication bus. The Bluetooth Low Energy (BLE) module on the main board is used for external communication between Myo and the client controller.[42]

The working principle of the information acquisition by this wearable-sensing system is presented in Fig. 4.5. The human forearm postures will be tracked and recorded by the IMU. This data includes acceleration and angular velocity information which can be fused to describe the forearm rotation angles. When the human performs assembly intentions, the electrical skeletal muscle activities from his forearm will be measured by the EMG sensors. This EMG information can be extracted to estimate human's finger motions such as wave-in, finger-spread, and fist. After being acquired and recorded, these two sets of data are further fused based upon the intention understanding algorithm to extract the practicable assembly intentions in human-robot collaborative tasks.

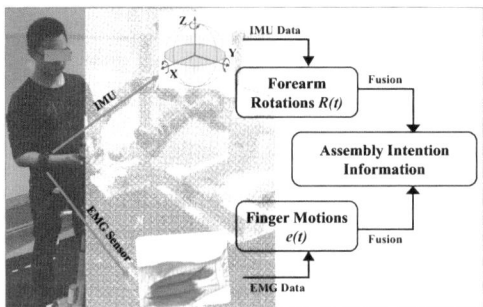

Fig. 4.5. The assembly   intentions represented by the forearm postures and muscle activity information.

4.4.3.2 *Wearable-sensing based teaching approach*

As shown in Fig. 4.5, when the human prepares to assemble a part in the collaborative task, his forearm posture information can be acquired and quantified by the IMU, which includes the raw 3-axis angular velocity data and the raw 3-axis acceleration data. Furthermore, these data can be fused into quaternions as

$$\begin{cases} q = [q_0, q_1, q_2, q_3]^T \\ q_0^{\,2} + q_1^{\,2} + q_2^{\,2} + q_3^{\,2} = 1 \end{cases}. \tag{4.5}$$

In order to calculate the forearm postures, Euler angles[43] are utilized to parameterize the forearm spatial rotations in the 3D work space. The Roll-Pitch-Yaw Euler angles can be represented by

$$R(t) = [\phi(t), \theta(t), \psi(t)]^T, \tag{4.6}$$

where t denotes the IMU sampling time, ϕ is the Roll rotation about the X-axis, θ is the Yaw rotation about the Y-axis, and ψ is the Pitch rotation about the Z-axis. Moreover, the Euler angles are able to be calculated by the quaternions as

$$R = \begin{bmatrix} \phi \\ \theta \\ \psi \end{bmatrix} = \begin{bmatrix} \arctan \dfrac{2q_0q_1 + 2q_2q_3}{1 - 2q_1^2 - 2q_2^2} \\ \arcsin(2q_0q_2 - 2q_1q_3) \\ \arctan \dfrac{2q_1q_2 + 2q_0q_3}{1 - 2q_2^2 - 2q_3^2} \end{bmatrix}. \tag{4.7}$$

Therefore, the human assembly intentions i_{WS_R} interpreted by the arm rotation can be represented as

$$i_{WS\_R} = [i_\phi, i_\theta, i_\psi]. \tag{4.8}$$

Meanwhile, the human finger motions can be calculated via the EMG signals which are collected from the human forearm's muscle activities. The EMG data acquired by the wearable-sensing system can be described as

$$E(t) = [e_1(t), e_2(t), \cdots, e_n(t)]^T,$$ (4.9)

where t is the sampling time of the EMG sensor, $e(t)$ is the output of each EMG sensor, and n is the number of EMG channels on the wearable-sensing system (n is 8 in Myo).

The raw EMG signal is a set of discrete points with positive and negative components. Along with the finger activities, the electric potentials generated by muscle cells have a distinct effect on the dispersion of the EMG signal. Therefore, to take advantage of the EMG data accurately, we adopt the standard deviation (StD) σ of the EMG data to extract the characteristics from the finger activities. The standard deviation could reflect the muscle activities observably. As shown in Fig. 4.6, the red line presents the variation of standard deviation with the EMG signals. A low standard deviation indicates that the human finger motions are slight, while a high standard deviation indicates that the EMG signal is motivated to spread out over a wider range by the human intention. In human-robot collaboration, the standard deviation can be calculated by

$$\sigma_i = \sqrt{\frac{1}{K} \sum_{k=1}^{K} \left(e_i(k) - \frac{1}{K} \sum_{k=1}^{K} e_i(k) \right)^2},$$ (4.10)

where $e_i(k), k = 1, 2, ..., K$ is a set of EMG signals, and K is the window size for determining the number of EMG data to be employed to calculate the stand derivation.

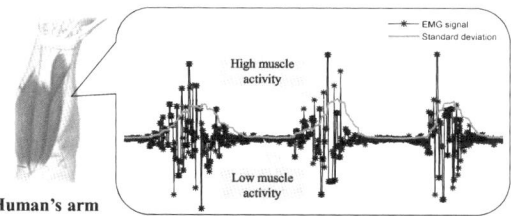

Fig. 4.6. Representing finger motions' effects by the standard deviation of EMG data.

Moreover, the human assembly intentions interpreted by the finger motions can be represented by

$$i_{WS\_\sigma} = [i_{\sigma1}, i_{\sigma2}, ..., i_{\sigma8}].$$ (4.11)

4.5   Robot Learning Strategies

4.5.1   *MaxEnt-IRL Based Learning Approach*

As presented in Section 4.2.1, if we regard human-robot collaboration process as a Markov decision process, the inverse reinforcement learning (IRL) is an effective approach to learn expert strategies from demonstrations.[44,45] As mentioned before, the human-robot co-assembly is able to be considered as a MDP with stochastic human actions. Therefore, this issue can be formulated as an IRL problem. In order to avoid ambiguities in choosing distributions, we employ maximum entropy inverse reinforcement learning (MaxEnt-IRL)[27] for the robot to learn from human demonstrations in this work. In MaxEnt-IRL, instead of assigning rewards subjectively in the MDP, the goal of this approach is to calculate the reward function $R = \{r_1, r_2, \cdots, r_k\}$ by learning from demonstrations. In the demonstrated assembly strategy ζ_i, the reward function, as expressed by Eq. (1.12), can be approximated by a linear combination of state feature functions with parameterized reward weights.

$$R(\zeta) = W^T f(\zeta) = \sum_{k=1}^{K} w_k^T f(s(k), a(k)),\qquad(4.12)$$

where $w_k = [w_{k1}, w_{k2}, \cdots, w_{kQ}]^T$ are a set of associated weights and each weight is employed to represent the preference on a specific assembly behavior in state k. $\|w\|_1 = 1$ and $w \geq 0$. $f = [f_1, f_2, \cdots, f_Q]^T$ are a set of bounded state features and each specifies the reward on a particular assembly behavior. They will be defined based on task customization requirements and human assembly preferences. Q is the number of features selected in each state. Moreover, we can get the demonstrated feature expectations of the assembly strategy ζ_i by

$$\widetilde{f(\zeta_i)} = \frac{1}{C} \sum_{i=1}^{C} f(\zeta_i),\qquad(4.13)$$

where C is the number of assembly strategy ζ_i in the demonstrations.

In the robot learning process, the feature expectation of the learned assembly strategy ζ^L by the robot can be expressed as

$$f(\zeta^L) = \sum_{i=1}^{C} P(\zeta_i) f(\zeta_i).\qquad(4.14)$$

When the robot learns from human assembly demonstrations, the feature expectation of the learner's assembly strategy should match the feature expectation from the human demonstration. Therefore,

$$f(\zeta^{L}) = \widetilde{f(\zeta_{i})}. \tag{4.15}$$

We assume that the MDP is deterministic in this work. Therefore, according to the MaxEnt-IRL principle, the distribution over assembly strategies under deterministic transitions can be defined as

$$P(\zeta_{i} \mid M, W) = \frac{e^{R(\zeta_{i})}}{Z(W)} = \frac{1}{Z(W)} \exp\left(\sum_{k=1}^{K} w_{k}^{T} f(s(k), a(k)) \right),$$

$$S.T.: f(\zeta^{L}) = \widetilde{f(\zeta_{i})} \tag{4.16}$$

where $Z(W)$ is the partition function.

Based on Eq. (1.16), it can be concluded that the robot's learning goal is to maximize the entropy of the distribution over assembly strategies from human demonstrations by optimizing the parameters in W. Furthermore, as presented by Eq. (1.17), optimizing the W to get the maximum entropy corresponds to maximize the likelihood of the demonstrated assembly strategies.

$$W^{*} = \arg\max_{W} \log P(\zeta_{i} \mid M, W)$$

$$= \arg\max_{W} \left(\sum_{k=1}^{K} w_{k}^{T} f(s(k), a(k)) - \log Z(W) \right). \tag{4.17}$$

4.5.2 *CNN Based Learning Approach*

When humans utilize the vision based teaching approach in human-robot collaborative tasks (as presented in Section 4.2.2), we can employ Convolutional Neural Network (CNN) for the robot to learn from human demonstrations. In this section, we introduce a CNN - based learning approach in human-robot collaboration.

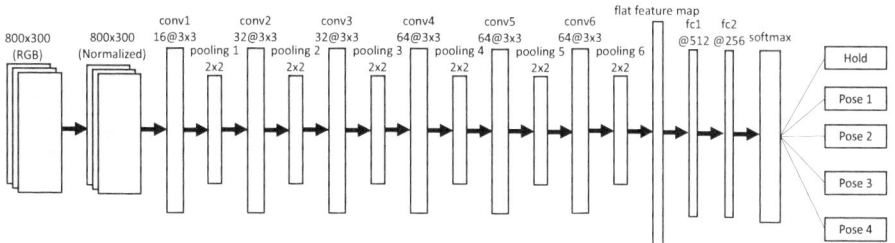

Fig. 4.7. Illustration of CNN structure.

The structure of CNN is illustrated in Fig. 4.7. The input of the CNN is an image patch extracted from the image of the shared workspace. In this work, the images of the shared workspace are sampled by a normal webcam camera with the resolution 1280 x 720 at 2Hz. The patch size on the original images is 1200 x 400 and this original image patch is resized to 800 x 300 as the input of the CNN (some samples of the input images are shown in Fig. 4.8). The input image patch is normalized before feeding into the convolutional layer.

Fig. 4.8. Some samples of the input images for CNN.

The output of CNN consists of the pose set corresponding to the collaborative assembly task and an additional class called hold, which means the robot should hold the current position. Six convolutional layers are used for feature learning, each convolutional layer is followed by a pooling layer with 2 x 2 maximum pooling. There are two fully connection layers with 512 and 256 neurons respectively after the flat feature maps. In the end, we use the classical softmax classifier.

Different from other deep learning cases whose datasets are manually labeled, the image frames of the workspace in the collaborative assembly process are automatically labeled based on the timestamps. Figure 4.9 illustrates the timing sequence to label the image time series data sampled in the human demonstration. First, we define a time interval Δt as human operation delay, which is the time interval from the end of the last sub-assembly process to the time point when humas start to guide the robot to the next pose. In this time interval, the sub-assembly at the pose P_k has been finished but the robot remained static. Thus, the images sampled in this period should be labeled by the next pose P_{k+1}. Second, the images sampled in the period when the semi-assembled chassis is transferring from pose P_k to the next pose P_{k+1} should be labeled by the next pose P_{k+1}. Third, the images sampled in any sub-assembly process when human is installing some new parts to the chassis should be labeled as "Hold".

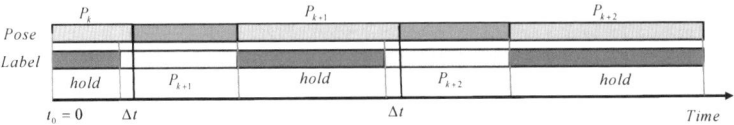

Fig. 4.9. The time sequence of image labeling.

4.5.3 *ELM Based Learning Approach*

In this section, we introduce an Extreme Learning Machine (ELM) based learning approach for the robot to learn human assembly strategies in human-robot collaborative tasks. ELM was developed for generalized single-hidden-layer feedforward neural networks (SLFNs) in which the hidden layer need not be alike.[46,47] In the robot learning process, the extracted wearable-sensing information of the assembly intention serves as the input to the ELM. In the hidden layer, the outputs of hidden nodes are mapping results by the activation function with respect to the input assembly intention features. Given a d dimensional assembly intention feature x, the feature mapping from hidden nodes can be described by

$$\mathbf{h(x)} = [g(a_1, b_1, \mathbf{x}), g(a_2, b_2, \mathbf{x}), ..., g(a_L, b_L, \mathbf{x})], \qquad (4.18)$$

where L is the number of hidden nodes in the ELM, $g(\mathbf{a}, b, \mathbf{x})$ is a nonlinear piecewise continuous function satisfying ELM universal approximation capability theorems,[46,48] $\mathbf{a}$ is the input weight vector, b is the hidden node bias, and $\{(\mathbf{a}_i, b_i)\}_{i=1}^{L}$ are randomly generated according to any continuous probability distribution.[49]

In ELM algorithms, $\mathbf{h(x)}$ maps the data from the d dimensional feature space to the L dimensional hidden-layer feature space $\mathbf{H}$. For the output layer, the output function for generalized SLFNs can be expressed as

$$f_L(\mathbf{x}) = \sum_{i=1}^{L} \beta_i h_i(\mathbf{x}) = \mathbf{h(x)}\beta, \qquad (4.19)$$

where $\beta = [\beta_1, \beta_2, ..., \beta_L]^T$ is the output weight vector between the hidden layer of L nodes to the M output nodes. Correspondingly, it can be seen that in human-robot assembly tasks, each output node $f_j(\mathbf{x})$, $j \in [1, M]$ of the ELM represents a type of assembly intention.

The final goal of assembly intentions learning by the robot is to find an optimal policy to understand what the human demonstrated to the robot in the teaching process. Compared to the traditional machine learning, the ELM tends to reach not only the smallest training error, but also the smallest norm of output weights.[49] Therefore, the robot learning process aims to minimize the approximation error as well as the norm of the output weights:

$$\underset{\beta \in \mathbf{R}^{l \times m}}{\text{Minimize}} \|\mathbf{H}\beta - \mathbf{T}\|^2 \text{ and } \|\beta\|, \qquad (4.20)$$

where $\mathbf{H}\beta$ is the actual output of the ELM, $\mathbf{H}$ is the hidden-layer output matrix:

$$H = \begin{bmatrix} h(x_1) \\ \vdots \\ h(x_N) \end{bmatrix} = \begin{bmatrix} g(a_1,b_1,x_1) & \cdots & g(a_L,b_L,x_1) \\ \vdots & \vdots & \vdots \\ g(a_1,b_1,x_N) & \cdots & g(a_L,b_L,x_N) \end{bmatrix}, \quad \text{and } T \text{ is the robot learning target}$$

matrix: $T = \begin{bmatrix} t_1^T \\ \vdots \\ t_N^T \end{bmatrix} = \begin{bmatrix} t_{11} & \cdots & t_{1m} \\ \vdots & \vdots & \vdots \\ t_{N1} & \cdots & t_{Nm} \end{bmatrix}$, where N is the number of feature samples of

human assembly intentions.

Moreover, the robot learning process can be formulized as a constrained-optimization problem with multi-output nodes:[49,50]

$$\text{Minimize}: L_{ELM} = \frac{1}{2}(\|\beta\|^2 + C\sum_{i=1}^{N}\|\xi_i\|^2), \tag{4.21}$$
$$\underset{\beta \in R^{l \times m}}{} $$
$$S.T. \ h(x_i)\beta = t_i^T - \xi_i^T, \ i \in [1, N]$$

where $\xi_i = [\xi_{i,1}, \xi_{i,2}, \cdots, \xi_{i,m}]^T$ is the approximation error vector of the m output nodes with respect to the input human intention feature sample in the robot learning process, and C denotes the regularization factor.

In human-robot collaborative tasks, the number of input human intention feature samples N is far more than the number of hidden nodes L. Based on the Karush-Kuhn-Tucker (KKT) theorem and Lagrange multiplier method,[49] the optimal learned policy β from human demonstrations can be got by

$$\beta^* = \left(\frac{I}{C} + H^T H\right)^{-1} H^T T, \tag{4.22}$$

where I is an identity matrix of dimension L.

4.6 Human-Robot Collaboration

Apart from having the robot imitate human demonstrations, it is necessary and meaningful to extend the existing work to make the robot actively assist its human partner in completing the shared tasks. In the human-robot collaboration process, we develop some approaches for the robot to assist its human partner to co-assemble the product by its learned assembly strategy from demonstrations, which contains the human assembly preferences and task customization requirements. We assume that the co-assembly task is executed step-by-step by the human and the robot using the product parts, which are common scenarios in practical manufacturing.

4.6.1 *Assisting Humans Based on MaxEnt-IRL*

As discussed in Section 4.3.1, once the human takes an assembly action $a_H(j-1)$ in the state $s(j-1)$, the collaboration system is transited to the state $s(j)$ with a certain probability which is consistent with the human's corresponding demonstration. Afterwards, the robot takes an action $a_H(j)$ in the state $s(j)$ to assist the human to assemble the product. As a result, the collaboration system is transited to a new state $s(j+1)$. Meanwhile, we get the reward of the robot's assisting action $a_R(j)$ in the collaborations as

$$r_R(s(j), a_R(j)) = w_j^T f(s(j), a_R(j)) . \tag{4.23}$$

According to the learned assembly strategy, we have a corresponding optimal reward $r^l(s^l(j), a^l(j))$ in this state. Therefore, in order to keep the robot assisting its human partner in line with the learned assembly strategy, these two rewards should approximate with each other as much as possible. Furthermore, by this principle, the expected robot action $a_R^*(j)$ for the system state $s(j)$ can be deduced by

$$a_R^*(j) = \arg\min_{a_R} \left| r_R(s(j), a_R(j)) - r^l(s^l(j), a^l(j)) \right| . \tag{4.24}$$

In human-robot collaboration, Eq. (1.24) is utilized for the robot to assist humans to guarantee the co-assembly process to be performed.

4.6.2 *Assisting Humans Based on CNN*

The robot can assist humans in collaborative assembly by deploying the trained CNN. The scenario of the shared workspace is sampled at a higher frequency (10Hz) than the data acquisition (DAQ) process. The images are cropped, resized and normalized with the same configurations as DAQ and fed into the trained CNN. The output of the CNN can be directly used to drive the robot. Among the output classes of the CNN, each pose label corresponds to a position control command and a constant non-zero speed control command to move the end-effector to a corresponding position and orientation with a given constant speed. The "Hold" label corresponds to a zero-speed control command to stop the robot immediately.

4.6.3 *Assisting Humans Based on ELM*

Using the learned knowledge, the robot is able to continue working online to assist the human in assembly tasks. When the human presents his/her assembly intentions online, the new intention features can be acquired by sensor systems (e.g. vision system and wearable-sensing system). Consequently, based on the robot's optimal learned policy, the online prediction outputs of each assembly intention via the ELM algorithms can be calculated by

$$\mathbf{f}(\mathbf{x}) = \mathbf{h}(\mathbf{x})\boldsymbol{\beta} = \mathbf{h}(\mathbf{x})\left(\frac{\mathbf{I}}{C} + \mathbf{H}^T\mathbf{H}\right)^{-1}\mathbf{H}^T\mathbf{T} . \tag{4.25}$$

Furthermore, according to the online output vector $\mathbf{f}(\mathbf{x})$ of possible human intentions, it can be seen that the predicted assembly intention of the given input features corresponds to the index number of the output node with the maximum value. Consequently, the online predicted assembly intention can be calculated by

$$I_p = \arg\max_{i\in[1,\,M]} f_i(\mathbf{x}) , \tag{4.26}$$

where $f_i(\mathbf{x}) \in \mathbf{f}(\mathbf{x})$. Therefore, via Eq. (4.26), the robot is able to predict human intentions online to assist the human in collaborative assembly tasks.

4.7 Experimental Results and Analysis

4.7.1 *Human-robot Co-assembly Based on MaxEnt-IRL*

4.7.1.1 *Task description*

The hybrid assembly tasks, which are accomplished sequentially by human-robot collaboration, are very common in manufacturing. In order to make it much more applicable and practical, we employ some general hybrid assembly tasks to verify and validate the efficiency and advantage of the developed teaching, learning, and collaboration approaches. As shown in Fig. 4.10, there are two different colors (red and blue) of parts on an assembly line, and each color contains three sizes (small, middle, and large). For different usages, these parts can be assembled according to customization requirements to be diverse products.

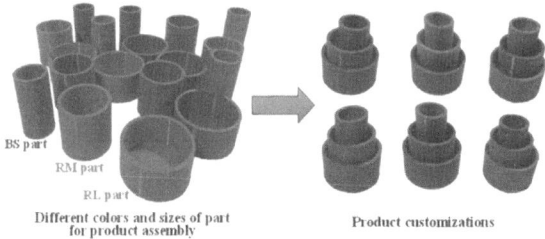

Fig. 4.10. Parts-to-products according to customization requirements.

Table 4.1. The executors' optional actions in each assembly step.

(1) RM to RL	(2) RS to RL	(3) RS to RM	(4) BM to BL
(5) BS to BL	(6) BS to BM	(7) BM to RL	(8) BS to RL
(9) BS to RM	(10) RM to BL	(11) RS to BL	(12) RS to BM

Once getting a new co-assembly task, the human re-teaches the robot using natural language instructions. As presented in Fig. 1.10, according to the task allocation, there are in total six kinds of parts (Red Small (RS), Red Middle (RM), Red Large (RL), Blue Small (BS), Blue Middle (BM), and Blue Large (BL)) for the executors (human and robot) to pick up in each step. Additionally, for any two parts assembly, the relatively small one should be put into the relatively large one (small to middle, or middle to large). Therefore, as shown in Table 4.1, the executors have twelve optional actions in each step and all the options are independent of each other. As a result, the task will present twelve different state features by these actions in each step.

4.7.1.2 *Learning from human demonstrations*

Based on the developed teaching and learning approaches based on MaxEnt-IRL, as shown in Fig. 4.11, the human teaches the robot online via the natural language to assemble products according to her assembly preference. The task is repeated 10 times to objectively detect the features of human assembly preferences and product customizations. After receiving the teaching instruction in each step, the robot will repeat it to the human by speech response. The teaching procedure of the first product is shown in Fig. 4.11 (1) ~ (6). First, the human picks up the RS part and puts it into the RM part. Afterwards, she puts the RM part into the BL part. The assembly process of the second product is presented in Fig. 4.11 (7) ~ (12), which demonstrates: (a) putting the BS part into the BM part; (b) putting the BM part into the RL part. Using the MaxEnt-IRL algorithm, the robot is able to update online its assembly cognition from the demonstrations.

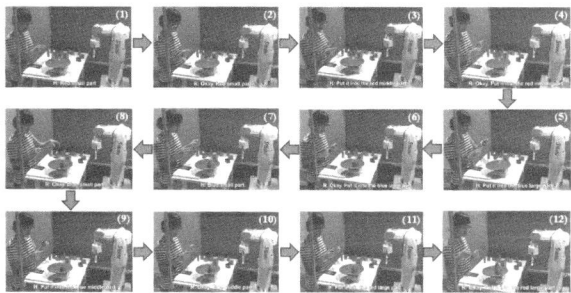

Fig. 4.11. Robot learning from the human assembly demonstrations.

4.7.1.3 *Human-robot co-assembly*

In the human-robot co-assembly process, the learned assembly strategy is employed online by the robot to assist the human to accomplish the above products. The parts' attributes, including positions, types, colors, and shapes, are detected by a 3D vision system. The co-assembly processes of these two products are shown in Fig. 4.12 and Fig. 4.13, respectively.

From Fig. 4.12 (1) ~ (2), it can be observed that the human puts the RS part into the RM part with the speech instructions. After making an action decision according to the dynamic task states using the TLC approach, the robot picks up the BL part and delivers it to the human with a speech response, as shown in Fig. 4.12 (3). Then the robot picks up the assembled product from the human and puts it into the container. Likewise, after the human puts the BS part into the BM part in Fig. 4.13 (1) ~ (2), the robot actively delivers the RL part to its human partner, as illustrated in Fig. 4.13 (3). Afterwards, it assists the human to put the completed product into the container. From the co-assembly results, we can conclude that the robot correctly assists its human partner in product assembly according to the customization requirements and human assembly preferences.

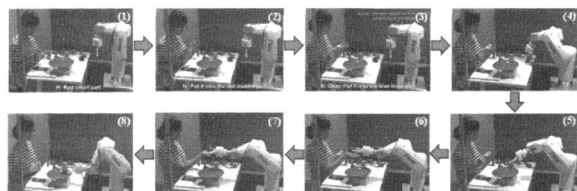

Fig. 4.12. Human-robot collaboration for the first product assembly.

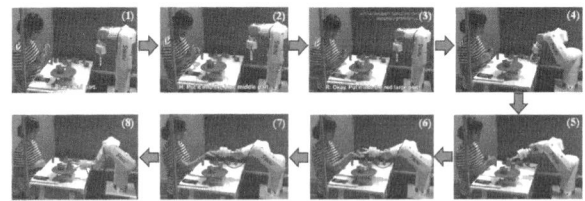

Fig. 4.13. Human-robot collaboration for the second product assembly.

4.7.1.4 *Evaluation*

In this experiment, we conduct an accuracy test of the robot collaborative action decision in human-robot co-assembly. According to the optional actions listed in Table 1, we randomly allocate 30 feasible customized assembly tasks and divide them into 3 groups equally. Each group is conducted by an independent individual, respectively. For each task, the human partner has a corresponding preference to accomplish it. In order to detect the human preferences objectively in the assembly process, each task is repeated 10 times.

The learned assembly strategies are generated in the teaching-learning process. Following this, they are employed as inputs for the human-robot co-assembly model to decide online the robot's collaborative actions. Like the descriptions in Fig. 4.12 and Fig. 4.13, the robot should make two action decisions to assist the human in each task. Hence, there should be 20 collaborative actions from the robot in each group. As shown in Table 4.2, the average accuracy of the expected action decision is 95%, which presents a high collaboration quality between the human and robot. However, if the features of human demonstrations are equally distributed, they are not able to represent the human assembly preference distinctly. Therefore, some unexpected robot actions will be generated in the human-robot collaboration. To solve this, more human demonstrations of each task should be presented to the robot, meanwhile, the human should perform the assembly demonstrations naturally according to his/her preferences without intentional misleading in the teaching process. The accuracy performance comparisons of our approach and some previous studies are shown in Table 4.3. We can evaluate the approaches' performance by their average output accuracy even the tasks are different. It can be seen that the proposed approach has a higher accuracy than these methods.

Table 4.2. The accuracy of the expected robot action decision.

Group No.	Robot Actions	Expected	Unexpected	Accuracy
1	20	19	1	95%
2	20	20	0	100%
3	20	18	2	90%

Table 4.3. Comparisons of our approach to the previous works.

Works	Algorithm	Average accuracy
Our Approach	MaxEnt-IRL	95%
Grigore et al. [51]	HMM	75.63%
Ryoo et al. [52]	SVM	72.9%
Mainprice et al. [53]	GMM	92%
Cohen et al. [54]	MIPM	83%

4.7.2 *Human-robot Co-assembly Based on CNN*

4.7.2.1 *Task description*

In this experiment, we have the human-robot team co-assemble a vehicle model. As shown in Fig. 4.14, the vehicle model contains four wheels, the front bumper, the rear bumper, the semi-assembled chassis, and the corresponding screws and washers for each component. In the human-robot collaboration, we make the robot hold the hulky semi-assembled chassis. When the human operator finishes a sub-assembly, the robot can collaboratively move it to the correct poses to assist the human operator to install the tires and bumpers of the vehicle conveniently and comfortably. Moreover, when the human operator intervenes with robot motions, the robot can stop immutably to avoid collisions.

Fig. 4.14. The vehicle model used in the collaborative task.

4.7.2.2 *Learning from human demonstrations*

To simplify the task, the pose P_i is represented by the orientation of the semi-assembled chassis with respect to the z-axis of the end-effector. The distribution of the poses is shown in Fig. 4.15. Each curve represents an assembly demonstration. The initial pose of the semi-assembled chassis is $P_0 = 0°$. First, the human operator turns the chassis to the next pose $P_1 \approx -80°$. Then the chassis is held at the pose P_1 for $30 \sim 40$ seconds until the assembly of the two wheels on the driver side is finished. The sub-assembled chassis is presented as a new state after the two wheels have been installed. Following this, the human operator turns the chassis to the pose $P_2 \approx 0°$, which is convenient for the human to install the front bumper. The pose is held by the robot for around 100 seconds because the installation of the front bumper is more time-consuming than the last sub-assembly process. The sub-assembly processes of the two wheels on the passenger side and the rear bumper are also indicated in the curve in the same way. Since human operators naturally demonstrate the assembly process and the poses are the accurate position feedback of the robot, there are some differences (typically is $\pm3°$) for each pose in different demonstrations. Therefore, the mean values of multiple demonstrations are applied as the target poses for the assembly task.

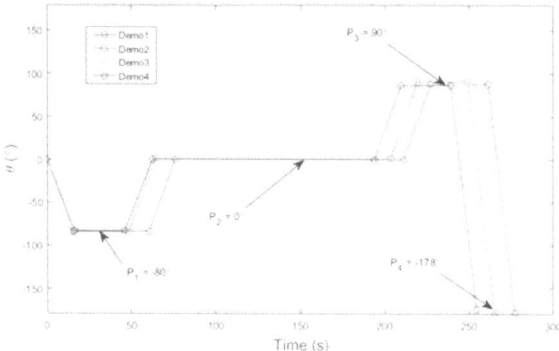

Fig. 4.15. Poses presented in human demonstrations.

In the learning efficiency perspective, the robot should accomplish the learning process in few demonstrations of specific tasks for the collaborative assembly applications. In our experiment, we performed four demonstrations. Table 4.4 illustrates the number of the images for each demonstration process. Since the images are sampled with a constant frequency at 2Hz and the time consuming of pose transferring is much less than that of sub-assembly process, the images for each pose which tend to move the robot is less than the images for hold state which include all the sub-assembly processes for this task. The total number of images is slightly different from each demonstration depending on the speed of the human operator to finish the task.

Table 4.4 Dataset of each demonstration process.

Class	D1	D2	D3	D4
:	38	39	34	39
Images of 0°	38	39	37	39
Images of 90°	39	37	39	38
Images of -178°	39	41	38	37
Images of Hold	510	514	486	462
Total	664	670	634	615

We deploy the training, validation, and testing with two different configurations. First, we only use the first demonstration to train and the third demonstration to determine the parameters of the neural networks. The fourth demonstration is used as test dataset for the trained neural networks. The training process runs for 100 epochs, meanwhile, the entire images of the third demonstration as the validation set are fed to the neural networks for every 500 iterations. The parameters of the neural networks are saved whenever we get a better result in validation. Figure 4.16 shows the process of this one-demonstration training configuration. The best validation result is 96.21% correct prediction with 54,000 iterations. The trained neural networks with the parameter corresponding to the minimum validation error get a correct prediction rate as 98.34% with the test dataset.

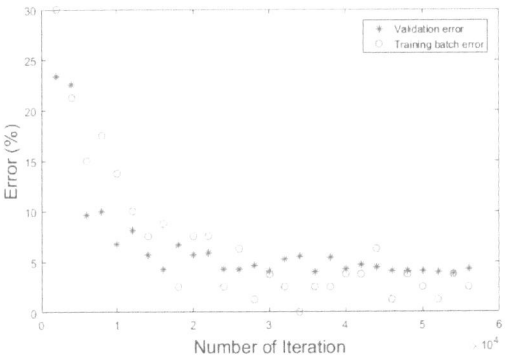

Fig. 4.16. The training process of one-demonstration training configuration.

Following this, we utilize the first and the second demonstrations to train the neural networks so that the training dataset increased to 1,334 images in total. The third and the fourth demonstrations are still used for validation and testing. Figure 4.17 presents the training process of this two-demonstration training dataset. The best validation result is 98.26% correct prediction with 120,000 iterations. The trained neural networks with the parameter corresponding to the minimum validation error get a correct prediction rate of 98.49% with the test dataset. The training, validation, and teasing results of both configurations are summarized in Table 4.5.

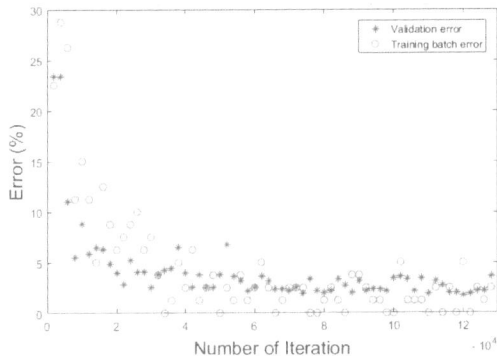

Fig. 4.17. The training process of two-demonstration training configuration.

Table 4.5. Training, validation, and testing results.

Training Dataset	Validation Dataset	Test Dataset	Validation (%)	Test (%)
D1	D3	D4	96.21	98.34
D1 & D2	D3	D4	98.26	98.49

4.7.2.3 *Human-robot co-assembly*

We employ a webcam to capture the real-time images of the shared workspace. Each image fed into the CNN generates a control command to directly drive the robot. Although the training and test errors are 1.74% and 1.51% respectively, the errors are introduced by the noise of the origin of the data (1%~2%). When the sub-assembled mechanism arrives in a new pose, but the human operator does not start to assemble any new parts, there are typically 3 ~ 5 image frames that are the same as each other. These frames might be classified as different labels, either the new pose or the "Hold", with the timestamp-based automatic labeling algorithm. However, it does not lead to incorrect robot motion or incorrect pose transferring in our test, because the robot arrives and stops at the new pose correctly. The CNN then outputs "Hold" when the human operator continues assembling the new parts onto the semi-assembled mechanism.

Some scenarios of the human-robot collaborative assembly are illustrated in Fig. 4.18 (a) ~ (f): (a) illustrates the initial state of the system; (b) illustrates that the robot is automatically turning the semi-assembled chassis to –80°, which is applicable for the human operator to install the wheels on the driver side; (c) illustrates that the robot holds the position of the semi-assembled chassis when the human is installing the wheels on the chassis; (d) illustrates that the robot starts to turn the next pose which is suitable for the human to install front bumper after the two wheels on driver side have been installed; (e) and (f) illustrate that the front bumper is installed by the human operator.

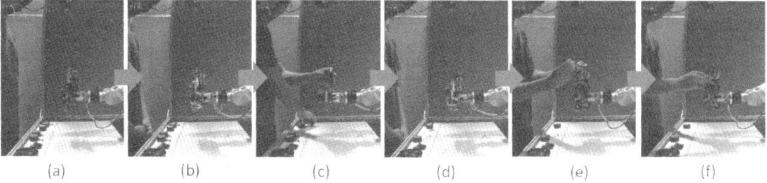

Fig. 4.18. Process of collaborative assembly with CNN implemented.

4.7.2.4 *Evaluation*

In the human motion recognition perspective, the template matching based approaches[55-57] need a variety of processes, such as background modeling, background subtraction, and template matching, to accomplish the human detection in dynamic environments. Table 4.6 illustrates the computational time of three different human detection algorithms. The detection speed generally does not meet the requirement of real-time motion control in human-robot collaborative assembly applications. The proposed approach can achieve a higher detection speed and can be used in real-time control.

Table 4.6. Comparisons of computational time of human detection.

Methods	Computational Time (ms)
Proposed Method	100
Multi-sensor based approach [55]	389
UKF-based Motion Tracking [56]	240
HOG descriptor based approach [57]	747

4.7.3 *Discussion*

Although these approaches are experimentally implemented in several typical assembly tasks, we can also extend their applications to more complicated human-robot collaboration scenarios through the similar teaching-learning-collaboration process. In the experiments, we also found some potential problems that need to be addressed during human teaching processes. For the natural language based teaching approach, its performance is usually affected by machine noise in working environments. To this end, we will develop a fuzzy recognition algorithm to improve human assembly instruction understanding based on the outputs of the Google cloud speech recognition platform. For the vision based teaching approach, its recognition accuracy is easily influenced by the background of the workspace. To solve this, we will refine the CNN structure to improve the system's antijamming capability. In addition, the recognition accuracy of these approaches is not 100%, and we still need to improve the robot learning methods to be more robust by integrating other advanced learning algorithms.

4.8 Conclusion

In this work, we have proposed a systematic framework of teaching-learning-collaboration for human-robot collaborative tasks in advanced manufacturing contexts. In this framework, we have presented several approaches which can be employed by humans to teach robots according to their working preferences via multi-modal demonstrations, including natural language based demonstrations, vision based demonstrations, and wearable-sensing based demonstrations. Following this, the learning algorithms, such as the maximum entropy inverse reinforcement learning, the convolutional neural network, and the extreme learning machine, have been developed for robots to learn from human demonstrations. Based on these algorithms, the robots are able to construct the task cognition and action planning policy independently. Moreover, we have proposed several human-robot collaboration approaches based on robots' learned knowledge to have the robots assist their human partners in finishing the shared tasks. We have conducted some practical human-robot co-assembly experiments on a collaborative robotic platform. Experimental results and findings demonstrated the efficiency and advantages of the proposed approaches in human-robot collaborative tasks.

This work was supported by the National Science Foundation under Grant IIS-1845779.

References

1. J. J. Craig, *Introduction to Robotics: Mechanics and Control, Volume 3.* Pearson Prentice Hall (2005).
2. L. Westerlund, *The Extended Arm of Man: A History of Industrial Robots.* Informationsforlaget (2000).
3. J. Krüger, R. Bernhardt, D. Surdilovic, and G. Spur, Intelligent assist systems for flexible assembly, *CIRP Annals Manufacturing Technology* **55**, 29–32 (2006).
4. G. Michalos, S. Makris, N. Papakostas, D. Mourtzis, and G. Chryssolouris, Automotive assembly technologies review: Challenges and outlook for a flexible and adaptive approach, *CIRP Journal of Manufacturing Science and Technology* **2**, 81–91 (2010).
5. W. Wang, R. Li, Z. Diekel, Y. Chen, Z. Zhang, and Y. Jia, Controlling object hand-over in human-robot collaboration via natural wearable sensing, *IEEE Transactions on Human Machine Systems* **49**(1), 1–12 (2018).
6. W. Wannasuphoprasit, P. Akella, M. Peshkin, and J. E. Colgate, Cobots: A novel material handling technology. In *Proceedings of International Mechanical Engineering Congress and Exposition (ASME'98 WA/MH 2),* Anaheim (1998).
7. W. Wang, Y. Chen, Z. M. Diekel, and Y. Jia, Cost functions based dynamic optimization for robot action planning. In *Proc. 2018 ACM/IEEE International Conference on Human Robot Interaction,* pp. 277–278 (2018).
8. D. Surdilovic and J. Radojicic, Robust control of interaction with haptic interfaces. In *Proceedings 2007 IEEE International Conference on Robotics and Automation,* pp. 3237–3244 (2007).
9. J. Krüger, T. K. Lien, and A. Verl, Cooperation of human and machines in assembly lines, *CIRP Annals - Manufacturing Technology* **58**, 628–646 (2009).

10. H. Bley, G. Reinhart, G. Seliger, M. Bernardi, and T. Korne, Appropriate human involvement in assembly and disassembly, *CIRP Annals - Manufacturing Technology* **53**, 487–509 (2004).

11. J. Shah and C. Breazeal, An empirical analysis of team coordination behaviors and action planning with application to human–robot teaming, *Human Factors: The Journal of the Human Factors and Ergonomics Society* **52**, 234–245 (2010).

12. T. Lien and F. Rasch, Hybrid automatic-manual assembly systems, *CIRP Annals-Manufacturing Technology* **50**, 21–24 (2001).

13. W. Wang, R. Li, Z. M. Diekel, and Y. Jia, Robot action planning by online optimization in human-robot collaborative tasks, *International Journal of Intelligent Robotics and Applications* **2**, 161–179 (2018). doi: 10.1007/s41315-018-0054-x.

14. W. Wang, N. Liu, R. Li, Y. Chen, and Y. Jia, HuCoM: A Model for Human Comfort Estimation in Personalized Human-Robot Collaboration, In *ASME 2018 Dynamic Systems and Control Conference*, pp. 1–6 (2018).

15. R. Schraft, E. Helms, M. Hans, and S. Thiemermann, Man-Machine-Interaction and co-operation for mobile and assisting robots. In *Proceedings of Fourth International ICSC Symposium on Engineering of Intelligent Systems (EIS 2004)*, Madeira, Portugal, 2004.

16. J. Shah, J. Wiken, B. Williams, and C. Breazeal, Improved human-robot team performance using chaski, a human-inspired plan execution system. In *Proceedings of the 6th International Conference on Human-Robot Interaction*, pp. 29–36 (2011).

17. J. Léger and J. Angeles, Off-line programming of six-axis robots for optimum five-dimensional tasks, *Mechanism and Machine Theory* **100**, 155–169 (2016).

18. J. Wind and A. Rangaswamy, Customerization: The next revolution in mass customization, *Journal of Interactive Marketing* **15**, 13–32 (2001).

19. B. D. Argall, S. Chernova, M. Veloso, and B. Browning, A survey of robot learning from demonstration, *Robotics and Autonomous Systems* **57**, 469–483 (2009).

20. J. Chen and A. Zelinsky, Programing by demonstration: Coping with suboptimal teaching actions, *The International Journal of Robotics Research* **22**, 299–319 (2003).

21. A. G. Billard, S. Calinon, and F. Guenter, Discriminative and adaptive imitation in uni-manual and bi-manual tasks, *Robotics and Autonomous Systems* **54**, 370–384 (2006).

22. M. Ferreira, P. Costa, L. Rocha, and A. P. Moreira, Stereo-based real-time 6-DoF work tool tracking for robot programing by demonstration, *The International Journal of Advanced Manufacturing Technology* **85**, 57–69 (2016).

23. L. Bodenhagen, A.R. Fugl, A. Jordt, M. Willatzen, K.A. Andersen M.M. Olsen, R. Koch, H.G. Petersen, and N. Kruger, An adaptable robot vision system performing manipulation actions with flexible objects, *IEEE Transactions on Automation Science and Engineering* **11**(3), 749–765 (2014).

24. J. Aleotti and S. Caselli, Learning manipulation tasks from human demonstration and 3D shape segmentation, *Advanced Robotics* **26**, 1863–1884 (2012).

25. M. Javaid, M. Žefran, and A. Yavolovsky, Using pressure sensors to identify manipulation actions during human physical interaction. In *24th IEEE International Symposium on Robot and Human Interactive Communication (RO-MAN)*, pp. 670–675 (2015).

26. W. Wang, R. Li, Y. Chen, Z. Diekel, and Y. Jia, Facilitating Human-Robot Collaborative Tasks by Teaching-Learning-Collaboration from Human Demonstrations, *IEEE Transactions on Automation Science and Engineering* **16**(2), 1–14 (2018). doi: 10.1109/TASE.2018.2840345.

27. B. D. Ziebart, A. L. Maas, J. A. Bagnell, and A. K. Dey, Maximum entropy inverse reinforcement learning. In *Proceedings of the 23rd AAAI Conference on Artificial Intelligence,* pp. 1433–1438 (2008).

28. A. Krizhevsky, I. Sutskever, and G. E. Hinton, Imagenet classification with deep convolutional neural networks. In *Advances in Neural Information Processing Systems*, pp. 1097–1105 (2012).

29. G.-B. Huang, Q.-Y. Zhu, and C.-K. Siew, Extreme learning machine: Theory and applications, *Neurocomputing* **70**, 489–501 (2006).

30. W. Wang, R. Li, Y. Chen, and Y. Jia, Human Intention Prediction in Human-Robot Collaborative Tasks. In *Proc. 2018 ACM/IEEE International Conference on Human-Robot Interaction*, pp. 279–280 (2018).

31. P. Abbeel and A. Y. Ng, Apprenticeship learning via inverse reinforcement learning. In *Proceedings of the twenty-first international conference on Machine learning*, pp.1–8 (2004).

32. https://cloud.google.com/speech/

33. Y. Jia, L. She, Y. Cheng, J. Bao, J. Y. Chai, and N. Xi, Program robots manufacturing tasks by natural language instructions. In *IEEE International Conference on Automation Science and Engineering (CASE)*, pp. 633–638 (2016).

34. L. She, S. Yang, Y. Cheng, Y. Jia, J. Y. Chai, and N. Xi, Back to the blocks world: Learning new actions through situated human-robot dialogue. In *15th Annual Meeting of the Special Interest Group on Discourse and Dialogue* (2014).

35. https://www.myo.com/

36. G. Loianno, C. Brunner, G. McGrath, and V. Kumar, Estimation, control, and planning for aggressive flight with a small quadrotor with a single camera and IMU, *IEEE Robotics and Automation Letters* **2**, 404–411 (2017).

37. H. Ahmed and M. Tahir, Improving the accuracy of human body orientation estimation with wearable IMU sensors, *IEEE Transactions on Instrumentation and Measurement* **66**(3), 535–542 (2017).

38. J. Wahlström, I. Skog, P. Händel, and A. Nehorai, IMU-based smartphone-to-vehicle positioning, *IEEE Transactions on Intelligent Vehicles* **1**, 139–147 (2016).

39. N. D. Bunt, J. C. Moreno, P. Müller, T. Seel, and T. Schauer, Online monitoring of muscle activity during walking for bio-feedback and for observing the effects of transcutaneous electrical stimulation. In *Converging Clinical and Engineering Research on Neurorehabilitation II,* Jaime Ibanez, Jose Gonzalez-Vargas, Jose Maria Azorin, Metin Akay, and Jose Luis Pons (eds). Springer (2017).

40. S. H. Roy, G. De Luca, M. Cheng, A. Johansson, L. D. Gilmore, and C. J. De Luca, Electro-mechanical stability of surface EMG sensors, *Medical & Biological Engineering & Computing* **45**, 447–457 (2007).

41. C. J. De Luca, M. Kuznetsov, L. D. Gilmore, and S. H. Roy, Inter-electrode spacing of surface EMG sensors: reduction of crosstalk contamination during voluntary contractions, *Journal of Biomechanics* **45**, 555–561 (2012).

42. W. Wang, R. Li, Z. M. Diekel, and Y. Jia, Hands-free Maneuvers of Robotic Vehicles via Human Intentions Understanding using Wearable Sensing, *Journal of Robotics,* 1–10, (2018). doi:10.1155/2018/4546094.

43. J. Diebel, Representing attitude: Euler angles, unit quaternions, and rotation vectors, *Matrix,* **58**, 1–35 (2006).

44. M. Herman, V. Fischer, T. Gindele, and W. Burgard, Inverse reinforcement learning of behavioral models for online-adapting navigation strategies. In *2015 IEEE International Conference on Robotics and Automation (ICRA)*, pp. 3215–3222 (2015).

45. S. Levine, Z. Popovic, and V. Koltun, Nonlinear inverse reinforcement learning with gaussian processes. In *Advances in Neural Information Processing Systems 24 (NIPS 2011)*, pp. 19–27 (2011).

46. G.-B. Huang and L. Chen, Enhanced random search based incremental extreme learning machine, *Neurocomputing* **71**, 3460–3468 (2008).

47. G.-B. Huang and L. Chen, Convex incremental extreme learning machine, *Neurocomputing,* **70**, 3056–3062 (2007).

48. G.-B. Huang, L. Chen, and C. K. Siew, Universal approximation using incremental constructive feedforward networks with random hidden nodes, *IEEE Trans. Neural Networks* **17**, 879–892 (2006).

49. G.-B. Huang, H. Zhou, X. Ding, and R. Zhang, Extreme learning machine for regression and multiclass classification, *IEEE Transactions on Systems, Man, and Cybernetics, Part B (Cybernetics)* **42**, 513–529 (2012).

50. G. Huang, G.-B. Huang, S. Song, and K. You, Trends in extreme learning machines: A review, *Neural Networks* **61**, 32–48 (2015).

51. E. C. Grigore, K. Eder, A. G. Pipe, C. Melhuish, and U. Leonards, Joint action understanding improves robot-to-human object handover. In *2013 IEEE/RSJ International Conference on Intelligent Robots and Systems (IROS),* pp. 4622–4629 (2013).

52. M. Ryoo, T. J. Fuchs, L. Xia, J. Aggarwal, and L. Matthies, Early recognition of human activities from first-person videos using onset representations, *arXiv preprint arXiv:1406.5309* (2014).

53. J. Mainprice and D. Berenson, Human-robot collaborative manipulation planning using early prediction of human motion. In *2013 IEEE/RSJ International Conference on Intelligent Robots and Systems (IROS)*, pp. 299–306 (2013).

54. L. Cohen, S. Haliyo, M. Chetouani, and S. Régnier, Intention prediction approach to interact naturally with the microworld. In *2014 IEEE/ASME International Conference on Advanced Intelligent Mechatronics,* pp. 396–401 (2014).

55. N. Bellotto and H. Hu, Multisensor-based human detection and tracking for mobile service robots, *IEEE Transactions on Systems, Man, and Cybernetics, Part B (Cybernetics)* **39**, 167–181 (2009).

56. M. Gupta, L. Behera, V. K. Subramanian, and M. M. Jamshidi, A robust visual human detection approach with UKF-based motion tracking for a mobile robot, *IEEE Systems Journal* **9**, 1363–1375 (2015).

57. N. Dalal and B. Triggs, Histograms of oriented gradients for human detection. In *IEEE Computer Society Conference on Computer Vision and Pattern Recognition (CVPR)*, pp. 886–893 (2005).

© 2020 World Scientific Publishing Company
https://doi.org/10.1142/9789811222849_0005

Chapter 5

Collaborative Industrial Robot Control: From Safe Motion to Multi-Robot Manipulation

John T. Wen, John Wason, Daniel Kruse, Yuan-Chih Peng, and Shuyang Chen

5.1 Introduction

It has been over five decades since the introduction of industrial robots.[1,2] They have transformed many industries, from automotive and semiconductor manufacturing to material handling and food processing. The vast majority of industrial robots today operate in teach-and-repeat mode based on interpolation of the taught way points using the teach pendant. Once the taught motion is finalized, the robot operates behind the closed cage without any human involvement. This programming-by-teaching process is elaborate and time-consuming, with many trial-and-modify steps to fine tune the final robot trajectories. There are off-line programming tools such as RobotMaster[3] and Octopuz[4] which uses CAD model and visualization to aid robot programming. However, the basic approach of teach and playback remains the same. The effort to teach a robot to perform a specific task also makes repurposing a robot for different tasks an expensive and time consuming proposition. Compounding the problem is that industrial robots have their own programming languages, e.g., INFORM for Motoman,[5] RAPID for ABB,[6] KAREL for FANUC,[7] V+ for Omron/Adept,[8] VAL3 for Stäubli,[9] KRL for Kuka,[10] etc., which are not interoperable. It is therefore rare to see robots from different vendors in the same manufacturing cell. External sensors, such as machine vision and force/torque sensor, has the potential to adapt the robot to variation in the workspace. But the incorporation of these sensor into the robot program is robot vendor specific and difficult to port to different systems. Furthermore, the use of sensors in industrial setting has been limited to look/sense-and-move variety, rather than continuous feedback for motion correction and modification. Human guidance is traditionally done through teleoperation, remotely using a joystick type of

117

input device. Vision and sometimes force feedback for contact or insertion types of tasks may be fed back to the operator, but the integration of sensors with operators is rarely done for industrial robots. There is a new breed of so-called collaborative robots which are light weight and have built-in joint torque sensing to detect collision. Baxter and Sawyer by Rethink Robotics and UR robots by Universal Robotics are examples of this class of robots. They are safer to operate around humans, but lack the payload capacity, speed, and precision the traditional industrial robots.

This chapter will describe our work in bringing sensor-based operation and human collaboration to industrial robots. We will consider industrial robots which are not human-collaborative in a traditional sense, as well as collaborative robots designed for human interaction. The goal is to demonstrate a general framework that integrates sensors and human input in a consistent, efficient, and friendly software and control architecture.

The glue to this architecture is the middleware that ties together the many components of the system, from robot controllers, sensors, to human interface devices. It is like a common language among the cacophony of devices to ensure efficient and effective communication. We will discuss a middleware initially developed in our lab, Robot Raconteur,[11] and its integration with the popular Robot Operating System (ROS).[12]

Our approach to sensor and human integration into the robot operation is through the use of the *outer loop* which sends commanded joint motion to the robot joint servo controller (the inner loop). The outer-loop controller determines the robot motion command based on sensor readings and human commands. It may be used to coordinate multiple devices, including possibly multiple robots (of different types, e.g., articulated robots and mobile bases), sensors (vision, point cloud, force, proximity, tactile, etc.), and humans (through input devices, e.g., gesture, joystick, verbal). These devices may operate at different sampling rates, which may not be at regular intervals (i.e., non-real-time). The outer-loop control will generate sensor-driven motion to achieve desired goals while ensuring safety.

Outer loop control implicitly assumes a very good joint level servo controllers that has fast response and high accuracy. However, the inner loop controller has its own characteristics, including dynamics, latency (time delay), and nonlinearity (configuration dependence). We will discuss characterization of the inner-loop controller, its impact on the outer-loop design, and its possible compensation.

Simulation is an important aspect of collaborative robot systems. It allows preview and visualization of robot operation and facilitates motion and task planning. There are powerful open source simulation and visualization software, ranging from rviz (ROS visualization tool) to OpenRave (kinematic simulation/planning and visualization) to Gazebo (dynamic simulation). Robotic companies may have their own simulation software, e.g., RobotStudio by ABB Robotics and MotoSim from Yaskawa Motoman . They are at varying levels of readiness for custom integration. We will discuss our experience in incorporating these tools in the overall software architecture, drawing on their respective strengths.

We have applied the approach described in this chapter to a multitude of industrial robots in various projects. To illustrate the capability and performance, we will draw on three examples: ABB IRB 6640 6-dof arm, Motoman SDA20 15-dof dual-arm robot, and Rethink Baxter 14-dof dual-arm robot augmented with a wheeled mobile base. The same approach to the software architecture is applied to all three cases, demonstrating the generality and versatility of the approach.

5.2   Middleware

Integrating advanced software capabilities with multiple networked devices from different vendors is a constant challenge for modern industrial automation. It could lead to rapidly escalating complexity and cost, and in many cases is limiting the adoption of automation. Consider robots from different manufacturers with off-the-shelf webcam, force/torque sensors, and input devices. For robot vendors, system integrators, and end users, combining all these components together to accomplish specified integrated tasks is demanding. Current state of practice involves the development of custom interfaces and programs in a custom software architecture. Some partial solutions are emerging based on data-centric peer-to-peer architectures. Robot Operating System (ROS) is an open-source middleware that is popular in the research community. There are ROS implementations developed for numerous robots and sensors, and there is a large repository of robotics related algorithms. ROS-Industrial (ROS-I), led by the Southwest Research Institute (SwRI), assists industrial users to leverage these ROS tools. Industry 4.0 and Industrial Internet of Things (IIoT) communities have developed middleware systems based on open platform communication/unified architecture (OPC/UA) or data distribution service (DDS) protocols. We will focus on the middleware Robot Raconteur (RR) which is an advanced augmented object-oriented middleware technology designed for automation/robotics systems. RR works with ROS through the RR/ROS bridge. It is has been used extensively at Rensselaer Polytechnic Institute and other sites.

5.2.1 *Comparison of Middleware Technologies*

There are several open-standard middleware technologies used for robotic integration.

ROS is an open-source robotics software architecture that is widely used in research, and has some use in industry (championed by the ROS-Industrial Consortium). It has a large user community and thousands of open-source packages available (though not well curated). However, it lacks plug-and-play or security and currently has limited support on platforms other than Linux.

ROS 2.0 is an update to ROS that utilizes DDS instead of the ROS 1.0 middleware. It is a promising approach as DDS is a far superior technology than the ROS 1.0 middleware. However, it is still under development and has limited package support.

DDS is a middleware intended for real-time and safety critical systems and is popular in the Industrial Internet community. It is a proven technology and has been implemented in safety-critical applications (e.g., avionics). The DDS standard uses the RTPS UDP transport protocol, which limits its compatibility with TCP, USB, and Bluetooth devices.

OPC/UA is modernized version of OPC which is widely used for Programmable Logic Controller (PLC) communication. It is a popular standard for Industry 4.0 and is incorporated in many standard interfaces, particularly PLC hardware devices. It is an object oriented interface and supports device discovery on networks.

Robot Raconteur has a number of capabilities and attributes that make it an attractive middleware choice in robotics and automation:

• Augmented Object-Oriented architecture: RR uses an object-oriented model with expanded functionality specifically designed for robotics and automation systems. While most object-oriented architectures have three member types (property, function, event), RR has eight member types: *Property, Function, Event, ObjRef, Pipe, Callback, Wire, Memory*. Each of these member types provide a unique way to interact with the service, and provide additional information such as quality-of-service (Wire vs Pipe) and direction of operation (Function vs Callback). This extra information helps developers clearly specify the data and functionality available in a service, and also makes transporting data across a network easier as each message contains detailed metadata.

• Plug-and-play: The augmented object-oriented objects, data structures, exceptions, and other types are defined in plain text "Service Definition" files. These service definitions are provided to the client at runtime, meaning that MATLAB, Python, and other scripting environments can automatically generate proxies upon connection. Combined with the inherently flexible transport protocols, this results in a true plug-and-play capability.

• Authentication and exclusive access control: With the built in authentication and exclusive access control, clients with sufficient privileges can request exclusive access to objects in a service to prevent crosstalk.

• Flexible transports: RR is transport agnostic and does not require any specific transport. Currently supported transports include: TCP, local, USB, Bluetooth, PCI Express. Support for the QUIC protocol is under development.

• Compatible with Linux, Windows, OSX, iOS, Android, OpenBSD, QNX, Arduino, and xPC Target. Libraries available for C++, Python, C#, Java, MATLAB, LabView, browser JavaScript, and xPC Target.

5.2.2 *Types of Device Interface*

Existing robotics, automation, and computer components use a mixture of technologies for communications. This results in costly and time-consuming system integration. The type of interface technology used by a device will determine how we interact with the device through the middleware. The following are the types of devices in a distributed architecture, all of which are used in the case studies described in this chapter:

• A device with a standard interface and driver for a specific operating system (OS, such as Windows, Mac, Linux), e.g., USB/Bluetooth. Examples include USB cameras, gamepad, force-reflecting joysticks.

• A device/system with standardized interface on a specific OS (e.g., ROS on Linux). Examples include Turtlebot, Baxter/Sawyer by Rethink Robotics, UR robots by Universal.

• A proprietary system with a custom API. Examples include ABB External Guided Motion (EGM), Motoman High Speed Controller (HSC), VAL III External Alter.

• Industrial fieldbus with standardized interfaces. Examples include DeviceNet, CANopen, Ethernet/IP, EtherCAT

• Generic TCP/IP and/or UDP/IP network interface. Modern industrial equipment with networking capability often expose services that can be accessed using TCP/IP or UDP/IP. These devices often utilize standardized industrial protocols or provide HTTP based web services. Example industrial protocols include OPC/UA,

DDS, and RR. Example HTTP web services standards include SOAP, REST, and WebSocket services. Network protocols and levels of standardization vary greatly between devices, leading to a challenging integration environment.

5.3   Robot Controller

As industrial robots typically operate in the teach-and-repeat mode, the torque-level joint servo controllers are carefully tuned to follow the commanded trajectory closely but cannot be otherwise modified. Instead, many industrial robot controllers allow for the adjustment of the joint displacement or its increment at a specified rate via an external interface, as illustrated in Fig. 5.1. The external command interface is offered by most major robot companies as an added feature to the standard robot controller. Examples include the High Speed Controller (HSC) of Yaskawa Motoman (2 ms),[13] External Guided Motion (EGM) of ABB (4 ms),[6] Low Level Interface (LLI) for Stäubli (4 ms),[9] and Robot Sensor Interface (RSI) of Kuka (12 ms).[14] The controller from Rethink Robotics for Baxter and Sawyer robots also allow external position or velocity commands, but, in contrast to the ones mentioned above, the interaction does not have real-time guarantee, and the rate can fluctuate significantly around 6 ms. We have slowed the loop to allow for a consistent sampling rate at 20 ms.[15] The external command feature allows outer-loop feedback to continuously adjust the joint motion based on sensor readings. The overall architecture is as shown in Fig. 5.2 with the external command determined by user input and sensor feedback.

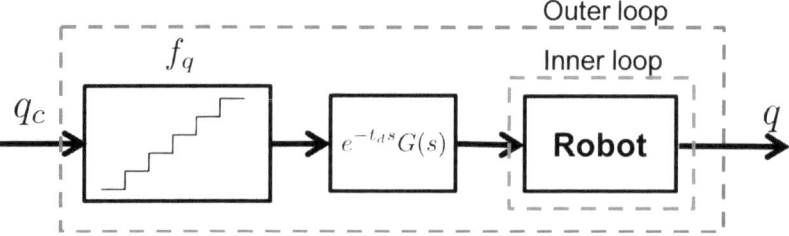

Fig. 5.1. Industry robot controller with external command option for outer loop feedback control. The inner loop dynamics is denoted by $G(s)$ (locally linear, nonlinear in general). External command time delay is t_d. Quantization effect is denoted by f_q. External command input available to the user is q_c.

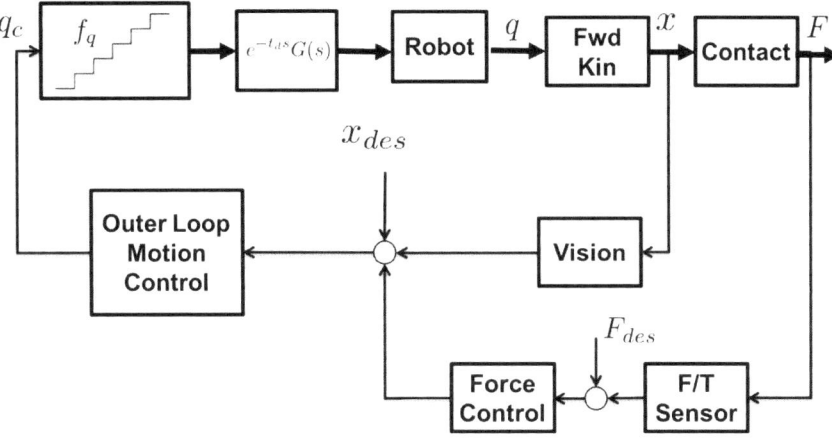

Fig. 5.2. The external command feature allows the incorporation of sensor feedback and user input (through x_{des}).

5.3.1   *Outer Loop Motion Control*

Resolved motion rate control or damped least square controller has long been used in robot control where the Cartesian motion is directly specified.[16,17] To use this approach for the outer loop motion control, consider the desired motion as given by the task space spatial velocity v_d (stacked angular and linear velocity vectors). The desired velocity v_d may be a combination of manual operator input (e.g., through a joystick), vision-guided motion (e.g., with χ_d determined from the camera view of a target), and force compliance (see Section 5.3.2). We propose the problem of determining joint motion command $\dot{q}_c$ as a quadratic program:

$$\min_{\dot{q}_c, \alpha_r, \alpha_p} ||J(q)\dot{q}_c - \alpha v_d||^2 + \epsilon_r(\alpha_r - 1)^2 + \epsilon_p(\alpha_p - 1)^2 \qquad (5.1)$$

where $J(q)$ is the arm Jacobian, $\alpha = \begin{bmatrix} \alpha_r I_3 & 0_3 \\ 0_3 & \alpha_p I_3 \end{bmatrix}$ in which α_r scales the angular velocity part of v_d, and α_p scales the desired linear velocity, ϵ_r and ϵ_p are weighting constants. If v_d is kinematically achievable, then $\alpha_r = \alpha_p = 1$ and $\dot{q}_c$ solves $J(q)\dot{q}_c = v_d$. If v_d is nearly infeasible, e.g., when the arm is near a singular configuration, then the linear and angular components of v_d are scaled so that the modified motion is feasible. Even though only the desired task space velocity is specified, it may be used for task space pose control. Let χ denote a parameterization of the Cartesian task space $SE(3)$, then we may choose $v_d = -K_\chi(\chi - \chi_d)$ where χ and χ_d are the actual and desired arm task space coordinates which would drive χ to χ_d if v_d is achievable.

In addition to trying to achieve the desired motion in (5.1), we may also impose equality constraints: $h_E(q) = 0$, and inequality constraints: $h_I(q) \geqslant \eta > 0$. The equality constraints may be useful to maintain certain direction of motion, e.g., at a constant gripper orientation. Inequality constraints may be needed to obey joint stops, steer away from singularities, avoid excessive joint motion, and prevent collision with obstacles.

To incorporate these constraints into the quadratic program (5.1), we convert the equality constraint to a differential constraint: $\frac{dh_E(q)}{dt} = \frac{\partial h_E(q)}{\partial q} \dot{q} = -k_E h_E$ which would incrementally drive h_E to zero.

For the inequality constraints $h_I(q)$ we again use the differential form of the constraint for determination of the instantaneous feasible direction:

$$\frac{dh_I}{dt} = \frac{\partial h_I}{\partial q} \dot{q} \geqslant \sigma. \tag{5.2}$$

where σ is a function of h_I. If h_I is a large positive value, the arm is far from this constraint. In this case, σ may be chosen large and negative, essentially making $\frac{dh_I}{dt}$ unconstrained. If h_I is near 0, i.e., the arm is near the constraint boundary, then σ should become positive so that h_I will move away from the constraint boundary. If h_I is negative, i.e., the constraint is violated, then σ should be a large positive value to quickly move the arm outside of the constraint region. An example shape of σ is shown in Fig. 5.3.

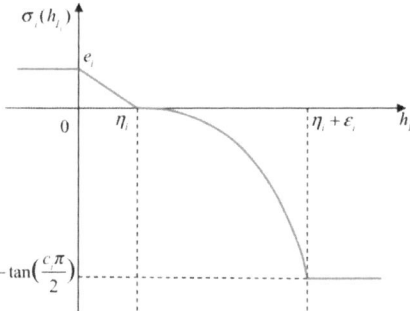

Fig. 5.3. Example σ function used for enforcing inequality constraints.

The typical components of the inequality constraints h_I are:
1. Joint limits. The joint limits are provided by the manufacturer and are selected to maximize the workspace of the robot while avoiding singularities: $q_{i_{\min}} \leq q_i \leq q_{i_{\max}}$.
2. Distance between robot and obstacles. The distance to obstacle can be measured by appropriate sensors, such as ultrasound sensors and cameras. We extend our

work in[18] by measuring the minimum distance d between the robot and the obstacle using the *BulletDiscreteBVH* collision checker that is a part of Tesseract.[19] To increase the collision checking speed, we can use simple bounding boxes to approximate the geometry of the robot, gripper, and the surroundings during collision checking. With a simplified collision geometry, h_I corresponding to collision may be updated at rates of 100 Hz or higher in common industrial workcell scenarios.

The differential forms of the equality and inequality constraints handling are all linear in $\dot{q}_c$, so adding them to the minimization (5.1) maintains convexity. Such quadratic program may be efficiently solved using available numerical computing software packages such as `cvx`.

When we apply the above approach to teleoperation (i.e., v_d is generated by operator input), the result is *safe teleoperation*, where the robot will stay close to the human commanded motion while remain inside the feasible region. The scheme guarantees collision avoidance, but could get stuck as there may be multiple nearest points to obstacles. In that case, the human operator is responsible for steering the robot away from the obstacle towards a feasible direction.

5.3.2   *Outer Loop Force Control*

For robots in contact with the environment, the impedance controller [20] has been an effective tool to regulate interaction. The basic idea is to command the robot to mimic a specified impedance (generalized mass-spring-damper) based on the measured contact force. We use generalized mass-damper for compliance control. Our focus is only on the contact force, therefore the target linear velocity for the contact, v_d, is generated from the measured force f as:

$$M_d \dot{v}_d + D_d v_d = B(f - f_d) \tag{5.3}$$

where (M_d, D_d) are the desired generalized mass and damper matrices, B is the compliance matrix specifying the compliance direction, and f_d is the target spatial force. The v_d generated from (5.3) may be added to the human input and/or vision guided motion to achieve hybrid motion and force control. Note that (5.3) is just integral force control with a first order filter. Integral force control has been demonstrated to have a good robustness property with respect to the measurement time delay, particularly in interaction with a stiff surface.[21]

The contact spatial force may be measured directly from a wrist-mounted force/torque sensor and the known geometry of the end effector. If such a sensor is not available, the spatial force at the end effector may be estimated from the joint torque sensor through the relationship $\tau = J^T(q)F$ where τ is the joint torque vector. The end effector spatial force F_T may then be estimated as $F = (J^T(q))^{\dagger}\tau$ where $(\cdot)^{\dagger}$ denotes Moore-Penrose pseudo-inverse. This method tends to be noisy and inaccurate when the arm is near a singular configuration. The first order filter in (5.3) would help address the noise. A deadzone for the spatial force error would help the force inaccuracy.

5.3.3 *Inner Loop Compensation*

The interaction between the outer loop command and the inner loop servo controller is affected by the inner loop dynamics and time delay. The inner loop dynamics is configuration dependent and only linear locally. Time delay could be as long as 20 ms (as in the case of Motoman HSC). Since the outer loop control only generates the *commanded* joint velocity, $\dot{q}_c$, the inner loop behavior can significantly compromise performance as q may significantly differ from q_c. Inner loop dynamics can cause significant tracking errors, particularly for trajectories with high velocity/acceleration. With outer loop feedback, this additional dynamics could even lead to instability particularly in force control with a rigid environment. We will discuss compensation schemes to ameliorate these adverse effects.

5.3.3.1 *Delay compensation*

Control loop time delay is not unique to robot control – it is a fact of life in process control, where there may be long transport delay due to material movement. Delay compensation using feedforward has long been proposed, the best known method is the Smith predictor , which directly cancels the delay and then applies feedback to the compensated system.[22] When the delay is reasonably constant and known, the scheme works well. There have been numerous enhancement since then. For example, the Åström variant [23] significantly improves the transient performance as it allows bandwidth tuning separately from delay compensation.

Smith predictor has been applied to robot control, particularly in the context of teleoperation.[24; 25] In, Ref. 26 we analyzed direct force feedback in the presence of significant delays in each joint, and compare the classic integral force feedback (which may be viewed as the generalized damper control) with two types of delay compensation, Smith predictor and Åström predictor. To analyze the stability and robustness, we consider a one-dimensional problem of a robot pressing on a spring and using the contact force as feedback. We show in this simple setup that both delay compensation schemes improve on the gain margin (robustness with respect to the environmental stiffness) and phase margins (robustness with respect to the delay). In the case of Åström predictor, the closed loop bandwidth and response rate for force setpoint convergence can also be tuned separately from disturbance rejection. Experiments conducted on our Motoman robot testbed with a very stiff environment show that both delay compensation schemes outperforms the integral feedback controller. The result will be shown in Section 5.5.2.

To extend Smith predictor, which was proposed for a single-input/single-output linear system, we consider all joint delays to be identical (the deviation is considered as an delay uncertainty, to be addressed with sufficient phase margin) and the arm is near a nominal configuration (the arm nonlinearity is also treated as uncertainty, to be addressed with sufficient gain and phase margins). The resulting system for the force control loop is shown in Fig. 5.4(a). The Smith predictor delay compensation, shown in Fig. 5.4(b) cancels the plant dynamics using an approximate model and replace it with the desired dynamics, $G_1(s)$. The impedance controller, $C(s)$, is then designed based on $G_1(s)$. The Åström modification, shown in Fig. 5.4(c) augments the Smith predictor with a feedforward to extend the tracking bandwidth. Since it does not change the feedback loop, the stability property is the same as the Smith predictor.

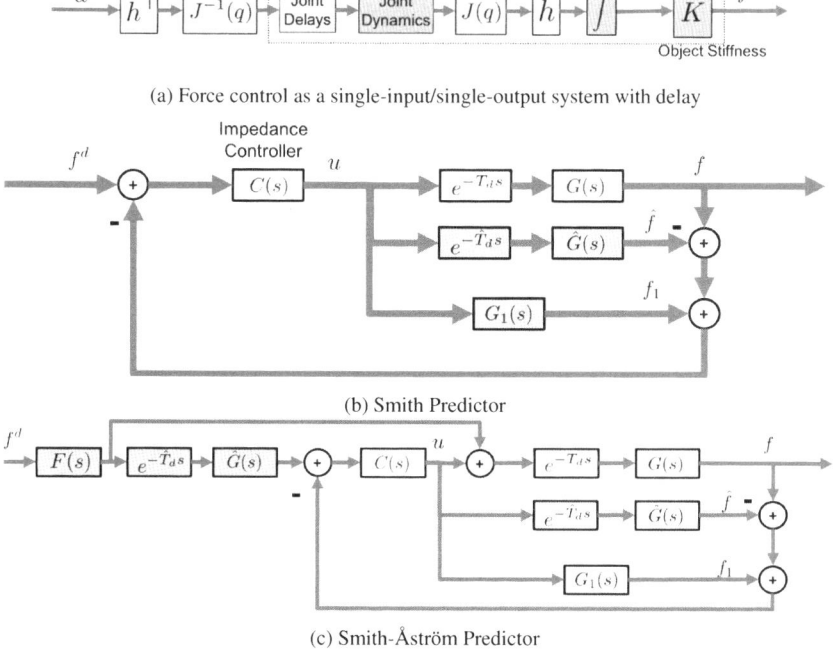

(a) Force control as a single-input/single-output system with delay

(b) Smith Predictor

(c) Smith-Åström Predictor

Fig. 5.4. Delay compensation for robot force control.

5.3.3.2   *Dynamics compensation*

The inner joint servo loop generally consists of well tuned proportional-integral-derivative (PID) type of controllers. The response around a given configuration is approximately linear around a given configuration (shown as $G(s)$ in Fig. 5.1). However, over the entire work space and at high velocity and acceleration, the response could become nonlinear. The typical step response at a configuration has a classic under-damped behavior and may be approximated by a first order lag cascaded with a second-order under-damped system:

$$G_I(s) = \frac{a}{s+a} \frac{\omega^2}{s^2 + 2\zeta\omega s + \omega^2} \tag{5.4}$$

where a is the bandwidth of the low-pass filter, and $\zeta(0 < \zeta < 1), \omega$ are the damping ratio and the undamped natural frequency of the second-order system, respectively. As an example, for the ABB IRB 6640 robot, step responses for various input steps are collected and fit the linear model. The robot joint output and the linear system step response are shown in Fig. 5.5(a). The Bode plot of the linear system is shown in Fig. 5.5(b), where $G(s) \approx 1$ in low frequency, so the actual joint motion follows the command motion (with perhaps a delay). At higher frequency, the amplitude rolls off and there is increasing phase lag. Because of the velocity and acceleration limits in the joint servo controller, the inner loop is nonlinear beyond these limits. Furthermore, these limits are configuration dependent.

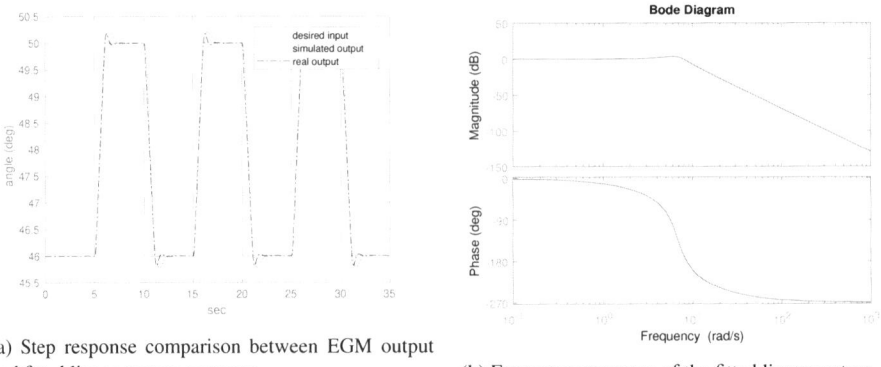

(a) Step response comparison between EGM output and fitted linear system response

(b) Frequency response of the fitted linear system

Fig. 5.5. Typical inner loop response at a given configuration. This response is obtained for ABB IRB 6640 using RobotStudio.

Around a given configuration subject to the velocity and acceleration limits, we may identify a linear system, and apply various known inverse dynamics approaches[27] to compensate for the inner loop dynamics. To operate fully within the work space and at the higher speed motion, nonlinearity must be addressed. However, such nonlinear effect is difficult to characterize. This type of nonlinear feedforward compensation issue has been widely studied, particularly for precision motion, such as in electronic manufacturing.[28] In, Ref. 28 a gradient descent iterative refinement approach has been applied to a galvanometer mirror for high speed laser scanning. If a linear model, $G(s)$, is known, the gradient descent direction is given by $G^*(s)e$ where $G^*(s)$ is the adjoint and $e = y - y_d$ is the output tracking error with y the actual output (joint angle), and y_d the desired output. Write $G(s)$ in terms of its state space parameters, $G(s) = C(sI - A)^{-1}B$, then $G^*(s) = G^T(-s) = B^T(-sI - A^T)^{-1}C^T$. Since A is stable, $G^*(s)$ would be unstable. For a finite length error signal $e(t)$, $G^*(s)e$ would show a very large input, making it impractical to implement. As described in,[28] we can instead implement a stable *noncausal* inverse as shown in Fig. 5.6. A key insight is that instead of using an analytical model of $G(s)$ to implement $G^*(s)e$, we can use the physical system or a good simulator (that captures the nonlinear effect, e.g., ABB's RobotStudio) to implement step (c) in Fig. 5.6. This would result in a completely model-independent iterative learning of the required input to track a desired output. Note that due to the noncausal nature of G^*e, an input with duration $[-T, T]$ is needed to track an output over $[0, T]$. In contrast to past work in iterative learning robot control,[29] our focus is on the outer loop and we apply gradient learning using a robot dynamics simulator instead of a linear learning rule or a model-based approach.

The approach described above is for a single-input/single-output system. As the inner-loop control tightly regulates each joint, the system is almost diagonal as seen from the outer loop. Hence, the same iterative learning procedure may be applied to all joints at the same time. In fact, if the inner loop is tuned to have about the same response, the same learning control may be applied to compensate for any of the joints. Iterative learning control may be employed to learn the ideal inputs for multiple sample trajectories. The result may then be used to train the dynamic inverse map of the inner loop by using, e.g., an artificial neural network. The structure of the neural network (number of neurons, number of hidden layers, etc.) and the selection of the training samples will need to be tuned to match with the performance requirements.

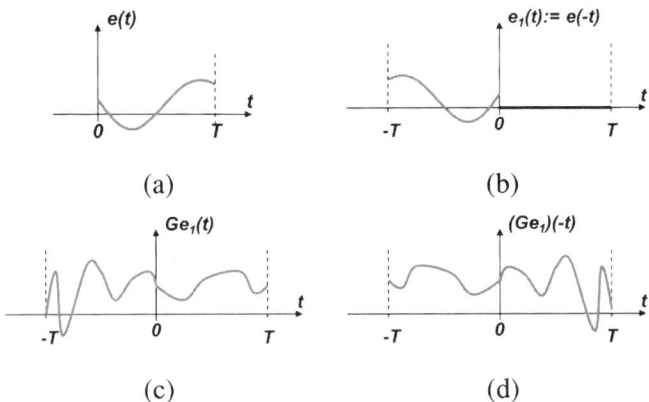

Fig. 5.6. Stable noncausal implementation of $G^*(s)e$ for iterative gradient update, where G is single-input/single-output. (a) Output tracking error (b) time inversion of the output tracking error, (c) filtering of output tracking error using G, and (d) time inversion of step (c).

5.4 Simulation

Simulation is becoming an increasing part of industrial robot control. It is used to visualize workspace, plan motion, and preview results. In the current practice, simulation is mostly based on kinematics and is used together with user input for way-point selection, robot motion planning and visualization. Many robot vendors (e.g., Yasakawa's Motosim, ABB's RobotStudio, Stäbli's Robotics Suite, Kuka's Kuka.sim, FANUC's RobotGuide, etc.) provide software simulation tools integrated with, but also restricted to, specific brands of robots. There are also third-party vendors, such as RobotMaster and Octopuz, that provide CAD-based simulation and design environments that work with multiple brands of robots. There are also open source tools for simulation and visualization, such as rviz, OpenRave, and Gazebo. This section will review the most common simulation tools and how they may be integrated into robot controller design. In Section 5.5.1.4, we discuss an example of using a mixture of proprietary and open source simulation tools for robot assembly tasks. This example extends beyond the current state of practice to include sensor-based feedback in the simulation environment.

5.4.1 *Proprietary Simulation Packages*

In a current state-of-practice industrial robot programming work flow, simulation is used to plan way-points, design tool paths, and test the logic of the task software. The use of simulation allows the operator to design the robot control software against CAD models of the workspace to achieve greater accuracy than would be possible attempting to teach a robot "in place" with a teach pendant. Using simulations also allows the designer to evaluate a robot workcell before physical construction with a virtual robot and rapidly iterate the design as needed.

Software for programming industrial robots using state-of-practice methods is typically produced by the robot vendors, is usually proprietary, and is often only able to simulate the vendors' robots. Examples of proprietary robot simulation packages include RobotStudio[30] by ABB Robotics, Motosim [31] for Yaskawa Motoman, Robotics Suite for Stäbli,[32] Kuka.sim[33] for Kuka, and RobotGuide[34] for FANUC. These simulation packages all offer similar functionalities, including graphical user interface, selection of robots and components from the robot vendor product line, import of CAD model for the workcell, emulation of the teach pendant operation, path planning, collision checking, attachment of tools/load, etc. There are certain features that would be useful but may not be available in all systems, e.g., incorporation of the external setpoint input feature as discussed in Section 5.3, robot and load dynamics, incorporation of sensors (possibly mounted on the robot) such as cameras, force/torque, proximity, etc. RobotStudio implements a virtual controller identical to the one implemented in the real robot. It supports off-line programming simulation, using *RAPID* programs and robot configuration files. RobotWare[6] is composed of a set of software files that are loaded into the controller and enables a number of functions, features, configurations, data and programs controlling the robot system. RobotStudio also emulates the external guided motion (EGM) mode and includes the inner loop dynamics as discussed in Section 5.3.3. It is ideally suited for tuning and evaluating control algorithms. Cameras elements are available in RobotStudio and there is a physics engine to simulate interaction with the environment. However, the interface available to the user is limited, so the implementation of sensor-based robot control such as visual servoing and force control is not difficult. Motosim supports INFORM programming for Motoman robots, but only provides kinematic simulation. Other robot simulation environments also appear to be kinematics-based as well.

There are also commercial software vendors that focus on robot simulation, path planning, visualization for multiple brands of robots, e.g., RobotMaster[3] and Octopuz.[4] These are mostly used as off-line programming tools and are kinematics-based. They only offer limited programmable user interface, and, as such, are not meant for sensor-based robot control.

5.4.2   *Open Source Software Simulation Packages*

The availability of powerful sensors and affordable network technology and computing power has spurred the demand for greater functionality such as sensor-guided motion, human-robot collaboration, and operator direction and intervention. The resulting robot control software requirement is beyond the capability of the current state of practice. Advanced robot control software is more flexible and takes advantage of the latest technologies, but its greater complexity also means more opportunities for errors. High-fidelity simulation is becoming a necessity to detect potential errors in the software before deployment on a physical robot. Simulation is also important for path planning. As automated path planners become more capable, they will require more powerful simulation tools for visualization. Numerous open-source software packages are available, with different levels of capability. A few examples we have found useful are as follows:

rviz, short for ROS Visualization, is a capable visualization tool for the ROS environment. rviz is capable of loading Unified Robot Description Format (URDF) files and displaying robot environments. The configuration of the environment is updated in real-time using data from the ROS environment, for example, through the *tf* topic. rviz is also capable of using plugins to expand its functionality. Examples include: marker display using real-time data from a ROS topic and the MoveIt! plugin that allows interactive path planning, display, and execution of motion plans. It is important to note that rviz itself is not a simulator. rviz is a visualization tool that can be used together with other simulation tools within ROS.

OpenRAVE is an open source simulation, planning, and visualization software package. Its primary use is for motion planning, and it has a number of built-in path planners with multiple available plugins. It is capable of kinematic simulations, dynamic simulations, and simulating various sensors. It is capable of loading OpenRAVE XML, COLLADA, or URDF model file formats. OpenRAVE is convenient to use because it has powerful Python and C++ APIs, and can be embedded in other software. Because of its modular design, it is possible to use only the functionality required. For instance, we have used OpenRAVE embedded in a Python program to load models and check for collision distances at various robot configurations.

Gazebo is an open source simulator package similar to OpenRAVE, with capabilities including physics simulation, visualization, and sensor simulation. Be default OpenRAVE uses the Open Dynamics Engine[35] physics engine, which is not suitable for most research or industrial uses due to its poor numerical stability and lax constraint enforcement. More advanced physics engines are available, including the Dynamic Animation and Robotics Toolkit[36] (DART) physics engine, which provide more accurate physics simulations, and Bullet.[37] Gazebo is also capable of simulating many types of sensors, including cameras, ray sensors, force-torque sensors, GPS, inertial measurement unit (IMU), magnitometer, sonar, and more. Gazebo uses its own file format called Scene Definition Format[38] (SDF). URDF models can be "spawned" into a Gazebo scene, but cannot be loaded directly. Certain robot vendors provide models that include dynamic parameters for Gazebo (e.g., Kinova[39]).

5.5 Case Studies

5.5.1 *ABB Robot*

To illustrate sensor-based robot control on an ABB industrial robot, we will use our project on robotic assembly of a large segmented structure, supported by the Advanced Robotics for Manufacturing (ARM) Institute. The panel segments may be of different sizes and shapes and are presented in slightly different locations. Traditional industrial robot programming approaches would be time consuming and laborious to account for different part locations and geometries. The overall goal of the project is to consider a scaled-down version of the assembly task and demonstrate the possibility of using an industrial robot in combination with vision and force sensors to achieve accurate part assembly with low cycle time and improved worker ergonomics. The current manufacturing practice relies on fixtures and tooling to meet the alignment requirement. Our approach is to integrate sensors with robot motion and user commands to achieve fixtureless assembly.

The testbed uses the ABB IRB 6640/180 robot[40] which is a 6 degrees of freedom robot manipulator with handling capacities up to 180 kg and furtherest reach of 2.55 m. This type of robot has high positioning repeatability of 0.07 mm and path repeatability of 0.3 mm such that it is suitable for industrial applications including material handling and spot welding.[40] For the vision system, Point Grey cameras are used.[41] A 20 MP camera is mounted over the panel pickup location to determine the panel location. Two 5 MP cameras are mounted on the robot end-effector to help with panel placement. A six-axis force/torque sensor[42] with 1 ms sampling time is mounted on the robot wrist.

5.5.1.1 *Software architecture*

Externally Guided Motion (EGM) is a feature of RobotWare 6.05, the ABB Robot Controller Software.[6] EGM enables external command of robot joint positions through a high-rate and low-latency (4 ms sampling, ∼8 ms lag) with interface. It is therefore ideally suited for sensor-based robot motion control. ABB provides a high fidelity dynamic simulation tool called RobotStudio,[30] which also supports EGM. This offers a convenient environment to test and preview robot task execution before implementing on the physical robot. We have integrated open source tools for motion planning (MoveIt!,[43] OpenRAVE[44]), visualization (R-Viz), collision detection (ROS-I Tesseract[19]), and simulation (Gazebo,[45] for contact dynamics) with RobotStudio and EGM through both ROS and RR. The overall system architecture is shown in Fig. 5.7. (Note that for this example RR has been used for development with MATLAB but is not used in the primary architecture.)

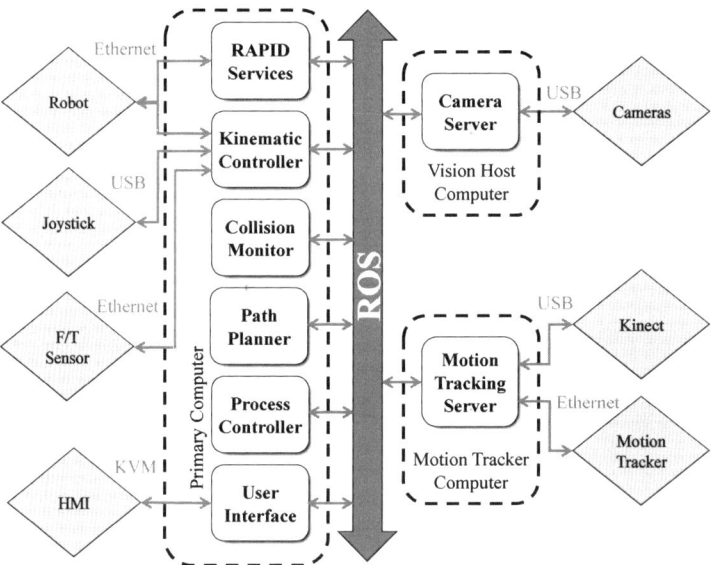

Fig. 5.7. Overall system architecture.

5.5.1.2 *Large panel pick-up operation*

By using the EGM feature, the outer loop robot controller is integrated with the MoveIt! path planner with the target pose obtained by camera and tag. The controller captures the intermediate points in the MoveIt! output and modifies the trajectory interpolation. This allows the controller to operate in several modes beyond the autonomous motion:

1. Shared control mode: The user may control the motion (forward or backward and variable speed) along the collision-free path generated by MoveIt! using a gamepad joystick.

2. Speed scaled mode: The motion along the path may be sped up or slowed down at different portions of the trajectory. This is useful when approaching a target.

3. Sensor control mode: The motion along the path may be terminated or modified based on sensor information. This is useful for force guided contacts.

Snapshots from the panel pickup operation is shown in Fig. 5.9. The robot is initially at Fig. 5.9(a). The camera at the overhead of the panel determines the pose of the panel. The first motion segment moves the robot to a configuration above the panel (Fig. 5.9(b)). The robot moves downward towards the panel until the force threshold of 250 N is reached (Fig. 5.9(c)). The vacuum is then engaged and the arm lifts up the panel (Fig. 5.9(d)). The collision-free motion is generated by MoveIt! using the Transition-based Rapidly exploring Random Tree (TRRT) algorithm.[46] The actual versus planned joint trajectories are shown in Fig. 5.10(a). The force measured by the robot wrist force/torque sensor is shown in Fig. 5.10(b). It shows that the force threshold triggers the motion termination and vacuum engagement. Once the panel is firmly attached, the weight of the panel now is felt by the measured force.

Fig. 5.8. The panel assembly testbed including the pick-up nest (right) and assembly nest (back).

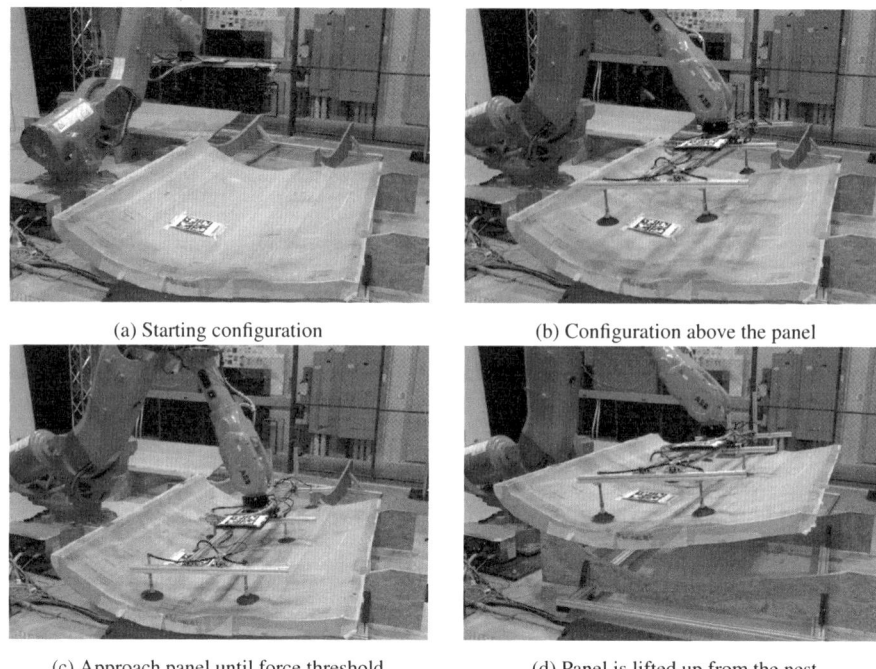

(a) Starting configuration   (b) Configuration above the panel

(c) Approach panel until force threshold   (d) Panel is lifted up from the nest

Fig. 5.9. Panel pick-up operation with vision and force guidance.

5.5.1.3   *Iterative refinement correction of the inner loop dynamics*

We have tested the iterative refinement approach for inner loop compensation of the ABB IRB 6640 robot using the ABB RobotStudio simulator. The resulting tracking improvement is striking in both the linear and nonlinear regimes as shown in Fig. 5.11. To generalize to an arbitrary input, we learn the required input for a large number of sample trajectories, and then encode these trajectories using an artificial neural network (ANN). The input of the ANN is a segment of the desired joint trajectory, $\{q_d(\tau)\}$, $\tau \in [t - T, t + T]$, and the output is the commanded joint position into the inner loop, $\{q_c(\tau)\}$, $\tau \in [t, t+T]$. Results from iterative refinement of various desired trajectories (including sinusoids and sigmoids) are used to train the ANN. This approach has worked remarkably well. As an example, see the tracking of a chirp signal in Fig. 5.12 for joint 1 of ABB IRB 6640. The input and output segments consist of 50 and 25 samples, respectively. There are two hidden layers each with 100 neurons. Figure 5.12(a) shows the uncompensated output with the robot output lagging behind the desired output and at smaller amplitudes. The linear model output also deviates from the robot output indicating nonlinear effects. Figure 5.12(b) shows the ANN generated commanded input which leads the desired

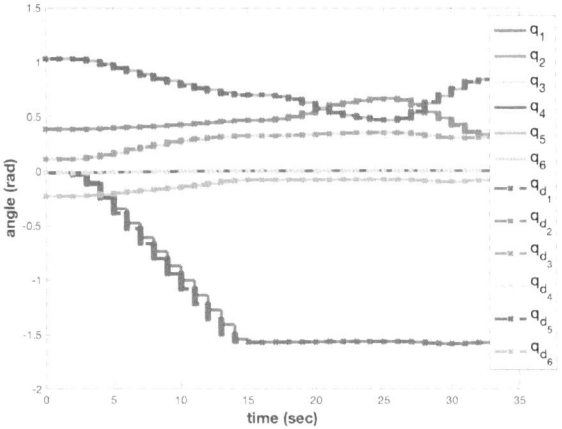

(a) Actual and desired joint angles.

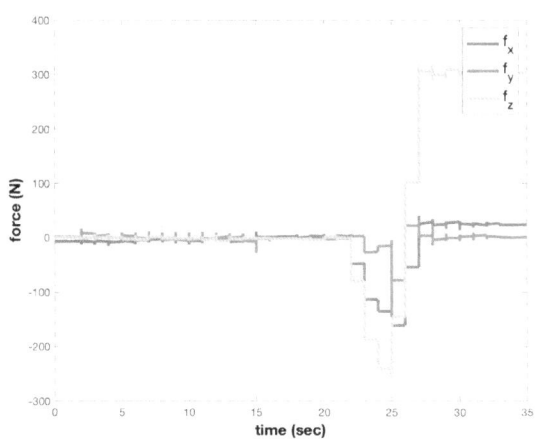

(b) Measured force at robot end effector.

Fig. 5.10. Motion and force plots during the panel pick-up operation. (a) Actual and desired joint angles (b) Force at robot wrist.

output to compensating for the lag effect and has high amplitude to compensate for the amplitude attenuation. The robot output tracks closely the desired output after a brief initial transient.

5.5.1.4 *Simulation*

The large panel placement task described in this section involves multiple components (robot, force torque sensor, multiple cameras, vacuum gripper, vacuum pressure sensors) and robot tasks (path planning, trajectory generation, force control,

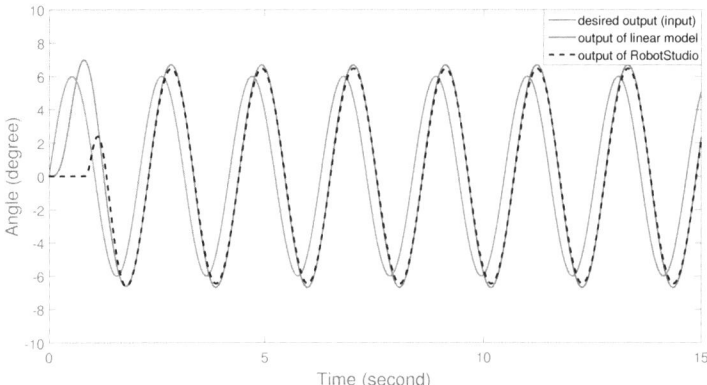

(a) Desired output (also the input into the inner loop), RobotStudio output, and linear model output.

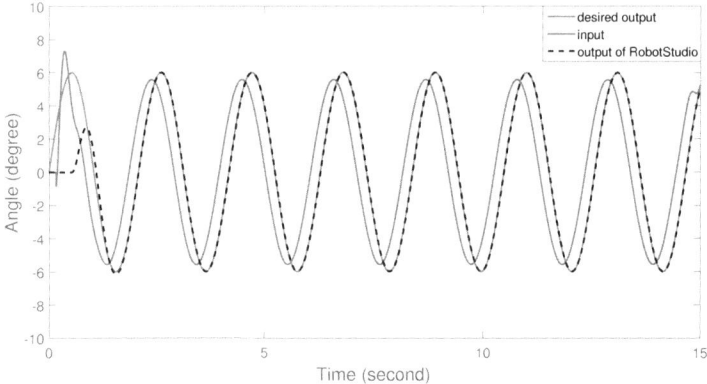

(b) Desired output, RobotStudio output (with modified input), and modified input based on iterative refinement.

Fig. 5.11. Trajectory tracking improvement with iterative refinement after 8 iterations. Desired trajectory is a sinusoid with $\omega = 3\ rad/sec$.

vision-guided motion). The control software orchestrates various software modules to perform the overall task. The complexity of this system prevents developing the software using only the physical testbed. We have assembled a number of tools for the full system simulation to assist the software development effort:

- *ROS Based Control Software*. The control software is based on ROS, and it is fully implemented in both simulation and physical experiment. The only difference is that the launch file for the simulation starts the simulated sensors (rviz camera streaming plugin and force/torque sensor simulation script).

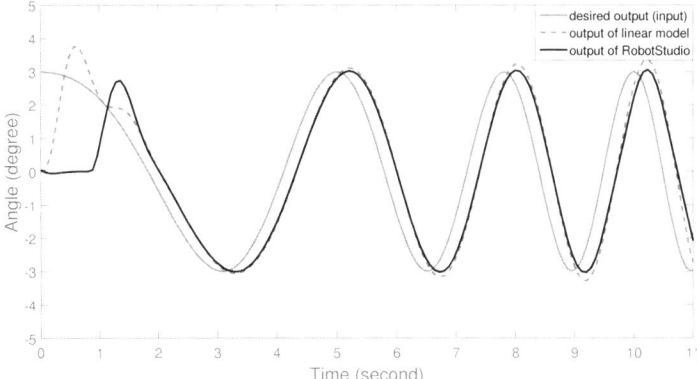

(a) The non-compensated case: desired output (also the input into the inner loop), RobotStudio output, and linear model output. Plots show the nonlinear effect at large amplitudes.

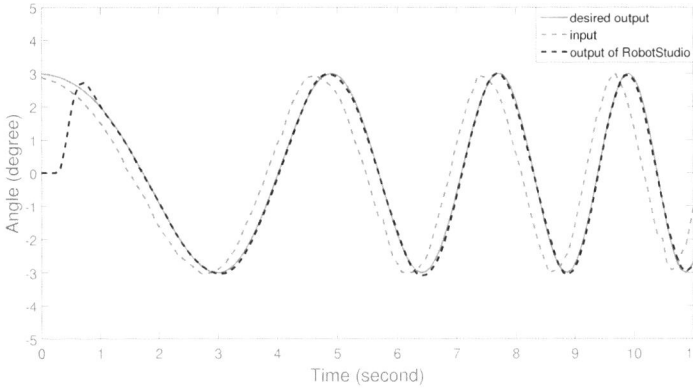

(b) The ANN compensated case: desired output, RobotStudio output (with modified input), and modified input based on the ANN generated inner loop input. Tracking error is significantly reduced.

Fig. 5.12. Comparison of tracking performance without and with the ANN compensation for a chirp signal.

- *rviz Camera Simulation.* Computer vision using cameras is critical to the operation of the testbed. We use an rviz plugin to simulate the cameras and publish images to ROS using the same topics as the real cameras, resulting in no changes required to vision processing software.

- *ABB RobotStudio.* ABB RobotStudio is used to simulate the dynamics of the robot and the low-level robot controller by using a simulated ABB IRC5 controller with EGM. The simulation is also capable of grasping and releasing panels. Because RobotStudio provides the full IRC5 controller implementation in simulation, there is no change required to the motion control software for simulation.

- *Force-Torque Sensor.* The force-torque sensor is simulated using a simple approximation with a stiff-spring contact between the gripper and panels, or between the panels and the nests.

A snapshot of the RobotStudio simulation with high fidelity panel and workspace models is shown in Fig. 5.13.

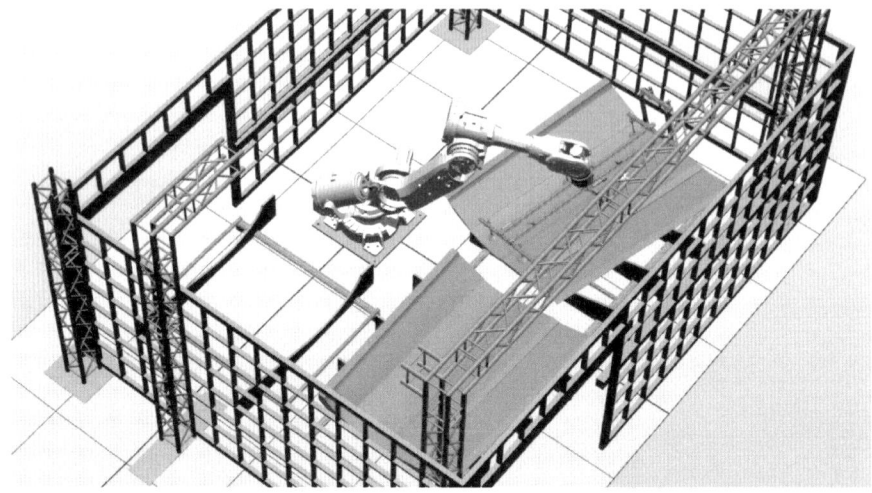

Fig. 5.13. RobotStudio simulation for the panel assembly process.

5.5.2 *Motoman Robot*

We have applied sensor-based control to a Yasakawa Motoman SDA10 robot, a dual-arm 15-dof industrial robot with two 7-dof arms and a 1-dof torso. The Yasakawa Motoman robot allows external interface through Motoman's High Speed Controller (HSC). The HSC interface provides joint angle read and incremental commanded joint angle write at 2 ms rate. The command input has significant delays (around 20 ms) due to the internal trajectory generation. The low-level robot control system takes a commanded correction to the current joint angle and calculates a trapezoidal trajectory profile for the joint motion. The resulting motion may be modeled sufficiently closely (except at transitions between motion segments) as a first-order-plus-dead-time system. For visual feedback, a Sony XCD-X710CR camera is mounted on the side of each wrist and angled in such a way that the end effector is in the field of view. Directly at the end of each arm is an ATI Mini45 force/torque transducer, with a rubber disc mounted at the end for a higher-friction contact.

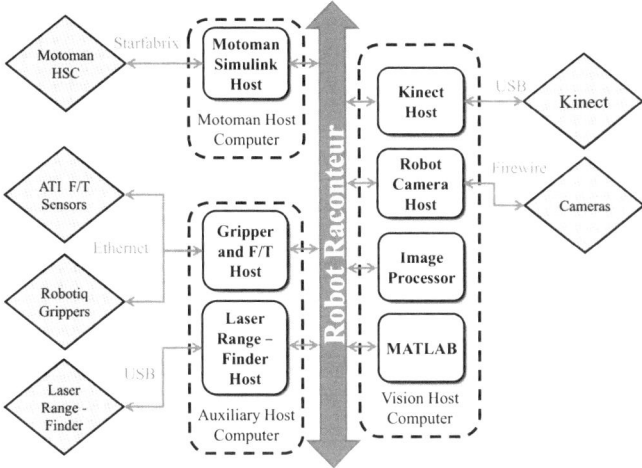

Fig. 5.14. Overall distributed control system architecture using the Robot Raconteur middleware.

5.5.2.1 *Software architecture*

The components of the overall system are coordinated through RR. The system architecture is illustrated in Fig. 5.14. Separate Robot Raconteur services are written (in C#) for the Motoman HSC interface, ATI force/torque sensor, cameras, image processing, and Kinect interface, residing on three separate computers linked together in a local area network via Ethernet and TCP/IP. The overall coordination is conducted by a MATLAB script that connects to these services as a client. This MATLAB environment does not run in real time and has no explicit timing guarantee. However, the performance is adequate with sampling times of ∼20 Hz in visual servoing and ∼90 Hz in hybrid motion-force control, on average.

5.5.2.2 *Human-guided dual arm manipulation*

The integrated system shown in Fig. 5.14 allows human guided motion and force control; the details may be found in Ref. 47. The Kinect SDK can detect and track 48 skeletal points on a human body at 30 Hz. This information may be used to construct a rich vocabulary for the user interface. Figure 5.15 shows the interpretation of human gesture for the desired pose for the object. The Kinect sensor extracts the user skeleton which is then mapped to the pose of the dual-arm robot. This pose is combined with generalized damper type of force control (5.3) and sent to the robot outer loop controller as described in Section 5.3.1. An example usage of these gestures in our overall system could be for a teleoperated pick and place task. The

tagged object is identified and picked up by the robot. An operator steps in front of
the Kinect and takes control using the *start* gesture. The operator then demonstrates
the desired trajectory for the object using their relative hand positions, coordinated
in real time with the current pose of the object. Once the object reaches the desired
goal, such as a conveyor belt, the *release* gesture is made to pass the object along
to the next phase of manufacturing.

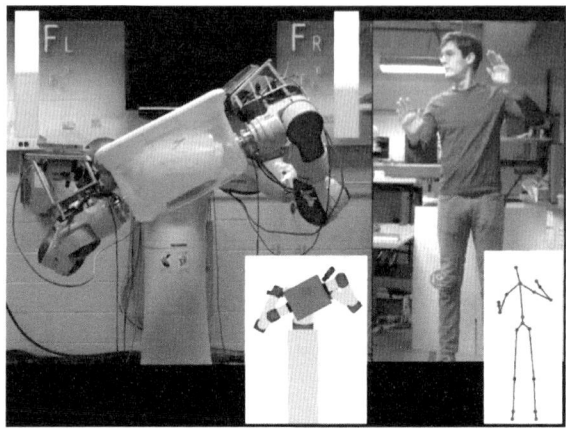

Fig. 5.15. Gesture-based user interface with Kinect.

The force controller gain needs to be adjusted based on the stiffness of the object, weight of the object, surface geometry, and input delay. This may be achieved
by choosing a gain that is robust for a range of possible object stiffness values or
adaptively adjusting the gain based on the measured force. Figure 5.16 shows the
stable squeeze force control of five objects of different stiffness, size, weight, and
surface geometry using a constant force feedback gain tuned to be robust over these
objects.

5.5.2.3   *Delay compensation in force control*

Transport delay could significantly affect closed loop stability. This is particularly
important in force control with robot in contact with a very stiff surface.[21] As discussed in 5.3.3.1 the stability is dependent on the pose (due to the arm Jacobian).
Using the Nyquist stability about multiple arm configurations as shown in Fig. 5.17
comparing the force control loop using the generalized impedance control alone
versus the impedance control with Smith predictor compensation, it is clear that
the Smith predictor enhances stability robustness with respect to the time delay (as
characterized by the phase margin). Force only and motion-force control exper-

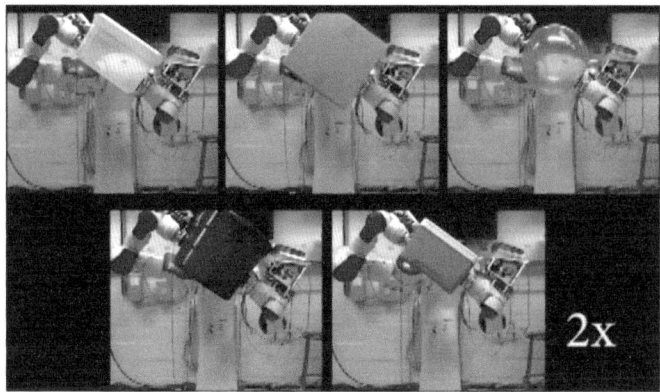

Fig. 5.16. Five test objects with different stiffness, size, weight, and surface geometry.

iments have been conducted using outer loop force control for a single arm and dual arm as shown in Fig. 5.18. In all cases, the uncompensated force control exhibits instability, while the Smith predictor compensation restores the stability. The Åström modification does not change the closed loop stability but does improve the tracking result by adding a feedforward term.

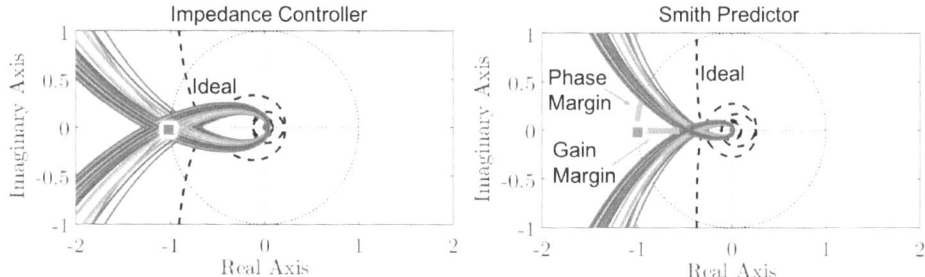

Fig. 5.17. Comparison of stability robustness between impedance control and Smith predictor over multiple arm configurations Nyquist plots show the robustness of the Smith predictor.

5.5.3 *Rethink Baxter Robot*

The Baxter robot made by Rethink Robotics consists of two 7-degree-of-freedom (DOF) arms connected to a rigid torso in a bimanual configuration. Each arm is composed of a 3-DOF shoulder, an elbow, and a 3-DOF wrist. The robot joints are actuated by a series of elastic actuators, whose links and motors are coupled with springs. This design provides not only safer actuation around humans but also a simple scheme for torque estimation by multiplying the known spring constant to

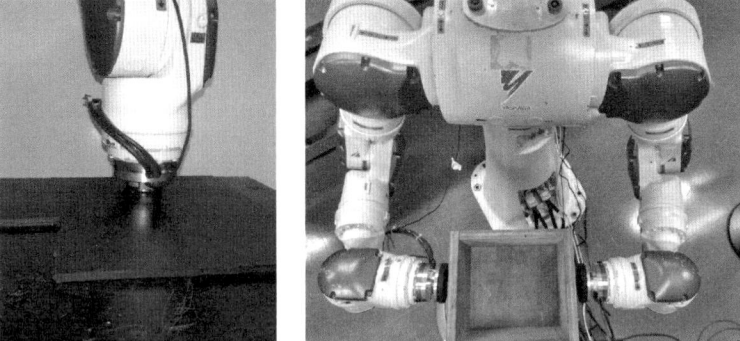

Fig. 5.18. Force control experimental setup for single and dual-arm force control.

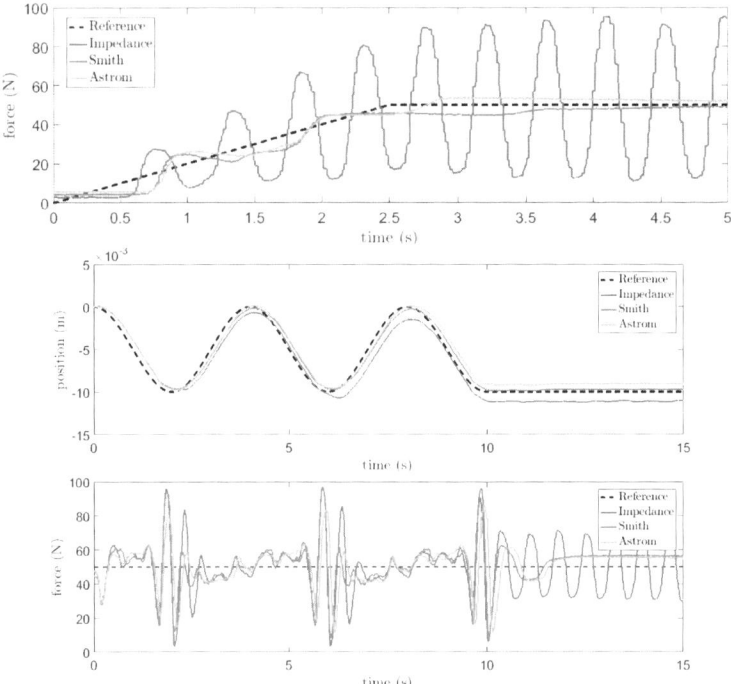

Fig. 5.19. Single arm force control comparison: force control only and motion and force control with the arm tracing out a circle on the surface.

the joint angle measured by a joint encoder.[48] The maximum payload of an individual Baxter robot arm is 2.2 kg. For the software communication and control, Baxter runs on Robot Operating System (ROS), which provides default services such as collision avoidance that halts the arm motion before colliding with itself, as well as gravity compensation that cancels the gravity load on the joints and the

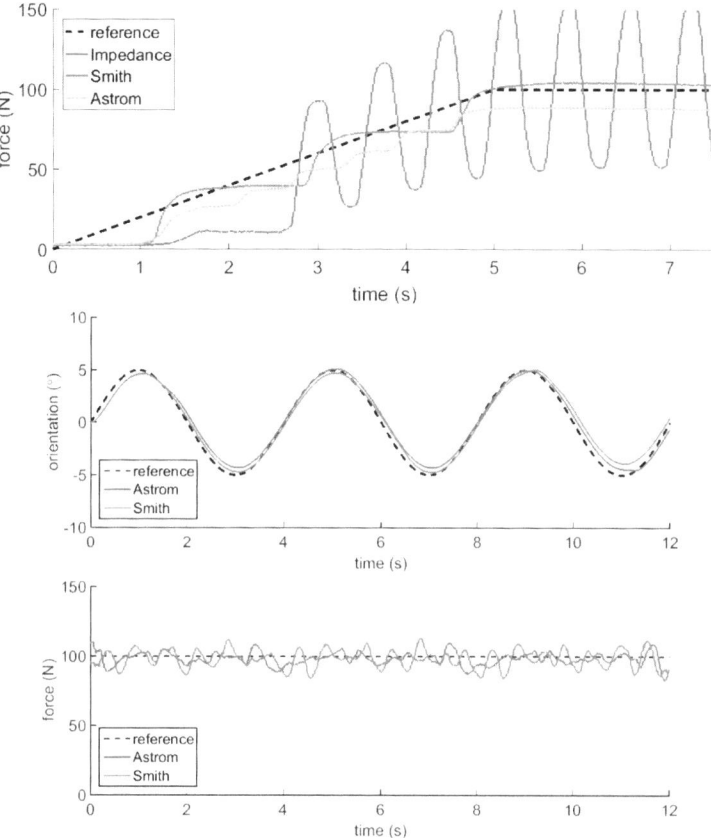

Fig. 5.20. Dual-arm force control comparison: force control only and force control with rotation about the forward axis.

external spring force on the shoulder joints. We use Robot Raconteur (RR)[11] as the communication and coordination layer and wrap the Rethink Robotics Python software development kit (SDK) in an RR service. Through the RR-ROS bridge, we are then able to access ROS services and topics to control the Baxters from high-level languages such as MATLAB.[49] Under this setting, the average system sampling time is about 8.67 ms (115.3 Hz) with a standard deviation of 0.6 ms. This rate is higher than the default ROS publication rate of 100Hz as we are using the Rethink Robotics SDK directly. As neither ROS nor RR is a real-time operating system (RTOS), this variation is unavoidable. There have been attempts to combine ROS with an RTOS (e.g., QNX) or real-time patch for Linux such as RT-PREEMPT, but such implementations are still at an experimental stage. Instead, we slowed the sampling period to 20 ms which is an upperbound of the sampling times to achieve a uniform sampling rate. Joint access command (reading joint angles and commanding joint position or velocity) execution time is measured in a Python loop. The average delay is very small, at about 63 μs with a standard deviation of 2.84 μs.

5.5.3.1 *Software architecture*

By mounting the Baxter robot on a converted power wheelchair, we have created a mobile manipulator, Baxter-on-Wheel (BOW), shown in Fig. 5.21. It consists of a dual arm robot, Baxter by Rethink Robotics, mounted on a converted power wheelchair. The arms and wheelchair may be controlled at the same time for coordinated operations. The initial design of the system has been described in Ref. 49 with improved sensing and control algorithms incorporated since then. Our focus is to empower mobility impaired individuals to gain more independence in daily living. The overall software architecture is shown in Fig. 5.21.

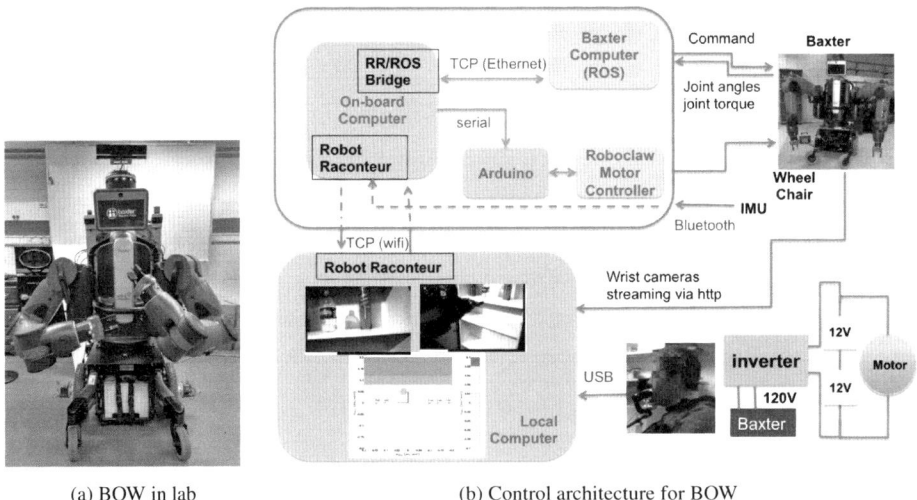

(a) BOW in lab   (b) Control architecture for BOW

Fig. 5.21. Baxter-on-Wheel (BOW) as a Baxter robot mounted on a stripped down wheel chair base and its control architecture based on RR and RR/ROS Bridge.

5.5.3.2 *BOW as an assistive robot*

BOW may be used as an assistive robot under the guidance of a remote user with limited input capability (e.g., individuals with tetraplegia). In Ref. 18 we showed that a 3-dof sip-puff mouth-operated input device may be used to command bow to navigate around furnitures and fetch objects from the shelf. This is accomplished through the outer loop velocity control mode of the Baxter with the user commanding the end effector position (switchable to orientation or other combinations) and other degrees of freedom autonomously resolved through the quadratic programming formulation as described in Section 5.3.1. Figure 5.22 shows the use of the input device to drive the BOW. In Fig. 5.22(a), the BOW detects the bench as an obstacle and the inequality constraint (5.2) in the outer loop controller prevents the BOW from colliding with it. The user then steers the BOW around the obstacle in Fig. 5.22(b), directs a BOW arm to grab a bottle from the shelf in Fig. 5.22(c), and returns it to the user in Fig. 5.22(d). Force control may also be added into the outer loop control using Baxter's built-in joint torque sensing as described.[50]

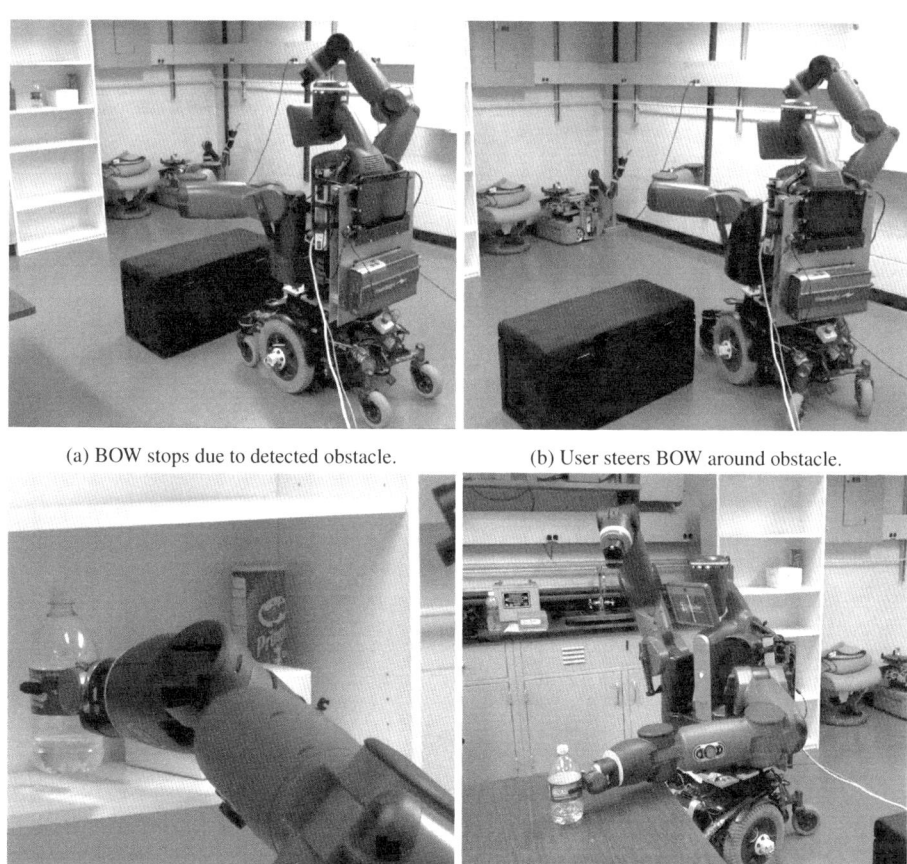

(a) BOW stops due to detected obstacle.   (b) User steers BOW around obstacle.

(c) User operates the gripper to grab bottle.   (d) User moves bottle back to target location.

Fig. 5.22. Using the 3-dof sip-puff input to command the BOW to fetch a water bottle from the shelf.

(a) Three Baxters holding a triangular box with six arms under force control.

(b) Three Baxters holding a triangular box with human motion guidance.

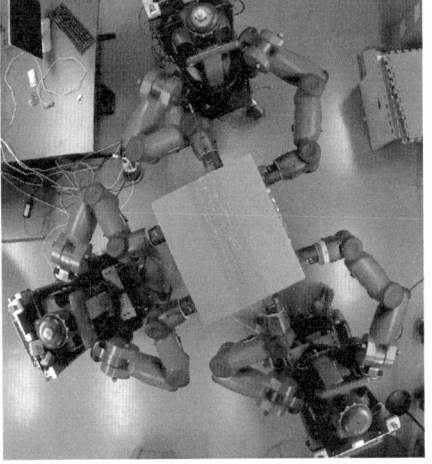

(c) Three Baxters holding a rectangular box with six arms under force control.

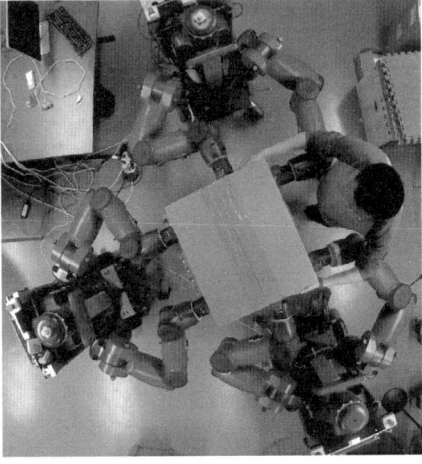

(d) Three Baxters holding a rectangular box with human motion guidance.

Fig. 5.23. Coordination of three Baxter robots to maintain contact forces to avoid slippage and follow human guidance.

5.5.3.3 *Multi-robot coordination*

One advantage of using Robot Raconteur and RR/ROS Bridge is the ability to coordinate three separate Baxter robots each one with its own ROS master node. Such coordination under ROS would require all three Baxter robots running under a single ROS environment with a single master node. This makes distributed control and scale-up more difficult. We have demonstrated three robots collaboratively holding a load together and manipulating it while maintaining the contact forces.[15] Figure 5.23 shows the three robots collaboratively manipulating a load under human hand guidance. The robots are under active force control to maintain required contact force within the friction cone as shown in Fig. 5.23(a) for a triangular box and Fig. 5.23(c) for a rectangular box. The control system also estimates the human motion intent based on the deviation of the contact force from the holding force requirement. These are shown in Figs. 5.23(b) and 5.23(d). Note that the load is beyond the capacity of a single arm so must be shared by all the supporting arms.

5.6   Conclusion and Future Work

Industrial robots today are ready to be integrated with sensors and human inputs to go beyond the traditional teach-and-playback paradigm. By using the external command interface provided by most robots, we can use outer loop control based on sensor and human inputs to direct the robot motion and its interaction with the environment. A unified quadratic programming formulation is posed for sensor-guided motion, human-directed motion, and force control. The inner control loop exhibits nonlinear dynamical response, including time delay. Compensating for these dynamics can improve stability, particularly for contact force control, and trajectory tracking performance. Results from three case studies are presented, including an ABB 6-dof arm, a Motoman dual-arm robot, and a dual-arm Baxter robot mounted on a wheel base.

5.7   Acknowledgment

The authors would like to thank Glenn Saunders for many of the mechanical setup and implementation in the experiments, Lu Lu for the assistive robot portion of this work, Shridhar Nath and Mark Vermilyea of GE for panel assembly portion of this work, and William Lawler for support with the software development. This work was supported in part by the New York State Empire State Development Division of Science, Technology and Innovation (NYSTAR) under contract C160142. The panel assembly work was sponsored by the ARM Institute through the Office of the Secretary of Defense under Agreement Number W911NF-17-3-0004.

References

1. J. Wallén, *The History of the Industrial Robot*. Linköping University Electronic Press (2008).
2. M. Hägele, K. Nilsson and J. N. Pires, *Industrial Robotics*. Springer (2008).
3. RobotMaster, RobotMaster:CAD/CAM for robots (Off-Line Programming). Available at https://robotmaster.com (Accessed March 29, 2018).

4. Octobpuz, Octopuz: Robot Programming and Simulation Software. Available at https://octopuz. com (Accessed March 29, 2018).

5. Yaskawa, *INFORM Manual* (2004).

6. ABB, *Application Manual: Controller Software IRC5: RoboWare 6.04* (2016).

7. FANUC Robotics America, *R-J3iB Controller KAREL Reference Manual* (2003).

8. Adept Technology, *V+ Language: User's Guide* (1997).

9. Stäubli, *Stäubli C Programming Interface for Low Level Robot Control* (2009).

10. KUKA Roboter, *Quickguide: KRL-Syntax* (2012).

11. J. D. Wason, Robot Raconteur version 0.8: An updated communication system for robotics, automation, building control, and the Internet of Things. In *IEEE International Conference on Automation Science and Engineering (CASE)* (2016).

12. M. Quigley, K. Conley, B. P. Gerkey, J. Faust, T. Foote, J. Leibs, R. Wheeler and A. Y. Ng, ROS: an open-source robot operating system. In *ICRA Workshop on Open Source Software* (2009).

13. E. Marcil, High-speed synchronous controller software specifications, Rev. B, Motoman Inc., West Carrollton, OH (2009).

14. M. Schöpfer, F. Schmidt, M. Pardowitz and H. Ritter, Open source real-time control software for the KUKA light weight robot. In *8th World Congress on Intelligent Control and Automation (WCICA)* (2010).

15. Y.-C. Peng, D. S. Carabis and J. T. Wen, Collaborative manipulation with multiple dual-arm robots under human guidance, *International Journal of Intelligent Robotics and Applications* **2** (2), 252–266 (2018).

16. D. E. Whitney, Resolved motion rate control of manipulators and human prostheses, *IEEE Transactions on Man-Machine Systems* **10** (2), 47–53 (1969).

17. S. Chiaverini, B. Siciliano and O. Egeland, Review of the damped least-squares inverse kinematics with experiments on an industrial robot manipulator, *IEEE Transactions on Control Systems Technology* **2**(2), 123–134 (1994).

18. L. Lu and J. T. Wen, Human-directed coordinated control of an assistive mobile manipulator, *International Journal of Intelligent Robotics and Applications* **1**(1), 104–120 (2017).

19. L. Armstrong, Optimization motion planning with `tesseract` and `trajopt` for industrial applications. Available at https://goo.gl/CihA8L (Accessed March 29, 2018).

20. N. Hogan, Impedance control: An approach to manipulation. In *1984 American Control Conference*, pp. 304–313 (1984).

21. L. Wilfinger, J. Wen and S. Murphy, Integral force control with robustness enhancement, *IEEE Control System Magazine* **14**(1), 31–40 (1994).

22. O. J. Smith, A controller to overcome dead time, *ISA Journal* **6**(2), 28–33 (1959).

23. K. Astrom, C. Hang and B. Lim, A new Smith predictor for controlling a process with an integrator and long dead-time, *IEEE Transaction on Automatic Control* **39**(2), 343–345 (1994).

24. P. Arcara and C. Melchiorri, Control schemes for teleoperation with time delay: A comparative study, *Robotics and Autonomous Systems* **38**(1), 49–64 (2002).

25. A. C. Smith and K. Hashtrudi-Zaad, Smith predictor type control architectures for time delayed teleoperation, *The International Journal of Robotics Research* **25**(8), 797–818 (2006).

26. D. Kruse and J. T. Wen, Application of the Smith-Astrom predictor to robot force control. In *IEEE Conference on Automation Science and Engineering (CASE)*, Gothenburg, Sweden (2015).

27. B. Potsaid and J. Wen, High performance motion tracking control. In *Proceedings of 2004 Conference on Control Applications*, Taipei, Taiwan (2004).

28. B. Potsaid, J. Wen, M. Unrath, D. Watt and M. Alpay, High performance motion tracking control for electronic manufacturing, *ASME Journal on Dynamics, Measurement, & Control* **129**(6), 767–776 (2007).

29. S. Arimoto, S. Kawamura and F. Miyazaki, Bettering operation of robots by learning, *Journal of Robotic systems* **1**(2), 123–140 (1984).

30. C. Connolly, Technology and applications of ABB RobotStudio, *Industrial Robot-an International Journal* **36**(6), 540–545 (2009).

31. Yaskawa, *MotoSim EG-VRC Operation Manual - for Windows* (2015).

32. Stäubli, Stäubli robotics suite. Available at https://www.staubli.com/en-us/robotics/product-range/robot-software/pc-robot-programming-srs (Accessed March 29, 2018).

33. KUKA, Kuka.Sim software. Available at https://www.kuka.com/en-us/products/robotics-systems/software/simulation-planning-optimization/kuka_sims (Accessed March 29, 2018).

34. FANUC, FANUC robotguide simulation software. Available at https://www.fanucamerica.com/products/robots/robot-simulation-software-FANUC-ROBOGUIDE (Accessed March 29, 2018).

35. R. Smith, Open Dynamics Engine. Available at http://www.ode.org (Accessed March 29, 2018).

36. DART, DART: Dynamic Animation and Robotics Toolkit. Available at https://dartsim.github.io (Accessed March 29, 2018).

37. Bullet, Bullet Real-Time Physics Simulation. Available at https://pybullet.org/wordpress (Accessed March 29, 2018).

38. SDFormat, SDF: Describe Your World. Available at http://sdformat.org (Accessed March 29, 2018).

39. Kinova Robotics, Gazebo for Kinova Robots. Available at https://github.com/Kinovarobotics/kinova-ros/wiki/Gazebo (Accessed March 29, 2018).

40. ABB, Product Manual-IRB6640. Available at Tech. Rep. 3HAC026876-001, ABB (2010).

41. Point Grey, FLIR Blackfly machine vision. Available at https://www.ptgrey.com/blackfly-usb3-vision-cameras (2018), (Accessed March 29, 2018).

42. ATI Industrial Automation, ATI F/T Sensor : Omega160. (2018). Available at https://goo.gl/5VhxRs (Accessed March 29, 2018).

43. S. Chitta, I. Sucan and S. Cousins, Moveit![ROS topics], *IEEE Robotics & Automation Magazine* **19**, 18–19 (2012).

44. R. Diankov, R. Diankov and J. Kuffner, OpenRAVE: A Planning Architecture for Autonomous Robotics, Tech. Rep., Robotics Institute Carnegie Mellon University (2008).

45. N. Koenig and A. Howard, Design and use paradigms for gazebo, an open-source multi-robot simulator. In *2004 IEEE/RSJ International Conference on Intelligent Robots and Systems (IROS) (IEEE Cat. No.04CH37566)*, vol. 3, pp. 2149–2154 (2004), doi:10.1109/IROS.2004.1389727.

46. L. Jaillet, J. Cortés and T. Siméon, Transition-based RRT for path planning in continuous cost spaces. In *IEEE/RSJ International Conference on Intelligent Robots and Systems (IROS)*, pp. 2145–2150 (2008).

47. D. Kruse, J. T. Wen and R. J. Radke, A Sensor-Based Dual-Arm Tele-Robotic System, *IEEE Transactions on Automation Science and Engineering* **12**(1), 4–18 (2015).

48. A. Smith, C. Yang, C. Li, H. Ma and L. Zhao, Development of a dynamics model for the Baxter robot. In *2016 IEEE International Conference on Mechatronics and Automation* (2016).

49. A. Cunningham, W. Keddy-Hector, U. Sinha, D. Whalen, D. Kruse, J. Braasch and J. T. Wen, Jamster: A mobile dual-arm assistive robot with Jamboxx control. In *IEEE International Conference on Automation Science and Engineering (CASE)* (2014).

50. L. Lu and J. T. Wen, Human-directed robot motion/force control for contact tasks in unstructured environments. In *IEEE International Conference on Automation Science and Engineering (CASE)*, pp. 1165–1170 (2015).

© 2020 World Scientific Publishing Company
https://doi.org/10.1142/9789811222849_0006

Chapter 6

Blended Shared Control in Collaborative Robotics

Zongyao Jin and Prabhakar R. Pagilla

6.1 Overview

Blended shared control is a method to continuously blend control inputs from traditional automatic control systems and the human operator for controlling machines safely and effectively. The automatic control system generates control inputs based on feedback of signals from sensor measurements. The human operator generates control inputs based on experience, task knowledge, and awareness of the environment in which the machine is operating. Such blending of inputs combines the benefits from both agents to achieve better performance of task execution as well as maintaining situational awareness to handle safety concerns and environmental uncertainties. The notion of blended shared control is particularly useful in collaborative robot applications, which enables keeping the human operator in the loop to initiate robot action and providing real-time intelligent assistance.

In this chapter, we first present the general concepts of shared control, its classification and applications with a brief survey of relevant literature. Blended shared control is then introduced with an emphasis on challenges involved in conflict-free blending of human and automatic control inputs. We present the following tools to overcome these challenges for a collaborative robot task: (1) task learning, (2) intent prediction, (3) subgoal adjustment and (4) input blending. We conclude the chapter by providing results from experiments conducted on a scaled hydraulic excavator for a typical trenching and truck-loading task.

6.1.1 *General Concepts*

Collaboration and cooperation among people in complex situations as a way to combine strength from multiple agents and completing tasks which could be otherwise impossible to finish has been a key for the development of human society.[1-3] Automatic control, traditionally considered as merely a powerful tool instead of a collaborator, is known to be able to execute well-defined and repetitive tasks with high precision and efficiency. Human operators, on the other hand, exhibit strong situational awareness for handling uncertainties in the environment and for adapting to changes during task execution. With rapid advances in the development of scientific tools in robotics, artificial intelligence, machine learning and automatic control, researchers have reconsidered the role of automatic control as a human collaborator.[4-6] Because of the potential for achieving a higher level of safety and performance, there has been a strong interest in the development of tools that address the challenges of collaboration between humans and robots.[7-9] Human-machine collaboration in the form of shared control (SC) has been explored in many studies in robotics and human-machine interfaces with a focus on assisting human operators with robotics and control technologies during task execution. Results have shown that shared control architectures offer more situational awareness and robustness over full autonomy, and provide additional benefits in terms of performance improvement, difficulty reduction, capability extension, and safety enhancement, etc.[10,11]

6.1.2   *Classification and Applications of Shared Control*

Shared control consists of methods which directly or indirectly combine human operator input with automatic control input in the control of dynamic systems,[12] i.e., the actions of the human operator are closely integrated into the closed-loop control system. While collaborative robotics for complex applications sometimes consist of many shared control methods, the methods from existing literature can be generally classified into the following distinguishable forms, each of which has distinct characteristics and target applications: collaborative control, traded control, indirect shared control, coordinated control, virtual constraint control, blended shared control.

The simplest forms of shared control are collaborative control and traded control. In collaborative control, a certain subset of control inputs are handled by a human operator, while the rest of the inputs are processed by the machine. This is commonly observed in automotive applications, where for example, in the cruising mode, steering action is handled by a human and throttle control is achieved by the closed-loop controller. With traded control, the control authority can be transferred completely to either the operator or the automatic control algorithms. This has been explored and applied to aircraft autopilot systems where the control authority is given to the computer while cruising, whereas more complex situations such as takeoff and landing are handled by human operators; in such applications, control authority switching is decided by the human operators. Recent studies[13,14] have suggested ways to adaptively change control authority between the human and the robot based on the ambiguity or confidence of the human operator's intent.

Indirect shared control, usually in the form of providing sensory information for human operators, has also been widely used. Instead of providing control input directly to the robot, the system offers feedback to the human operators to make adjustments or improvements. In Maske et al.,[15] providing operational instructions to operators through Graphical User Interfaces (GUIs) has resulted in improved execution performance for excavator earth-moving tasks. Haptic feedback to human operators has been used for UAV collision avoidance,[16] vehicle blind spot warning,[17] and highway merging scenarios.[18]

When controlling a multiple degrees-of-freedom (DOF) robot, difficulties arise for human operators when the inverse kinematics is not intuitive or when there are too many DOF for the human to manipulate simultaneously. Coordinated control reduces such difficulty by taking care of the kinematics and having humans to give command in a lower dimension space which is usually more intuitive to understand. For example, (1) in the control of quadrotor motion, human operators provide commands in the Cartesian space and the control algorithm coordinates the rotors to execute the Cartesian motion desired by the human operators[19] and (2) in control of robotic manipulator end-effector motion, human operators specify the motion of the end-effector and control of each joint motion to execute the motion is handled in software via the inverse kinematics.[20]

In virtual constraint control methods, assistance is provided to human operators by disabling input commands leading to hazardous results. In Hanson and Servin,[21] a large-scale manipulator with forwarder machine is designed with the shared control capabilities of allowing a human operator to give inputs in the Cartesian space. While executing the operator's command, the underlying software provides a protection mechanism such that the commands resulting in singularities or exceeding physical limits are ignored. Researchers working on the development of smart wheelchairs have been using virtual constraint control to protect such systems from colliding with the physical environment[22-24] where inputs that may result in collisions are voided or handled by providing force feedback to the user.

A classification of various types of shared control strategies with a brief description is provided in Table 6.1. The blended shared control category, which is the focus of this chapter, is subsequently described in more detail in Section 6.1.3.

Table 6.1. Classification of shared control strategies.

Name	Description
Collaborative Control	A subset of control inputs are handled by human operator, the rest are processed by the automatic control.
Traded Control	Control authority can be transferred to either the human operator or the automatic control.
Indirect Shared Control	Additional sensory information is provided to human operators for feedback and assistance.
Coordinated Control	Human operators command robot in an intuitive coordinate frame and individual joint control is coordinated by automatic control.
Virtual Constraint Control	Automatic control overrides human operators command to overcome physical or computational constraints.
Blended Shared Control	Human operator intent is predicted to generate automatic control input which is blended continuously with the human operator input for action command.

6.1.3 *Blended Shared Control*

Blended shared control (BSC) is a form of a shared control scheme where human and automatic control inputs are combined continuously to control the robot. BSC scheme is more seamless in the sense that the human operator, through either individual joint control or control coordination, always has access to the control of the robot and to initiate actions; the automatic control, by predicting the operator's intent, keeps providing assistance in the form of closed-loop control input and is dynamically combined with the human input in real-time to jointly act on the robot. The BSC scheme is particularly relevant for applications where the environments are dynamic, unstructured and uncertain. In such environments, it is difficult to efficiently execute tasks using only automatic control or full autonomy since comprehensive sensing of the environment could be impractical or prohibitively expensive. Furthermore, when safety is of paramount importance, the quick decision-making abilities and situational awareness of human operators provide a level of robustness that is hard to replicate with full autonomy. However, by providing some level of control assistance via BSC to the human operator, one can reduce the difficulty of operating robots in such environments, improve task performance, and enhance safety during task execution.

Studies on blended shared control have shown promising results towards applying such techniques to surgery robots, smart wheelchairs, and construction excavators. In Refs. 25–27, researchers applied shared control methods on wheelchair navigation problems for collision avoidance where human and automatic control inputs were blended to drive the robots. The blending parameters in these studies were designed by optimizing various cost functions relating human input to obstacle collision or the probability distribution of velocity versus collision. In robotic surgery applications, researchers have demonstrated that by utilizing BSC on tissue grasping related surgical tasks, it is possible to reduce the probability of tissue crash injury[28, 29] caused by over-application of grasping force. In selecting the blending parameter, in one case, researchers used a model dynamically predicting tissue type, in another case, blending parameter was assigned with a fixed value based on experiments.

In the heavy construction industry, there are significant risks associated with operating heavy machinery in an uncertain task environment without human involvement. Thus, the industry has always resorted to human operators controlling the excavators, except in remote mining operations. However, operating machines such as hydraulic excavators efficiently require a certain skill level and experience. With the industry growth trends observed in recent years, there has been a shortage of skilled human operators. The BSC scheme has the potential to overcome the skill-gap issue by providing intelligent assistance to novice operators to improve task execution performance. Studies in Refs. 15, 30–33 investigated some of these BSC solutions coupled with the concepts of task learning and intent prediction, and some promising experimental results were presented.

In addition to the difficulty of operating robots and the uncertainty in the task environment, another distinct feature of many collaborative applications is that operations with similar patterns have to be executed over many cycles; the operations are similar but lack well-organized repetition. Thus, prior to addressing issues such as intent detection/prediction and input blending, one has to learn the task in such a way that the learned results can be interpreted and executed by automatic control easily. Learning of a task in itself could be another significant and key element of the BSC scheme. The concept of subgoals as discussed in Refs. 15, 30, 31, 34 has been used for such interpretation in BSC, where the specific task is first learned through demonstration and divided into subgoals that can be executable by automatic control. Then, control blending is performed based on the prediction of the human operator's intent. Hence, there are a number of challenges in terms of developing comprehensive blended shared control strategies for such general applications in collaborative robotics. Based on the aforementioned challenges and to investigate and develop tools to address these challenges, one can formulate the following key questions:

(1) How does one learn the task and segment it into well-defined subgoals?
(2) How does one ascertain and quantify the intent of the operator in terms of moving from one subgoal to another?
(3) How does one adjust nominal subgoals based on changes in target objects during operation as detected by the human operator?
(4) How does one change the blending parameter (the parameter that decides the extent of the human operator input and automatic control input in the total command input) in real-time to facilitate operator intent and subgoal achievement?

In the following sections, some preliminary strategies developed for answering these questions are presented. Experiments conducted with these strategies on a scaled hydraulic excavator platform in a typical trenching-and-truck-loading task environment where the human operator commands the robot with two joysticks are described. The excavator application is a relevant candidate for BSC research because

(1) operating excavators without intelligent assistance demands significant training with the joystick-interface; an operator typically controls four robot arm degrees of freedom independently and simultaneously by two joysticks with four motion axes as shown in Fig. 6.1; and
(2) similar joystick-based operational interfaces, with cyclic tasks lacking well-organized repetition, are common in other machines such as cranes, backhoes, forklifts, bulldozers, etc.

Thus, BSC methods developed based on the excavator application have the potential to be generalized to many industrial robots and to improve performance as well as combine benefits from both agents.

In the rest of the chapter, we first provide technical details of the methods developed to address these challenges. We then provide details of the excavator experimental platform and results of experiments conducted to validate some of the

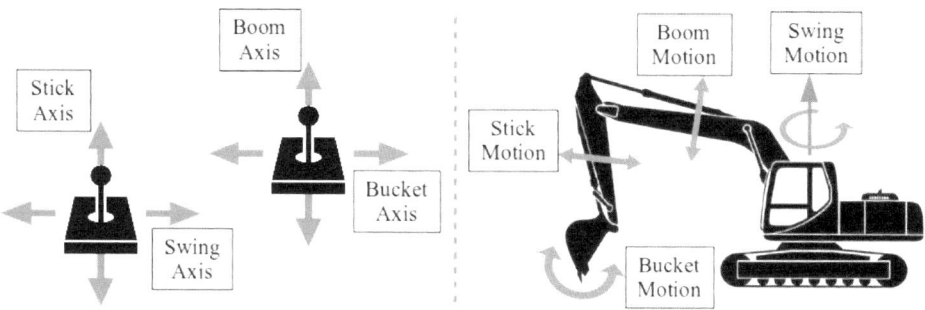

Fig. 6.1. Excavator operation interface via joysticks.

technical developments. We conclude the chapter by providing some remarks and specific future directions that hold promise in terms of immediate impact on improving BSC in collaborative robotics.

6.2 Task Learning

The collaborative robotic applications where BSC schemes are useful typically involve tasks that are ill-defined for traditional automatic control. To address the challenges of task quantification, some very general methods have been developed from machine learning perspectives.[35] provides a survey on robot learning from demonstration, and recent developments show that the available methods can be generally divided into two categories, namely, policy learning and subgoal learning.

6.2.1 *Policy and Subgoal Learning Methods*

Policy learning methods have been effective in grid world applications, for example chess games, and employ iterative searching and propagating reward calculations in the entire space with finite states and finite actions. However, they are less effective in robotic applications where robots work in continuous space with infinite possible state transitions and actions to take at each state. For applications where robots are operated by humans, the nature of tasks involved allows us to make reasonable assumptions to simplify the learning structure. Human operators in general do not perform well in operations that involve multi-tasking;[36] they have a tendency to decompose a complicated task into a number of subgoals, and by completing all the subgoals in some particular sequence the overall task is accomplished.

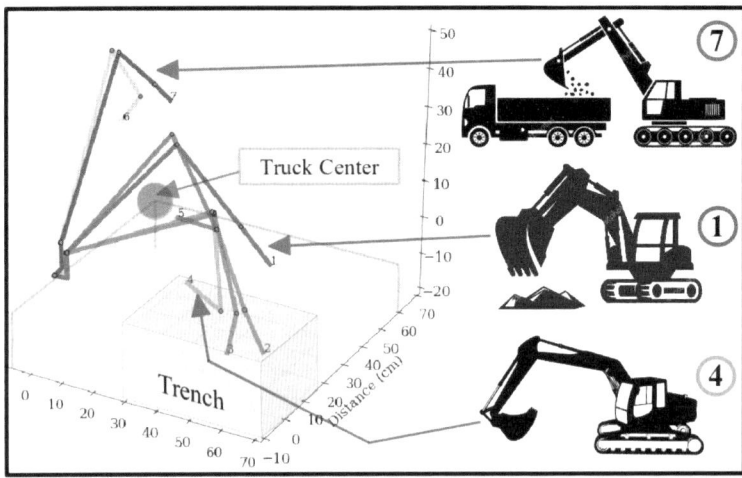

Fig. 6.2. Illustration of subgoals in joint space.

Subgoals, in the context of human operated robot tasks, can be points in the robot joint space which correspond to different robot configurations, or points in the Euclidean workspace corresponding to different end-effector positions. To illustrate the concept of subgoals, consider the excavator shown in Fig. 6.2 performing a trenching-and-loading task. Seven nominal subgoals, visualized by wire-frame, are shown. By repeating such subgoals in a correct sequence, the operator will be able to complete the task. Each subgoal in this case is a point in the joint space, but can be instantiated by a robot configuration via forward kinematics, as 1, 4, and 7 are shown on the right. Note that transitioning between subgoals is executable by either human operators (easy for skilled operators, but may be hard for novice operators) or some straight forward closed-loop control algorithms.

Subgoal learning methods[15,31,34] extract from finite recorded data distributions of points, where operator input patterns or robot states commanded by the operator change in noticeable ways indicating the transition from one subgoal to another. With such distributions extracted, statistical methods are employed to cluster and locate subgoals. Once the subgoals are learned, they can serve as reference for intent prediction and automatic control since they roughly define the critical steps toward task completion. Hence, subgoal learning methods can be considered as more suitable for BSC applications involving human-machine interaction.

6.2.2 *Discovering Subgoal Distributions*

To discover from data the distributions of points which potentially encode the subgoal-changing behavior, we introduce the concept of operator primitives. It is similar to the notion of action primitives described in Maske et al.[37] in the sense that they both map the operator's joystick input into broader categories as depicted in Fig. 6.3. The concept of operator primitives is a generalization of action primitives for human operated robotic tasks where precision is not critical, since in those tasks humans are necessary because of the need for their decision making ability as opposed to their ability to execute actions precisely. The operators tend to give commands in a broad sense, e.g., when we set $N = 3$ in Fig. 6.3, the three primitives could be positive input, negative input, and zero or near-zero noise perturbation. The variable N hence controls the resolution of such a map.

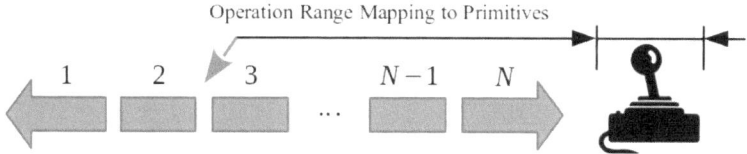

Fig. 6.3. Mapping between joystick input and primitives.

With such generalization and considering that most human operated robots are operated with an independent joystick signal channel commanding each joint velocity, we formulate the definition of operator primitives in the following manner. Let o_j be the operator primitive variable for joint j, then at any time, o_j can take N values given by $w \in \{1, 2, \cdots, N\}$ which encodes the categories. In the case of the hydraulic excavator case, we can set $N = 3$, which means that each independent human input (via a joystick) for an actuator controlling a DOF can take three distinct values; for example, 1 for forward motion of the joystick, 2 for backward motion, and 3 for near zero; these distinct values are mapped to the joint velocity. Also, the primitive-categorized states of an m-DOF robot can be mathematically captured by the concept of operator primitives such that at any given time, the operative primitives vector is given by $\mathbf{o} = [o_1, o_2, \cdots, o_m]$; note that each o_j could be 1, 2 or 3 depending on the joystick input for the j-th actuator. In order to assign joint motion actions to fall into one of the three categories (1, 2, 3), we use the K-Means algorithm to cluster the data. We initialize the cluster means

$\mu_{jw}, w \in \{1, 2, 3\}$ for joint j by

$$\begin{cases} \mu_{j1} = \underset{t}{\mathrm{argmax}}[x_j(t)] \\ \mu_{j2} = \frac{1}{2}\{\underset{t}{\mathrm{argmax}}[x_j(t)] - \underset{t}{\mathrm{argmin}}[x_j(t)]\} \\ \mu_{j3} = \underset{t}{\mathrm{argmin}}[x_j(t)] \end{cases} \qquad (6.1)$$

where $x_j(t)$ is the state of joint j at time t. Then we update the cluster (primitive category) assignment and the means by Lloyd's algorithm,[38] i.e., updating the cluster assignment by finding the index w such that

$$\underset{w}{\mathrm{argmin}}\{||x_j(t) - \mu_{jw}||_2\}. \qquad (6.2)$$

We then follow by updating μ_{jw} with the new cluster assignment by

$$\mu_{jw} = \frac{1}{\eta}\sum_t \{x_j(t)\mathbb{1}(w)\} \qquad (6.3)$$

where $\mathbb{1}(w)$ is the indicator function which takes the value of 1 if $x_j(t)$ gets assigned to cluster w and 0 otherwise, and η is the total number of elements assigned to cluster w. We iterate on such process until the means converge. The rest of the segmentation is processed using the same methods as mentioned in Ref. 39.

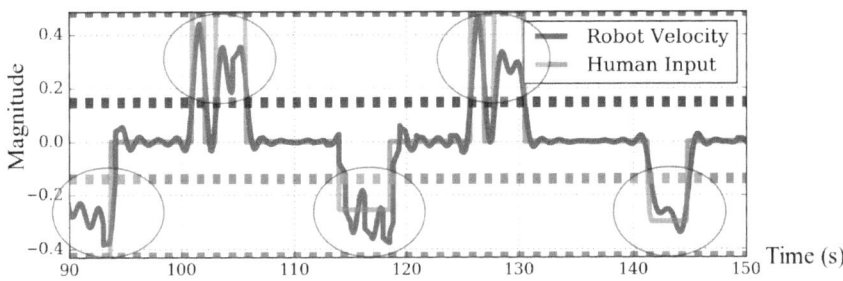

Fig. 6.4. Operator input overlapped with joint velocity of excavator bucket.

The difference in formulation between the operator primitives and the action primitives as in Refs. 15, 37 is that the action primitives are defined based on the robot joint velocities and operator primitives are based on the operator's joystick input. Hence, the operator primitives capture the operator's inputs directly from the joystick space. A significant advantage of the operator primitives in heavy construction setting is that they are not affected by drastic changes in workload or contact force. For example, during a digging process, the operator may not change the command input combination, hence the joint velocities ideally should not change drastically. However, the workload or contact force may change dramatically before and after the end-effector touches a hard surface, which will likely cause changes in robot joint velocities, thus, affecting the action primitives. Therefore, operator primitives provide better encoding of operator's behavior and are less sensitive to perturbations due to the environment. One can observe this from the experimental data shown in Fig. 6.4, where the regions highlighted with circles refer to situations where the joint velocity for the bucket was significantly affected by hard contact during digging. But the operator's intent, as reflected from the joystick input, did not change.

6.2.3 *Subgoal Identification and Execution Sequence*

Since the data processed by operator-primitive-based segmentation encode the potential distribution of subgoals, and the number of subgoals may vary depending on the task complexity and operator styles, Bayesian non-parametric clustering (BNPC) can be employed as an appropriate inference method. In BNPC formulation, the Chinese Restaurant Process (CRP) prior handles the uncertain number of clusters by assuming a potential infinite number of clusters with only a finite number of them active. With the exchangeable property of such formulation, Gibbs sampling is usually used as the iterative inference tool.[34,40] However, the traditional BNPC was developed for inference with data for which the cluster label ordering needs to be unique but does not depend on time. Because of the dynamical nature of the robot motion in the sense that subgoals have to be finished in a time sequence in order to bring the task to its completion, we also want to encode temporal information from demonstration. The fact that data points are sampled in real-time with time stamps makes this possible. The idea behind temporal ordering is that for all clusters we want to label them sequentially in increasing order according to the point in that cluster associated with the earliest time stamp; let $\overline{\tau}_J$ be the time stamp corresponding to that data point. We define τ_i as the time stamp associated with data point x_i, then

$$\overline{\tau}_J = \operatorname*{argmin}_i(\tau_i), \ \forall z_i = j \tag{6.4}$$

where z_i is the cluster assignment of data point i. The inference of z_i is a result of the BNPC formulation. Let $P(z_i = j|z_{-i}, \theta_j)$ be the probability of x_i having label $z_i = j$, then

$$P(z_i = j|z_{-i}, \theta_j) \propto P(z_i|z_{-i})P(x_i|\theta_j) \tag{6.5}$$

where z_{-i} is the cluster assignments of all other data points except i, x_i is the data point itself, j is the assigned cluster for x_i, and θ_j is the parameter for the base distribution. The CRP prior $P(z_i|z_{-i})$ in (6.5) is given by

$$P(z_i = j|z_{-i}) = \begin{cases} \frac{n}{n-1+\alpha}, & \text{from an existing cluster} \\ \frac{\alpha}{n-1+\alpha}, & \text{starting a new cluster} \end{cases} \tag{6.6}$$

where n is the number of data points assigned to cluster j and α is the concentration parameter controlling how many clusters will be generated. By assuming the base distribution is normal with zero mean and unit variance,[40] the likelihood $P(x_i|\theta_j)$ in (6.5) is then

$$P(x_i|\theta_j) = \begin{cases} \mathcal{N}(x_i, \frac{n\bar{x}_j}{n+1}, \mathbb{I}) & \text{from an existing cluster} \\ \mathcal{N}(x_i, 0, \mathbb{I}), & \text{starting a new cluster} \end{cases} \tag{6.7}$$

where $\bar{x}_j$ is the mean of cluster j, $\mathbb{I}$ is the identity covariance matrix.

The BNPC/TO implementation is provided in Algorithm 1, where χ is the data set with ν data points and each data point contains the m-dimensional robot joint information at each sample time. Because of the linearity of the normal distribution,

---

Algorithm 1 BNPC/TO

Input: Data set $\chi \in \mathbb{R}^{(m+1)\times\nu}$, concentration parameter $\alpha \in \mathbb{R}^+$, number of iterations $k \in \mathbb{N}^+$

Output: Cluster assignment for each data point, distribution mean and covariance for each cluster

1: **Initialization** Assign each point to a distinct cluster
2: **while** Number of iterations $\leq k$ **do**
3:     Unassign observation from its original cluster
4:     Calculate $\mathrm{argmax}\{P(z_i|z_{-i})P(x_i|\theta_j)\}$ and assign new cluster label accordingly
5: **end while**
6: **Finalization** Sort clusters re-assign labels increasingly according to $\bar{\tau}_J$

---

we can scale the base distribution to fit the scale of the data set, or take affine transformations on the data set to fit the assumed base distribution.

6.3 Intent Prediction

Based on the set of learned subgoals, the actions of the human operator can be used to predict which subgoal is sought. In predicting the intent of the operator's input to seek a particular subgoal, we incorporate both the empirical knowledge of the task process and the operator's input in real-time. In order to encode such information, we construct a factor graph representing their dependencies as shown in Fig. 6.5(a), where L denotes the last visited subgoal, X is the current joint position, V denotes

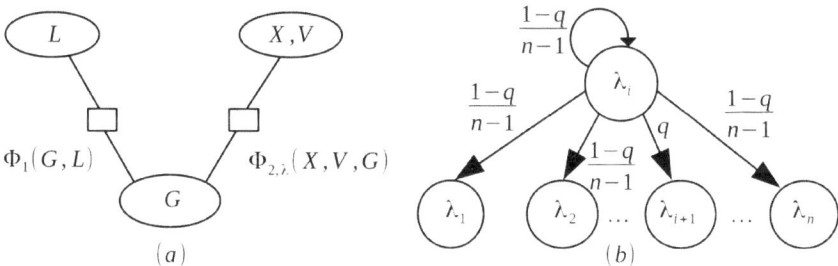

Fig. 6.5. Factor graph and Markov Chain for prediction.

the current joint velocity, G is the predicted next subgoal that the operator wishes to reach, Φ_1 denotes the function encoding the dependency between the last visited and the predicted subgoal, and $\Phi_{2,\lambda}$ denotes the dependency between the current position, velocity, and the predicted subgoal. The parameter λ contains information of all the subgoals which is known. Let $P(G|X, V, L)$ denote the probability of going to subgoal G given current position X, velocity V, and last visited subgoal L. Let $\Phi_1(G|L)$ be the probability of going to subgoal G given last visited subgoal L and $\Phi_{2,\lambda}(G|X, V)$ be the probability of going to subgoal G given current position X and velocity V. Then,

$$P(G|X, V, L) \propto \Phi_1(G, L)\Phi_{2,\lambda}(G, X, V). \qquad (6.8)$$

In the following we describe a method to compute $\Phi_1(G|L)$ by employing the notion of empirical stochastic transition matrix (ESTM) and $\Phi_{2,\lambda}(G|X, V)$ by employing the notion of the dynamic angle difference exponential (DADE).

6.3.1 *Encoding Empirical Knowledge*

In order to encode the empirical knowledge of subgoal transitions, a Markov Chain with n states is constructed. Figure 6.5(b) shows the transitions occurring at state i in such a Markov Chain, where $q \in [0, 1]$ denotes the probability that the task will be completed in the ordered sequence. It depicts that, at any given state (each subgoal λ_i is a state in terms of the Markov Chain), the probability of going to the next subgoal is given by $q \in [0, 1]$ which reflects the confidence level that one has that the task will be completed in the ordered sequence. While jumping to any other subgoal or staying in the same subgoal all have the same probability of $\frac{1-q}{n-1}$. Based on such a construction, to encode the information we define the ESTM as

$$
T = \begin{bmatrix}
\frac{1-q}{n-1} & q & \frac{1-q}{n-1} & \cdots & \frac{1-q}{n-1} \\
\frac{1-q}{n-1} & \frac{1-q}{n-1} & q & \cdots & \frac{1-q}{n-1} \\
\vdots & \ddots & \ddots & \ddots & \vdots \\
\frac{1-q}{n-1} & \frac{1-q}{n-1} & \ddots & \ddots & q \\
q & \frac{1-q}{n-1} & \cdots & \cdots & \frac{1-q}{n-1}
\end{bmatrix}.
\tag{6.9}
$$

Let T_{ij} denote the element in the i-th row and j-th column of T. Then, the probability of transitioning to subgoal j, namely G, given the last visited subgoal i, namely L, is given by

$$
\Phi_1(G, L) \propto P(G|L) \propto T_{ij}.
\tag{6.10}
$$

6.3.2 *Integrating Dynamic Prediction*

To incorporate into our prediction the effect of dynamic measurements and operator input in real-time, we introduce the idea of dynamic angle difference. Figure 6.6(a) shows the angles between current action, which is the velocity commanded by the operator in real-time, and closed-loop actions of going to each of the subgoals. In Fig. 6.6(a), $\lambda_1, \lambda_2, \cdots, \lambda_n$ denote the positions of subgoal $1, 2, \cdots, n$ in joint

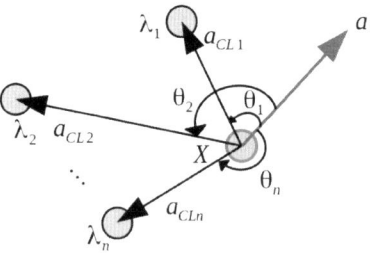

Fig. 6.6. Dynamic angle difference.

space, respectively; a denotes the operator's current action; $a_{CL1}, a_{CL2}, \cdots, a_{CLn}$ denote the closed-loop actions of an automatic controller for going to subgoal $1, 2, \cdots, n$, respectively, $\theta_1, \theta_2, \cdots, \theta_n \in [0, \pi]$ denote the angle between current action and closed-loop subgoal-tracking actions. We postulate that the dynamic probability of operator's action a of going to subgoal j is inversely proportional to the dynamic angle difference θ_j. In other words, the subgoal with the smallest angle between closed-loop action and operator's current action is our predicted target.

We can construct such a probability by defining

$$\Phi_{2,\lambda}(G, X, V) \propto P(G|X, V) \propto \frac{1}{\theta_j}. \tag{6.11}$$

However, such a construction potentially has two drawbacks. It approaches singularity when θ_j is close to zero. The output of such a function also would overweigh the probability from the stochastic matrix when the angle is small. To overcome these issues we propose the dynamic probability as given by the following dynamic angle difference exponential:

$$P(G|X, V) \propto e^{-\theta_j} \tag{6.12}$$

where

$$\theta_j = \arccos(\frac{a \cdot a_{CLj}}{||a|| \cdot ||a_{CLj}||}). \tag{6.13}$$

Therefore, DADE addresses the problem of singularity and normalizes the output such that the probabilities of ESTM and DADE are in the same scale.

The resulting equation for subgoal prediction is then given by

$$P(G|X, V, L) \propto T_{ij} \cdot e^{-\theta_j} \tag{6.14}$$

and the predicted subgoal is the one with the maximum probability among all possible scenarios, i.e.,

$$\underset{j,\lambda}{\mathrm{argmax}}\{T_{ij} \cdot e^{-\theta_j}\} \tag{6.15}$$

where i is the index of the last visited subgoal, which is known, j is the index of a possible target subgoal, and λ is a known parameter of $\Phi_{2,\lambda}$ which includes all the positions of learned subgoals using BNPC/TO algorithm.

6.4 Subgoal Adjustment

6.4.1 *Motivation*

In collaborative robot applications where operators are required to perform tasks that are mostly cyclic where each cycle is similar but lacks well-organized repetition, subgoals can change significantly due to task operation based on certain situations associated with the underlying conditions. For example, Fig. 6.7 shows gradual but significant accumulative changes of the trenching area and depth in a construction task with excavators. These changes typically can be adapted by making small adjustments in subgoals during each task cycle while having the operation pattern to remain largely the same. Execution of such tasks will benefit significantly from the application of BSC in which the robust situational awareness of human and the precision and efficiency of automatic control can be combined to improve task performance. However, BSC methods which consider only nominal subgoals without making any adjustments resulting from the task operation over time will not be able to provide effective assistance in off-nominal situations. Since nominal subgoals are assumed all the time, there could be gradual deterioration of automatic control assistance. Human operators, with their unique sensory abilities, environmental awareness and domain knowledge, can generally make decisions and take actions to adapt to those changes. Predicting and modeling these subgoal changes precisely in advance may not be feasible. Yet, meaningful interpretations of such decisions or actions can be obtained in real-time via operator intent, and can be encoded into dynamic subgoal adjustment which will lead to improving the long-term performance of blended shared control.

6.4.2 *Characteristics of Operator Behavior*

Based on our observations of excavator operators during task execution, subgoal adjustments are realized by making small modifications to the initial/nominal subgoals. Such observations are generally supported by studies and results from extensive research in psychology,[41,42] i.e., complex human behavior is learned through the modification of simpler behaviors, especially when environmental changes are gradual. For example, operators in excavator trenching usually make small adjustments to the subgoals in each subsequent cycle to compensate for the environmental changes, since it is an intuitively simple way to stay productive, such as removing as much dirt. With this viewpoint, we make the following assumption. If the operator commands a velocity for each robot joint, and if the operator could make a correct

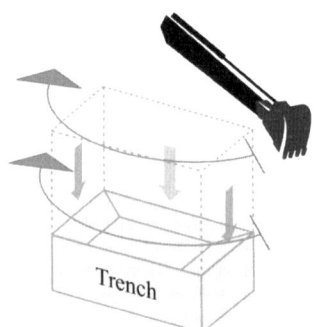

Fig. 6.7. Gradual but significant accumulative changes in target object.

adjustment to compensate for the subgoal changes, then the operator knows the level of adjustment needed for each robot joint. It is assumed that such knowledge is instantiated in the operator's actions taken for each robot joint near the subgoal which needs to be adjusted. In the following, we will describe how to adjust the subgoals based on operator actions by utilizing the notions of a hyper-rectangle (which embeds the subgoal with proper volume) and skill weighted action integral (which accounts for the amount of adjustment needed).

6.4.3 *Detection of Subgoal Adjustment Actions*

In order to detect operator's subgoal adjustment information, with the assumption that such behavior appears near the target subgoal, we define an Adjustment Encoding Hyper-Rectangle (AEHR), denoted by Δ to enclose the subgoal vicinity. It is a generalization of the rectangle to higher dimensions and is dynamically created and centered at the predicted target subgoal. The AEHR also dynamically changes its center and length of the edges when the prediction updates the target subgoal. The AEHR either lies within the m-dimensional robot joint space, denoted by Ω, or overlaps with it. This process is illustrated in Fig. 6.8 with a two-dimensional visualization of the AEHR in the robot joint space Ω. As shown in Fig. 6.8(a), the prediction result is λ_j according to operator's action vector $a(t)$ at time t; hence, the AEHR is created and centered at λ_j. However, at time $t+\delta$, as shown in Fig. 6.8(b), the prediction updates the target to λ_n based on the new action vector $a(t+\delta)$; thus, the AEHR changes its center and edge length accordingly. The AEHR thus defines a dynamic region around the target subgoal whose size is dependent on the position of the last visited subgoal and predicted target subgoal.

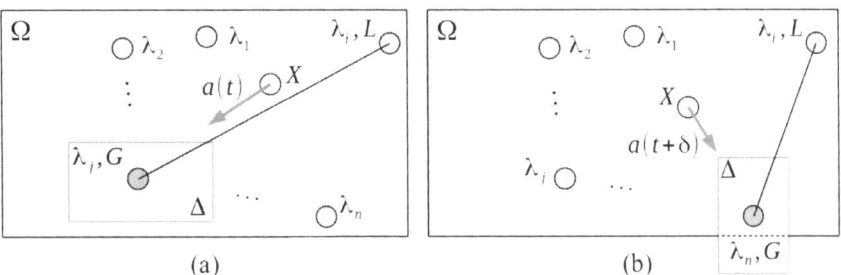

Fig. 6.8. Joint space Ω and adjustment encoding hyper-rectangle Δ in 2D.

We propose a method for finding the volume of AEHR via its edge lengths by employing a Hyperbolic Slope Transition Function (HSTF). If we keep the edge lengths constant, then we will have an issue when the last visited subgoal and the predicted subgoal are close to each other, the AEHR may very well encompass both of them which effectively shuts down the prediction updates. If the edge lengths are chosen as constant fractions of the distance between the two subgoals, we encounter another problem when the two subgoals are very far from each other, that is, the size of the AEHR would be very large which reduces the active region for the prediction algorithm. We want the size of AEHR to be large enough to accumulate and encode sufficient adjustment information from the operator and small enough such that the prediction is updated for active assistance as much as possible.

The solution we propose for this problem is to define the HSTF to be the ratio of the edge length of the AEHR and the distance of the predicted subgoal along the direction of that edge length. Further, we set an upper limit on this ratio to ensure that the AEHR is not too large when the distance between the last visited subgoal and predicted subgoal is large. We construct the HSTF function as a single function that is smooth and easy to implement in practice. When the subgoals are close, we define

$$\delta_r = d_r \tag{6.16}$$

where δ_r, $r \in 1, 2, \cdots, m$, denotes the edge lengths of Δ and d_r denotes the normalized distance between subgoals along the r-th coordinate of the m-dimensional joint space Ω. The normalized distance $d_r \in [0, 1]$ is given by

$$d_r = \frac{|\lambda_{ir} - \lambda_{jr}|}{\underset{p,q}{\operatorname{argmax}}|s_p - s_q|} \tag{6.17}$$

where λ_{ir} and λ_{jr} denote the distance of subgoals i and j along the r-th coordinate of the m-dimensional joint space, and s_p and s_q denote two arbitrary points along the same coordinate. When the subgoals are far from each other, we set a constant limit for each δ_r by

$$\delta_r = \mu \tag{6.18}$$

where $\mu \in [0, 1]$ is the constant upper limit. We then connect (6.17) and (6.18) together smoothly by constructing the HSTF given by

$$\delta_r = \Gamma^\mu_{\kappa,\xi}(d_r) = \xi d_r + \frac{1 + \tanh[\kappa(\xi d_r - \mu)]}{2}(\mu - \xi d_r) \tag{6.19}$$

where $\kappa \in \mathbb{R}^+$ and $\xi \in (0, 1)$ are two design parameters; κ controls by how much (6.19) resembles the combination of (6.17) and (6.18) and ξ is selected based on κ to ensure that the maximum slope of (6.19) is less than (6.17).

An example illustration of the HSTF and its motivation is provided in Fig. 6.9. In Fig. 6.9(a), the parameter selections are $\mu = 0.2, \kappa = 20, \xi = 0.95$. In Fig. 6.9(b), two examples of the relationship between subgoals and edge length of Δ for a one-degree of freedom revolute joint are provided to illustrate this idea; in this figure, the bottom case corresponds to the subgoals close to each other and the top case corresponds to the subgoals far from each other; also note that $\mathrm{argmax}|s_p - s_q| = 180^o$ is the maximum operational range of the one DOF revolute joint.

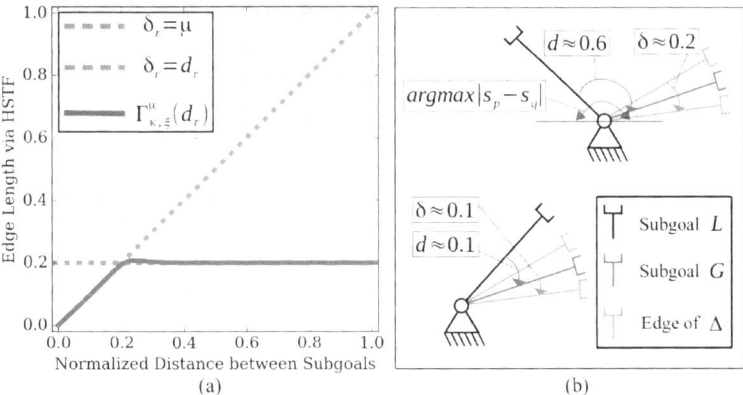

Fig. 6.9. (a) Hyperbolic Slope Transition Function and (b) examples.

6.4.4 *Encoding Adjustment Information via Integration*

To encode operator adjustment actions within the AEHR, we define a method for interpreting and encoding such information via a Skill Weighted Action Integral (SWAI) ρ, which is defined as

$$\rho = \beta \int a(t) \mathbb{1}(\Omega \cap \Delta | X \neq G)\, dt \qquad (6.20)$$

where β is a positive design scaling parameter (controls how much the designer wants to scale the integration results based on knowledge of the skill level of the operator), $\rho \in \mathbb{R}^m$ is the vector denoting the adjustment for the target subgoal, and the action vector is given by

$$a(t) = [a_1(t)\ a_2(t)\ \cdots\ a_m(t)]^T \in \mathbb{R}^m \qquad (6.21)$$

where $a_1, a_2, \cdots, a_m$ denote operator commands for each robot joint. The indicator function $\mathbb{1}(\Omega \cap \Delta | X \neq G)$ is given by

$$\mathbb{1}(\Omega \cap \Delta | X \neq G) = \begin{cases} 1, & X \in (\Omega \cap \Delta) \text{ given } X \neq G. \\ 0, & otherwise \end{cases} \tag{6.22}$$

The indicator function provides a means for SWAI to encode subgoal adjustment information only when the robot is within the intersection of Ω and Δ and when it has not reached the target subgoal. Figure 6.10 provides an illustration of such conditions. Figure 6.10(a) illustrates this concept by showing that in Δ, the robot trajectory τ is perturbed by the operator's subgoal adjustment actions $a(t), a(t + \delta)$. The closed-loop subgoal (G) tracking actions are denoted by $a_{CL}(t), a_{CL}(t + \delta), a_{CL}(t+2\delta)$, the positions of the robot are denoted by $X(t), X(t+\delta), X(t+2\delta)$. Notice that at the time $t + 2\delta$, the operator may be satisfied with the adjustment and take no additional action, thus, $a(t+2\delta) = 0$ is not shown. Figure 6.10(b) illustrates another scenario where the SWAI finishes encoding adjustment information since the robot has left the AEHR without reaching the target subgoal.

An important observation is that only actions taken by the operator are encoded by the SWAI, which represent the operator's subgoal adjustment information. It is hard to extract such information from sensing only the robot states in a blended shared control scheme because the operator's action always gets blended with the automatic control input.

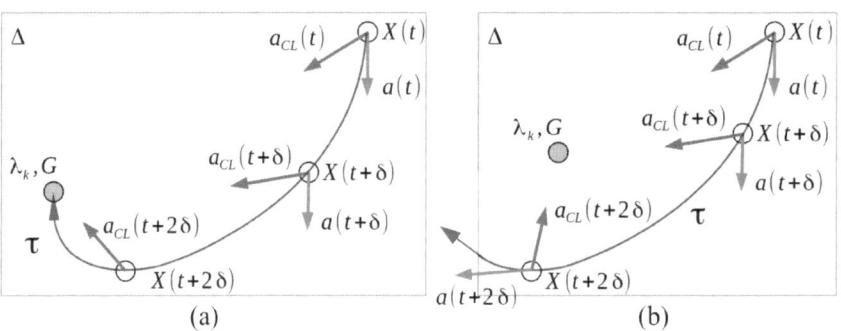

(a)   (b)

Fig. 6.10. Skill weighted action integration in the target subgoal vicinity.

Once the robot either reaches the subgoal or leaves the AEHR as shown in Fig. 6.10, we update the last visited subgoal L to the previous prediction result G which is the subgoal λ_k in subgoal set λ. Then, adjustment to this subgoal is made in the m-dimensional robot joint space by

$$\lambda_k^+ = \lambda_k^- + \rho \tag{6.23}$$

where λ_k^+ denotes the adjusted position, λ_k^- denotes its previous/nominal position.

One additional aspect is that once the robot enters Δ, we stop the prediction updates and keep the last predicted subgoal as the target subgoal; we also fix the blending parameter (which determines weighting between the human operator input and the automatic control input in calculating the total input; described in the next section) such that the human operator's blending weight is always higher than that of the automatic control input for tracking the target subgoal. Therefore, shared control assistance can still provide active assistance but the operator can always override the assistance to make arbitrary adjustments.

6.5 Blended Shared Control with Conflict Awareness

In the shared control framework, we want to blend the operator's inputs with the closed-loop action of tracking the predicted subgoal based on our prediction confidence, namely, the probability with which we can predict the most likely subgoal. Meanwhile, we also want to resolve conflicts, or yield control authority to the operator when the operator may not want to visit any of the learned subgoals; for example, in situations of emergent safety concerns. Based on (6.12), we define a parameter called the deviation threshold angle (DTA) θ_d to encode such awareness. We say that if $\forall \theta_i, i \in 1, 2, \cdots, n, \theta_i > \theta_d$, then the blending scheme will yield control authority to the human operator. That is, if all the angles from DADE are greater than the threshold value, we assume that the operator is going to a point not previously registered in the subgoals, and we yield control authority to the human operator. Otherwise, we will share the control authority between the human operator and the closed-loop subgoal-tracking action according to our prediction probability. The conflict awareness in the proposed blending scheme updates the starting point and considers conflicts for all subgoals from the entire joint space in real-time, unlike the ones considered in[39] where only conflicts between a single pair of starting and destination points are considered.

In blending control inputs according to the prediction probability, we need to normalize the prediction result in order to make it a valid probability. We consider the prediction probability to be given by

$$p^* = P(G = k | P, V, L) = \frac{T_{ik} \cdot e^{-\theta_k}}{\sum\limits_{j,\lambda} T_{ij} \cdot e^{-\theta_j}} \tag{6.24}$$

which renders $P(G = k | P, V, L) \in [0, 1]$, and k is the index of our predicted next subgoal from the previous section. Once we have $p^* \in [0, 1]$ as a valid probabil-

---

Algorithm 2 Real-Time BSC/CA

Input: Operator control input u_h, automatic control input u_e, probability p^* of predicted subgoal, dynamic angle difference vector $\theta \in \mathbb{R}^n$, threshold parameter θ_d

Output: Blended control input u_b

    Initialization $\bar{p} = p^*$

    if $\arg\min \theta > \theta_d$ **then**

3:      $\bar{p} = 0$

    end if

    Calculate $u_b = (1 - \bar{p})u_h + \bar{p}u_e$

---

ity, we blend the operator's input, denoted by u_h, with the real-time closed-loop subgoal tracking controller input, denoted by u_e, through

$$u = (1 - p^*)u_h + p^* u_e \qquad (6.25)$$

where u is the blended control input to the robot.

Taking into account the DTA-based conflict-awareness, we specify the total control input as

$$u_b = \begin{cases} (1 - p^*)u_h + p^* u_e, & \exists \theta_i < \theta_d, \ i \in 1, 2, \cdots, n \\ u_h, & \text{otherwise} \end{cases} \qquad (6.26)$$

where u_b is the final blended control input with conflict-awareness. The real-time implementation of this BSC method is given in Algorithm 2.

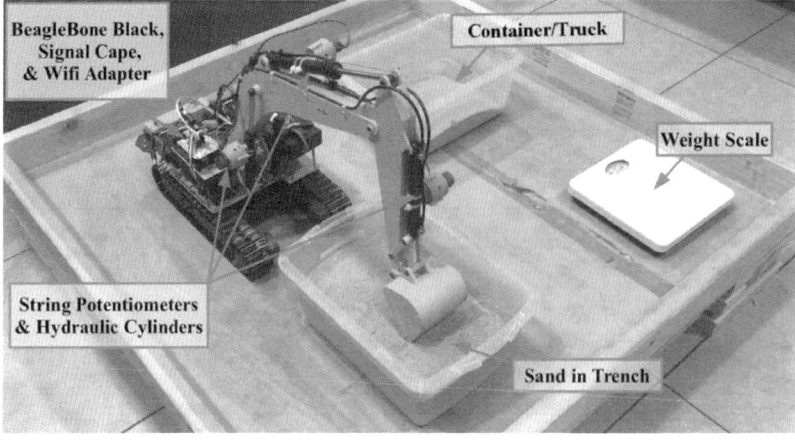

Fig. 6.11. Truck loading environment with a scaled hydraulic excavator.

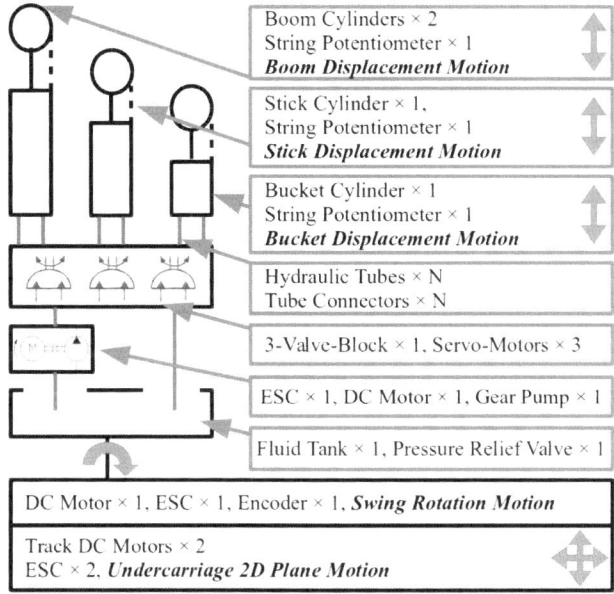

Fig. 6.12. Excavator operation.

6.6 Physical Platform and Experiment Design

In order to test our algorithms on a physical excavator platform, a trenching and truck loading environment was setup with a 1/12-th scaled hydraulic excavator system as shown in Fig. 6.11. Details of the hydraulic excavator system hardware and its software system are provided in the following and the complete kinematic and dynamics of the excavator system can be found in Ref. 30.

Figure 6.12 illustrates the operation of the 4-DOF hydraulic excavator. In this setup, four sensors are employed to track the displacement of the three cylinders (for boom, stick, bucket motions) and rotation of the swing motor (swing motion). The system components consist of a laptop for implementation, a Logitech F710 wireless controller with two standard joysticks as the human operator interface, a Beaglebone Black with AM335x 1GHz ARM Cortex-A8 processor and GPIO pins for collecting sensor data and output of actuation signals, a custom designed PCB board for signal connectors, and a WiFi router for communication.

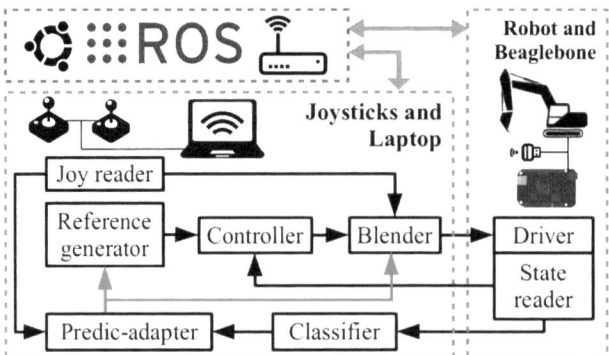

Fig. 6.13. Software structure and control flow.

The system software is built on Ubuntu Linux and Robot Operating System (ROS)[43] with different nodes; a node is an atomic program unit in ROS and it is used to describe different functions communicating between each other. A detailed ROS software network structure and control flow is provided in Fig. 6.13. The nodes running on the laptop-side include joy reader (reads joystick inputs), reference generator, controller, blender, classifier (generates learned subgoals), and Predic-adapter (predicts target and encodes subgoal changes). On the Beaglebone-side, a state reader and a driver node are employed for low-level actuation and sensing of the excavator. ROS topics, through which messages/information are published and subscribed, are programmed to transmit the computed information.

Two sets of experiments were designed based on the excavator setup mimicking the human-machine interaction applications to test the effectiveness of our algorithms. The first set of experiments test the efficiency improvement for novice operators with the BSC/CA provided by our algorithms alone, a truck loading experiment was designed with participation of 8 novice learning operators (NOs) and 1 skilled demonstration operator (SO). The second set of experiments test the effectiveness of the subgoal adjustment algorithms along with the BSC algorithms, a similar but modified task was designed with the participation of 10 novice operators, 1 skilled operator.

6.7 Experimental Results

Since some of the developed methods can yield meaningful results independently, we present the results of task learning, intent prediction by themselves first, and then the integrated results on performance improvement for BSC and subgoal ad-

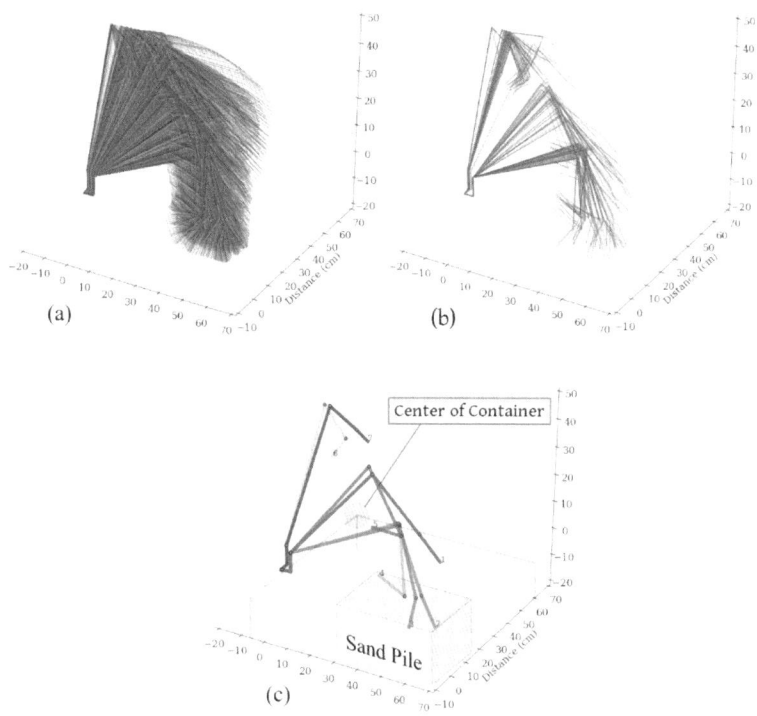

Fig. 6.14. Visualization task learning process and results.

justment BSC based on learning and prediction.

6.7.1 *Task Learning and Intent Prediction*

Learning the subgoals from the skilled operator is a key element for blended shared control, but can be applied to task learning for full autonomy as well. The learning process consists of having the skilled operator demonstrate the task, recording the robot states, processing the recorded data with operator primitive based segmentation, and identifying the subgoals via Bayesian non-parametric clustering with temporal order specification. Figure 6.14 illustrates the process and results of task learning, specifically, (a) shows the complete dataset of recorded robot states, (b) presents the distribution of subgoals after the complete dataset has been processed by operator primitive segmentation, and (c) provides the final subgoals with temporal order clustered via BNPC/TO.

Once the subgoals are learned, employing the prediction algorithm during a task process, one can ascertain with what probability the operator is attempting to visit the predicted subgoals. Such a process is demonstrated in Fig. 6.15 where the plot shows that in one task cycle, the evolution of prediction probabilities associated with the operator's input of visiting each of the subgoals in one complete task cycle.

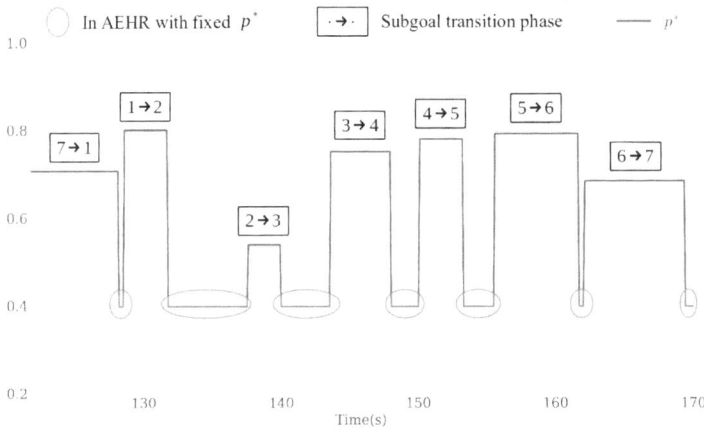

Fig. 6.15. Blending parameter trajectory from skilled operator.

6.7.2 *BSC Performance Improvement*

Since the overall purpose of developing blended shared control algorithms is to improve the performance in collaborative robotic tasks, an integrated BSC experiment is designed in the following manner. The novice operators first familiarize themselves with the excavator operation with an operational instruction guide (which is always available to novice operators during the entire experiment). We refer to this as the preparation stage (PSt). After this initial training, novice operators are asked to execute the task. We call this stage the manual stage (MSt). Each task cycle is timed and the amount of sand each operator loaded to the truck is weighed. Then the skilled operator performs the same task as demonstration to the machine. The machine will learn from the skilled operator's demonstration and execute the learning algorithms for task quantification as the foundation for providing intelligent assistance to the novice operators. We call this stage as the demonstration stage (DSt). Lastly, the novice operators are asked again to execute the same task three cycles under the same condition, except for this time, there is assistance from our BSC algorithms. The process is timed and the amount of sand collected is weighed for each operator again. We call this the blended stage (BSt).

Figure 6.16 shows the improvement in performance of the eight novice operators due to assistance in terms of the average cycle time and the amount of sand moved per minute. On average, the cycle time improved from 63.17 s to 32.84 s and the sand moved per minute increased from 1.25 lb to 3.91 lb. This constitutes an improvement in cycle time of 52% and weight per minute improvement of 213%.

To further illustrate the improvement with and without assistance, in Fig. 6.17 we present three sets of data which show normalized joint states of the excavator for the same task from a novice operator without intelligent assistance (a), a skilled operator (b), and the same novice operator with intelligent control (c). Each trial is a repetition of the same task for the same duration of 120 s. From the figure, one can observe that the novice operator's improvement in performance with BSC assistance is more consistent between cycles and closely matches the states of the skilled operator.

6.7.3 *Subgoal Adjustment BSC*

In order to test whether the subgoal adjustment algorithms are able to provide more flexibility to the BSC scheme and offer sustainable performance improvement, another series of experiments were designed in a similar manner with modifications. Based on a similar typical excavator trenching and truck loading task, 10 novice operators and one skilled operator were asked to participate in the experiments. The experiments were divided into various stages: preparation stage (PSt), manual stage (MSt), demonstration stage (DSt), BSC stage (BSC-St), and BSC with subgoal adjustment stage (BSC/SA-St).

In PSt, the basics of excavator operation and trenching and truck loading task are explained to the NOs. We provide them with excavator operational instruction guide (which is always available to novice operators), and have our NOs familiarize themselves with the excavator operations. After the notification from NOs of being

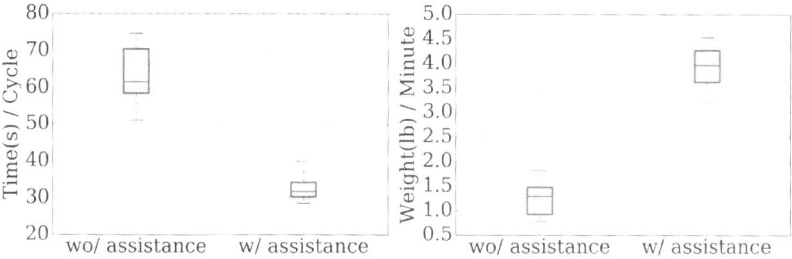

Fig. 6.16. Box plots of productivity and efficiency improvement.

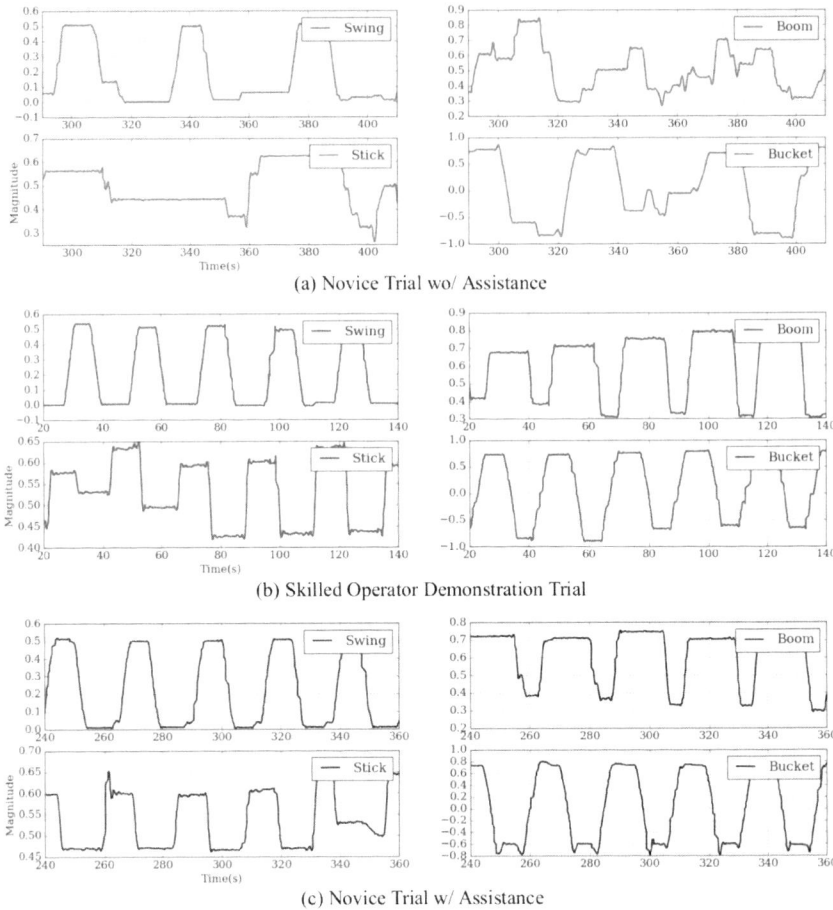

(a) Novice Trial wo/ Assistance

(b) Skilled Operator Demonstration Trial

(c) Novice Trial w/ Assistance

Fig. 6.17. Excavator states from different operation trials.

ready for the task, we move to MSt and ask the NOs to start executing the task for three cycles (each cycle consists of picking up a bucket of sand, moving the actuator to the location of the container and dumping into the container) without algorithm assistance. The process is timed and the amount of sand loaded to the truck is weighed. We then transition into DSt where we have the SO demonstrate the task, record the excavator states, and run the learning algorithm to learn the subgoals from the SO's demonstration. With the learned subgoals, we start the BSC-St and activate the BSC algorithm with intent prediction to provide active assistance. The NO's are asked to execute the same task for nine cycles. The time and weight data are collected and analyzed for each of the three cycles. Finally in the BSC/SA-St, we repeat the process of BSC-St but provide active assistance with

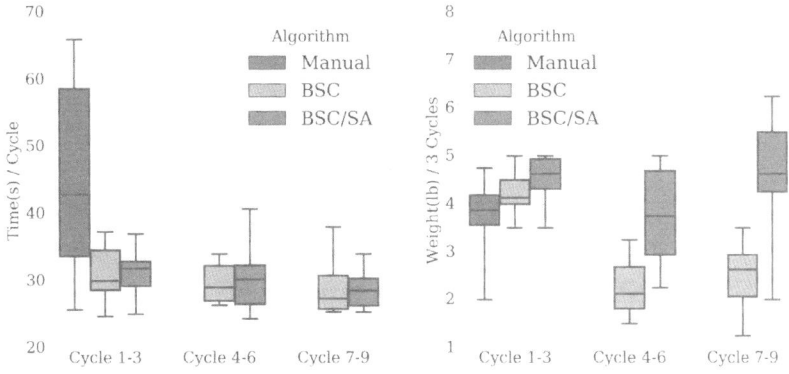

Fig. 6.18. Performance comparison for each three out of nine task cycles.

the the proposed subgoal adjustment BSC algorithm. The data are collected and analyzed in the same manner as in BSC-St.

Figure 6.18 provides a comparison of the operator performance for each of the three task cycles. We observe that for the first 3-cycles when there is no significant shape change of the target object, the two BSC algorithms were able to improve the operator performance from the manual operation without significant quality difference. On average, the cycle time improved from 45.53 s (MSt) to 31.10 s (BSC-St) and 31.13 s (BSC/SA-St), and the sand moved per 3 cycles improved from 3.78 lb (MSt) to 4.25 lb (BSC-St) and 4.55 lb (BSC/SA-St). For the last two 3-cycles, we observed that the time improvement from the two BSC schemes, with respect to manual operation, stays very similar to the first 3 cycles. However, the performance in terms of the amount of sand moved per 3-cycles is different for the two BSC schemes. For the intent prediction BSC, the amount of sand moved on average goes down from 4.25 lb (cycle 1-3) to 2.28 lb (cycle 4-6) and 2.56 lb (cycle

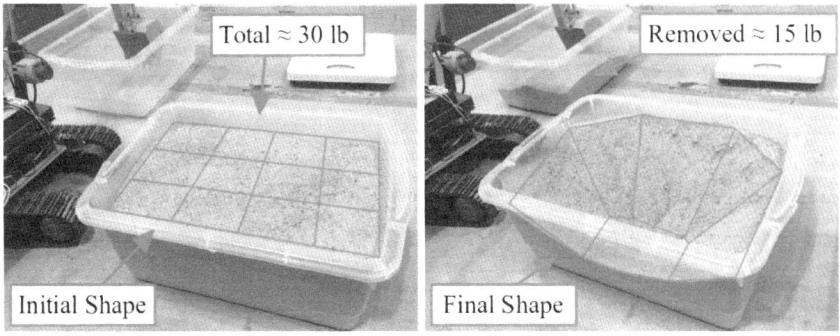

Fig. 6.19. Real shape change of the target object after nine task cycles.

7-9), because of target object shape change versus nominal subgoals. However, for the subgoal adjustment BSC, the weight performance on average changes from 4.55 lb (cycle 1-3) to 3.75 lb (cycle 4-6) and 4.65 lb (cycle 7-9). The subgoal adjustment BSC maintains its assistance quality almost throughout in the presence of gradual but significant shape change of the target object as shown in Fig. 6.19. Furthermore, the recorded performance in the later cycles is still better than manual operation for the first 3-cycles when the task operation is relatively easier. In addition, we observed that although the weight per 3-cycles data from the BSC/SA-St shows sustainable performance improvement, the data spread is relatively wide. One possible reason could be that in our implementation, we fixed the value of the skill level parameter of SWAI since it is hard to evaluate one's skill level and operation style in our case. However, for industry applications, that problem could be solved by designing a standardized test to rate the skill level of operators and relate that to the selection of skill level parameter.

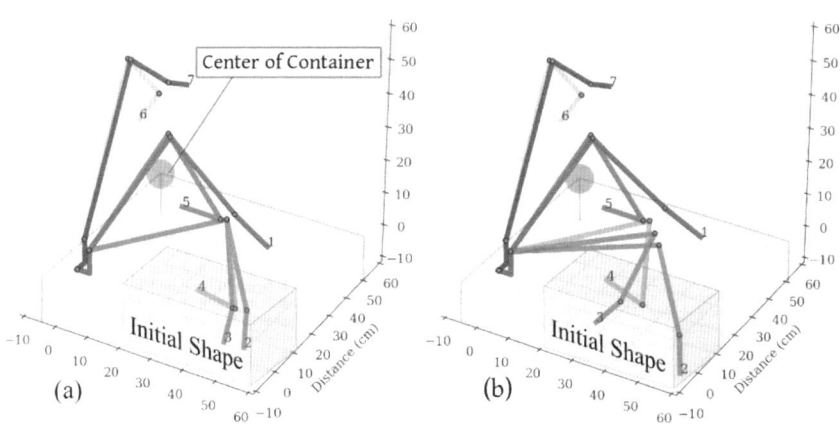

Fig. 6.20. Visualization of subgoal adjustments made and initial shape.

To illustrate the effectiveness of our algorithm from other perspectives, we present in Fig. 6.20 a visualization of subgoal adjustments made by the SO. In the visualization, each subgoal is realized by converting its position in robot joint space to its configuration space of the excavator through forward kinematics. In Fig. 6.20, (a) shows the original learned subgoals and the initial target shape, and the initial target shape is shown again along with the adjusted subgoals in (b) to emphasize the amount of adjustment.

6.8 Summary

In this chapter, general concepts and novel methods are presented for key components required in BSC methods (task learning, intent prediction, subgoal adjustment, and inputs blending) and their synthesis. Among the proposed methods, we have introduced new concepts in task learning such as operator primitive based segmentation, Bayesian non-parametric clustering with temporal ordering; intent prediction using empirical stochastic transition matrix and dynamic angle difference exponential; subgoal adjustment embedding with adjustment encoding hyper-rectangle, hyperbolic slope transition function, and skill weighted action integral; and blended shared control strategy with conflict awareness. Experimental results on a scaled excavator platform indicate the effectiveness in performance improvement of the proposed method.

There are, however, still many open problems for improving the efficiency of BSC, examples include: (1) how does one utilize the magnitude of the operator's input to update the automatic controller gain dynamically; (2) how does one combine adaptive and robust control to BSC such that the automatic control offers better robustness to handle changes in payload weight, contact force, robot parameters; and (3) how to integrate haptic feedback to provide more sensory information and augment operator learning.

References

1. M. Tomasello, *A Natural History of Human Thinking*. Harvard University Press (2014).
2. N. Sebanz, H. Bekkering and G. Knoblich, Joint action: Bodies and minds moving together, *Trends in Cognitive Sciences* **10**, pp. 70–76 (2006).
3. S. S. Obhi and N. Sebanz, Moving together: Toward understanding the mechanisms of joint action, *Experimental Brain Research* **211**(3), 329 (2011), doi:10.1007/s00221-011-2721-0.
4. R. Parasuraman, T. B. Sheridan and C. D. Wickens, A model for types and levels of human interaction with automation, *IEEE Transactions on Systems, Man, and Cybernetics - Part A: Systems and Humans* **30**(3), 286–297 (2000), doi:10.1109/3468.844354.
5. M. A. Goodrich and A. C. Schultz, Human–robot interaction: A survey, *Foundations and Trends® in Human–Computer Interaction* **1**(3), 203–275 (2008), doi:10.1561/1100000005.
6. E. de Visser and R. Parasuraman, Adaptive aiding of human-robot teaming: Effects of imperfect automation on performance, trust, and workload, *Journal of Cognitive Engineering and Decision Making* **5**(2), 209–231 (2011), doi:10.1177/1555343411410160.
7. T. B. Sheridan, *Telerobotics, Automation, and Human Supervisory Control*. MIT Press, Cambridge, MA, USA (1992).
8. E. Hollnagel and D. D. Woods, Cognitive systems engineering: New wine in new bottles, *International Journal of Human-Computer Studies* **51**(2), 339–356 (1999), https://doi.org/10.1006/ijhc.1982.0313.

9. F. Flemisch, D. Abbink, M. Itoh, M.-P. Pacaux-Lemoine and G. Weßel, Shared control is the sharp end of cooperation: Towards a common framework of joint action, shared control and human machine cooperation, *IFAC-PapersOnLine* **49**(19), 72–77 (2016), https://doi.org/10.1016/j.ifacol.2016.10.464.

10. V. Dimitrov and T. Padır, A shared control architecture for human-in-the-loop robotics applications. In *The 23rd IEEE International Symposium on Robot and Human Interactive Communication*, pp. 1089–1094 (2014), doi:10.1109/ROMAN.2014.6926397.

11. D. P. Losey, C. G. McDonald, E. Battaglia and M. K. O'Malley, A review of intent detection, arbitration, and communication aspects of shared control for physical human-robot interaction, *Applied Mechanics Reviews* **70**(1), 010804 (2018), doi:DOI: 10.1115/1.4039145.

12. A. Enes and W. Book, Blended shared control of zermelo's navigation problem. In *Proceedings of the 2010 American Control Conference*, pp. 4307–4312 (2010), doi:10.1109/ACC.2010.5530818.

13. Y. Li, K. P. Tee, W. L. Chan, R. Yan, Y. Chua and D. K. Limbu, Continuous role adaptation for human-robot shared control, *IEEE Transactions on Robotics* **31**(3), 672–681 (2015), doi:10.1109/TRO.2015.2419873.

14. M. J. A. Zeestraten, I. Havoutis and S. Calinon, Programming by demonstration for shared control with an application in teleoperation, *IEEE Robotics and Automation Letters* **3**(3), 1848–1855 (2018), doi:10.1109/LRA.2018.2805105.

15. H. Maske, E. Kieson, G. Chowdury and A. Charles, Learning task-based instructional policy for excavator-like machines. In *IEEE International Conference on Robotics and Automation*, Brisbane, Australia (September 2018).

16. A. M. Brandt and M. B. Colton, Haptic collision avoidance for a remotely operated quadrotor uav in indoor environments. In *2010 IEEE International Conference on Systems, Man and Cybernetics*, pp. 2724–2731 (2010), doi:10.1109/ICSMC.2010.5641798.

17. J. Chun, I. Lee, G. Park, J. Seo, S. Choi and S. H. Han, Efficacy of haptic blind spot warnings applied through a steering wheel or a seatbelt, *Transportation Research Part F: Traffic Psychology and Behaviour* **21**, 231 – 241 (2013), https://doi.org/10.1016/j.trf.2013.09.014.

18. C. Guo, C. Sentouh, J. C. Popieul, B. Soualmi and J. B. Haué, Shared control framework applied for vehicle longitudinal control in highway merging scenarios. In *2015 IEEE International Conference on Systems, Man, and Cybernetics*, pp. 3098–3103 (2015), doi:10.1109/SMC.2015.538.

19. P. Wang, Z. Man, Z. Cao, J. Zheng and Y. Zhao, Dynamics modelling and linear control of quadcopter. In *2016 International Conference on Advanced Mechatronic Systems (ICAMechS)*, pp. 498–503 (2016), doi:10.1109/ICAMechS.2016.7813499.

20. L. Sciavicco, B. Siciliano and B. Sciavicco, *Modelling and Control of Robot Manipulators, 2nd Edition*. Springer-Verlag, Berlin, Heidelberg (2000).

21. A. Hansson and M. Servin, Semi-autonomous shared control of large-scale manipulator arms, *Control Engineering Practice* **18**(9), 1069–1076 (2010), https://doi.org/10.1016/j.conengprac.2010.05.015.

22. J. Philips, J. del R. Millan, G. Vanacker, E. Lew, F. Galan, P. W. Ferrez, H. V. Brussel and M. Nuttin, Adaptive shared control of a brain-actuated simulated wheelchair. In *2007 IEEE 10th International Conference on Rehabilitation Robotics*, pp. 408–414 (2007), doi:10.1109/ICORR.2007.4428457.

23. G. Pires and U. Nunes, A wheelchair steered through voice commands and assisted by a reactive fuzzy-logic controller, *Journal of Intelligent and Robotic Systems* **34**(3), 301–314 (2002), doi:10.1023/A:1016363605613.

24. L. Kitagawa, T. Kobayashi, T. Beppu and K. Terashima, Semi-autonomous obstacle avoidance of omnidirectional wheelchair by joystick impedance control. In *Proceedings 2001 IEEE/RSJ International Conference on Intelligent Robots and Systems. Expanding the Societal Role of Robotics in the the Next Millennium (Cat. No.01CH37180)*, vol. 4, pp. 2148–2153 (2001), doi:10.1109/IROS.2001.976388.

25. C. Ezeh, P. Trautman, C. Holloway and T. Carlson, Comparing shared control approaches for alternative interfaces: A wheelchair simulator experiment. In *2017 IEEE International Conference on Systems, Man, and Cybernetics (SMC)*, pp. 93–98 (2017), doi:10.1109/SMC.2017.8122584.

26. L. Devigne, V. K. Narayanan, F. Pasteau and M. Babel, Low complex sensor-based shared control for power wheelchair navigation. In *2016 IEEE/RSJ International Conference on Intelligent Robots and Systems (IROS)*, pp. 5434–5439 (2016), doi:10.1109/IROS.2016.7759799.

27. J. G. Storms and D. M. Tilbury, Blending of human and obstacle avoidance control for a high speed mobile robot. In *2014 American Control Conference*, pp. 3488–3493 (2014), doi:10.1109/ACC.2014.6859352.

28. T. K. Stephens, N. J. Kong, R. L. Dockter, J. J. O'Neill, R. M. Sweet and T. M. Kowalewski, Blended shared control utilizing online identification, *International Journal of Computer Assisted Radiology and Surgery* **13**(6), 769–776 (2018), doi:10.1007/s11548-018-1745-3.

29. K. Shamaei, Y. Che, A. Murali, S. Sen, S. Patil, K. Goldberg and A. M. Okamura, A paced shared-control teleoperated architecture for supervised automation of multilateral surgical tasks. In *2015 IEEE/RSJ International Conference on Intelligent Robots and Systems (IROS)*, pp. 1434–1439 (2015), doi:10.1109/IROS.2015.7353556.

30. M. Allain, S. Konduri, H. Maske, P. R. Pagilla and G. Chowdhary, Blended shared control of a hydraulic excavator, *IFAC-PapersOnLine* **50**(1), 14928–14933 (2017), https://doi.org/10.1016/j.ifacol.2017.08.2541.

31. Z. Jin, P. Pagilla, H. Maske and G. Chowdury, Methods for blended shared control of hydraulic excavators with learning and prediction. In *2018 IEEE Conference on Decision and Control (CDC)*, Miami Beach, FL, US (January 2019).

32. Z. Jin, P. Pagilla, H. Maske and G. Chowdury, Blended shared control with subgoal adjustment, in *2018 IEEE Conference on Systems, Man, and Cybernetics (SMC)*, Miyazaki, Japan (January 2019).

33. A. Enes R., Shared control of hydraulic manipulators to decrease cycle time, PhD Dissertation, School of Mechanical Engineering, Georgia Tech. (2010).

34. B. Michini, T. J. Walsh, A. A. Agha-Mohammadi and J. P. How, Bayesian nonparametric reward learning from demonstration, *IEEE Transactions on Robotics* **31**(2), 369–386 (2015), doi:10.1109/TRO.2015.2405593.

35. B. D. Argall, S. Chernova, M. Veloso and B. Browning, A survey of robot learning from demonstration, *Robotics and Autonomous Systems* **67**, 469–483 (2009).

36. R. F. Adler and R. Benbunan-Fich, The effects of task difficulty and multitasking on performance, *Interacting with Computers* **27**(4), 430–439 (2015), doi:10.1093/iwc/iwu005.

37. H. Maske, E. Kieson, G. Chowdhary and C. Abramson, Can co-robots learn to teach? *CoRR* **abs/1611.07490** (2016), arXiv:1611.07490.

38. S. Lloyd, Least squares quantization in PCM, *IEEE Trans. Inf. Theor.* **28**(2), 129–137 (2006), doi:10.1109/TIT.1982.1056489.

39. H. Maske, G. Chowdhary and P. R. Pagilla, Intent aware shared control in off-nominal situations. In *2016 IEEE 55th Conference on Decision and Control (CDC)*, pp. 5171–5176 (2016), doi:10.1109/CDC.2016.7799060.

40. R. M. Neal, Markov chain sampling methods for dirichlet process mixture models, *Journal of Computational and Graphical Statistics* **9**(2), 249–265 (2000), doi:10.1080/10618600.2000.10474879.

41. B. Skinner, *Science And Human Behavior*. Free Press (1953).

42. R. Miltenberger, *Behavior Modification: Principles and Procedures*. Cengage Learning, Belmont, CA (2015).

43. M. Quigley, K. Conley, B.P. Gerkey, J. Faust, T. Foote, J. Leibs, R. Wheeler and A.Y. Ng, ROS: An open-source robot operation system. In *ICRA Workshop on Open Source Software* (2009).

© 2020 World Scientific Publishing Company
https://doi.org/10.1142/9789811222849_0007

Chapter 7

Learning and Coordination of Movement Primitives for Bimanual Manipulation Tasks Using Concurrent Synchronization

Ashwin Dani, Iman Salehi, Harish Ravichandar, and Gang Yao

7.1 Introduction

Coordination of multiple robots is very useful in advanced manufacturing applications, where the robots can be used to pick up, transport, and manipulate heavy and/or deformable objects, performing a wire harness assembly or a screw assembly. This chapter focuses on methods that involve coordination between the two arms. Dual arm manipulation can be broadly classified into uncoordinated and coordinated manipulation.[1] Coordinated dual arm manipulation can further be categorized into goal-coordinated and bimanual manipulations. In goal-coordinated manipulation, the two arms are not interacting with each other but they are coordinating to achieve a same end goal, such as filling up a box with wooden pallets, sanding different parts of a workpiece to achieve a time-efficient sanding operation, bimanual cleaning operations.[2] In contrast, bimanual manipulation requires the arms to interact with the same object. Naturally, bimanual manipulation requires two arms to synchronize and move with a defined transformation to carry out a common goal, such as tying a knot by pulling different parts of the string, uncurling the curled wires in wire harness assembly, carrying heavy wooden/metal pallets, transporting large deformable objects like fabric, composite materials. In this chapter, we present coordinated control laws to synchronize motions of two arms for bimanual manipulation, where the learning and coordination for bimanual manipulation tasks are considered. The synchronization of arms is achieved by considering transformations such as a fixed rigid transformation, reflection/mirror transformation or time-varying transformations. The dynamics of the task for one of the arms are first learned from demonstration data using dynamic movement primitives (DMPs). In the same spirit as Chung and Slotine; Chun et al.[3,4] a concurrent tracking and synchronization laws based on contraction analysis are derived for the two arms to track the trajectory generated by the DMP and achieve coordination of two arms.

In this chapter, DMP representation is used for encoding both discrete and periodic motion. Kinesthetic demonstration obtained from robotic arm manipulator is used to learn the DMP. The demonstration may include the motion (position, velocity, acceleration) in robot joint space or robot task space represented using 3D positions and orientation angles. If the dynamics of end effector pose (position+orientation) are learned using DMPs, inverse kinematics solution is required to convert the end effector pose to joint angles during implementation using robot arm manipulators. Learning the dynamics of two arms using independent sets of DMPs does not take into consideration the task-specific spatio-temporal constraints of the two arms. Hence, the two arms controlled using independently learned sets of DMPs might fail to complete the bimanual task, especially under perturbations (e.g., one arm is pushed while dual-arm wooden pallet transportation operation is in action). This issue can be circumvented by synchronizing the motions of two arms according to task-specific constraints. The end-effector motion dynamics of one of the arms is modeled using a set of DMPs. The learned set of DMPs is used as the desired trajectory for one arm, while a pose transformation is applied to obtain the desired end-effector trajectory for the second arm. The transformation can be different based on the task objectives, and it can be any combination of translation, rotation, and reflection. The transformation depends on the geometry of the object, which can be estimated using vision based estimation algorithms (see e.g., Refs. 5–9).

For ensuring tracking of the desired trajectories of both the arms, a tracking controller is designed for each arm. The desired trajectory for one of the arms is obtained using a DMP and the other arm is obtained using a task space transformation between two arms. In addition, the synchronization between both the arms is essential in bimanual manipulation tasks for ensuring the temporal and spatial constraints between two arms are satisfied at all times. The synchronization between the motions of two arms is achieved by adding tracking error from one arm as feedback to the controller of another arm, called as a coupling term. The gains of the feedback term are selected such that the error dynamics for the two arms are contracting.[10] Solutions of contracting dynamics are robust to external perturbations and exponentially forgets the initial condition. Hence, the solutions of the error dynamics converge towards each other. The contraction ensures robust tracking of the desired trajectory of two arms in the task space even under perturbations.

The synchronization laws presented in this chapter are generic and can be used for synchronization of more than two arms coordinating in different configurations, e.g., (a) a cyclic configuration, (b) all-to-all configuration. In cyclic structure, every agent is coupled only with the next and prior agents and all the couplings are bidirectional couplings.[3,4,11] In all-to-all structure, every agent is coupled with all the other agents in the system and similar to the cyclic structure, all the couplings are bidirectional. For dual-arm manipulation, both of these configurations coincide with each other.

Three different experiments are presented. These experiments are inspired by some of the commonly occurring tasks in manufacturing and assembly operations. Some examples include bimanual motion coordination for holding a flexible wire with two hands for an insertion into a pin operation, coordinating motions of two hands to pull a box in which an object is kept which is being supported by the other arm, motion coordination for bimanual surgeon's knot tying operation or bimanual paper folding operation for origami folding.[12,13]

Experiment 1: In the first experiment, a wooden pallet transportation task is conducted using a Baxter robot. End effector data is collected in task space and a DMP is learned based on the position and orientation data. For this task, the end-effector task space pose transformation between two arms in a nearly fixed transformation. Using the tracking and synchronization control laws the task of moving the wooden pallet from one location to other is performed. This experiment shows utility of the bimanual coordination approach for manufacturing tasks involved in wire harness assembly mentioned above. Perturbations are added to one of the arms while the pallet transportation task is in motion. The results show that the other arm synchronizes its motion to the perturbed arm's motion exponentially fast. The synchronization feature is important so that the robot does not drop the object while the transportation task is in process.

Experiment 2: In the second experiment, a capability of adaptation to the change in goal location is demonstrated while the task is in progress. It is shown in experiments that with the change in reaching goal location of one of the two robot arms in task space, the other arm is able to synchronize its motion to the new location without disturbing the bimanual manipulation task. Such a capability is very useful in the manufacturing tasks such as sliding a box on the table with one of the robot arms and an object kept in the box is supported by the other robot arm.

Experiment 3: In the third experiment, a knot tying task is carried out using coordination of two arms. DMP is learned for encoding task space motion of one of the two arms. The knot tying task requires the other arm to move with a reflection transformation. Knot tying operations are ubiquitous in robotics manufacturing. For example, tying knots during surgery using robot arms, tying knots in parachute packing operations, etc. An implementation of knot tying task on Baxter robot is presented.

Related Work

Several works have introduced control designs that enable coordination between the two arms. Classical approaches consider force or motion control of closed chains formed by the arms and an object. Methods involving input-output linearization,[14,15] hybrid/force control,[16–19] impedance control,[20–23] neuro-adaptive control[24–26] have been used to either maintain a desired object pose or track a desired pose trajectory. In contrast, this chapter treats the two arms as separate agents and focuses on their coordinated motion. Earlier work has demonstrated the use of a leader-follower architecture in the coordinated motion of the two arms.[27–29] In such configurations, the leader is assumed to be the desired or optimal trajectory and the follower arm is controlled to follow the trajectory (after suitable transformations) of the leader arm. In, Refs. 30–32 methods that rely on visual feedback to coordinate the arms via visual servoing are developed. Such methods ensure that the motion of the arms minimizes the error between the observed features and the desired features of both the arms. Motion planning of multiple arms is studied for coordinated motion of dual arm manipulators and grasp planning using multiple robots.[33–39] Motion planning-based methods are capable to joint space control that take into account obstacles. Control architectures for formation control of multiple robot arms has been studied in Refs. 40–42.

Another approach for creating robot trajectories is based on learning from demonstration (LfD), which requires demonstration of the task to be performed by the robot. Learning-based approaches[43,44] leverage statistical learning to teach robots new tasks from demonstrated data and provide the ability to perform those tasks by adapting to the changes in the workspace. One of the LfD algorithms, called DMP, represents both learnable point attractor systems and limit cycle attractor systems which can be used to encode discrete and periodic trajectories, respectively.[45] Besides the attractor system, DMP consists of a learnable autonomous forcing term which is guided by a canonical system. DMPs can be used to learn motion trajectories such as point-to-point reaching motions, grinding, polishing operations, etc. which involve either discrete or periodic motions of the end-effector in workspace. DMP can also encode the periodic motion and its transient behavior[46] for single arm motion learning. In this representation, an oscillator, which is a stable limit cycle is used as a canonical system that guides the forcing term. In Ref. 47, the online obstacle avoidance feature is incorporated into a DMP by simple addition of repelling force around obstacles in acceleration term. In Ref. 48, simultaneous goal and parameter learning is carried out for a pouring task. In Ref. 49, learning of DMPs in joint space is discussed for the adaptation of DMP learned in joint space. In Refs. 50, 51, a method of learning DMPs from multiple demonstrations by finding the styles in the shapes of desired attractor landscapes from multiple demonstrations without losing the useful properties of DMPs is discussed. DMPs are also used in joining movement sequencing where smooth and natural transitions in position and velocity are generated with modifications to original DMPs.[52,53] DMP has been used for formation control of multi-agent systems in Refs. 54, 55.

Apart from DMP, there are other LfD approaches that learns the end-effector motion trajectories by considering a joint state in the workspace.[56,57] In our prior work,[58-60] the dynamics of reaching motions are learned using neural networks (NN) and Gaussian Mixture Models (GMMs) under contraction analysis constraints. In Ref. 61, this work is extended to periodic motions. For bimanual coordination, an LfD approach is developed in Ref. 43 to classify bimanual motions based on the spatial relationship between the motion trajectories of both the arms. In Ref. 44, Hidden Markov Models (HMMs) and Gaussian Mixture Regression (GMR) are used to learn bi-manual tasks from several demonstrations. While learning-based methods generally perform well in circumstances similar to those encountered during training, they might fail in unfamiliar circumstances. In Ref. 62, an iterative learning controller for two-handed tying a knot is designed. LfD methods using non-rigid registration for bimanual manipulation tasks are presented in Ref. 63. In Table 7.1, a classification of contributions related to coordinated manipulation that appeared in the literature based on approaches and methods is provided.

Table 7.1. An overview of literature on bimanual manipulation.

Approaches	Methods	Literature
Classical	Input/Output Linearization	14, 15
	Hybrid/Force Control	16, 17
		18, 19
	Impedance Control	20
		21–23
	Neuro-adaptive Control	24
		25, 26
	Leader-Follower Architecture	27
		28, 29
	Visual Servoing Coordination	30
		31, 32
	Motion Planning	33, 34
		35, 36
		37
		38, 39
	Formation Control	40–42
LfD	GMM - Bimanual Coordination	43
	GMM with HMM	44
	DMP	46, 64
		47, 52
		48, 49
		38, 50
		51, 53
		54, 55
	GMM - Multivariate Robot Motions	56
	Iterative Learning Control	62
	GMM with Lyapunov	57
	NN with Contraction	58, 61
	GMM with Contraction	59, 60

Contributions

The contributions of this chapter are as follows.

- Provide an overview of literature for bimanual manipulation.
- Design the control laws for desired trajectory tracking and synchronization

of multi-agent system modeled with DMPs by using contraction analysis. The contraction analysis provides an exponential convergence to the desired trajectory, which is important for maintaining accuracy and productivity in the manufacturing tasks using robots.

- Demonstrate robustness of synchronization laws under perturbations which is very important for dual arm manipulations. When perturbed all the agents first synchronize and then resume tracking the desired trajectory, which is important in tasks such as manipulation with objects in workspace with two arms. The robustness property is important to prevent carried object from being dropped while performing bimanual heavy load transportation task.

- Specific control laws and constraints for tracking and synchronization are derived for performing the bimanual task. This property is useful for performing bimanual coordination tasks such as carrying a rigid object using two arms, or tying a knot or stripping a wire using two arms of a robot.

- Simulation and experimental results are presented which shows the tracking and synchronization, robustness of synchronization under perturbations. An example of moving wooden flanks is presented, where two arms must synchronize their motion with a rigid relative transformation. This experiment is motivated from many manufacturing operations that are found in industrial setting such as carrying large and heavy payload. Another experiment for tying a knot is presented, where two arms synchronize their motion with a reflective transformation between them. This experiment is motivated from manufacturing operations such as wire stripping operation or straightening of curled wires in wire harness assembly, tying knots in medical robotics applications.

Rest of the chapter is organized as follows. In Section 7.2, relevant preliminary mathematical concepts are revisited. In Section 7.3, modeling of multi-agent system represented using a system of DMPs and corresponding control design is presented. In Section 7.4, analyses of control design for tracking and synchronization control objective are provided. In Section 7.4.3, coordinate transformation between desired behavior of multiple agents is provided that can be used to generate desired behavior of agents given behavior of one of the agents. In Section 7.5, results from two experiments are provided that implements the multi-agent control framework for bimanual manipulation task using Baxter robot.

7.2 Preliminaries

In this section, brief review of dynamic movement primitives and contraction analysis is presented.

7.2.1 *Review of Dynamic Movement Primitive*

The DMP consists of a transformation system which drives the system to the goal location, and a canonical system which drives the forcing term that generates the desired shape of the trajectory.

The DMP that encodes both rhythmic and transient motions is given by

$$\ddot{y}(t) = \Omega^2 \left(\alpha_y \left(\beta_y \left(g - y(t) \right) - \frac{\dot{y}(t)}{\Omega} \right) + f \left(\phi(t), r(t), \tilde{w}, w \right) \right) \quad (7.1)$$

where y is the state of the system in (7.1), $g \in \mathbb{R}$ is the goal location, $f : \mathbb{R} \times \mathbb{R} \times \mathbb{R}^M \times \mathbb{R}^N \to \mathbb{R}$ is the forcing term to generate the desired behavior, where M and N are the number of basis functions encoding the transient and periodic motion respectively, $\tilde{w} \in \mathbb{R}^M$, $w \in \mathbb{R}^N$ are the weights of the basis functions, such that system in (7.1) represents the desired trajectory closely, $\alpha_y \in \mathbb{R}^+, \beta_y \in \mathbb{R}^+$ are the constant gains driving the system towards the goal location. In the following sub-sections, the forcing term $f(\cdot)$, the canonical system that drives the forcing term, the set of basis functions used to encode transient and periodic behavior are presented. Further, the construction of $f(\cdot)$ term for encoding discrete motions, i.e., point-to-point reaching is also described.

7.2.1.1 *Forcing term $f(\cdot)$ for periodic motions*

The forcing term $f(\cdot)$ in (7.1), driven by the canonical system is obtained by using the following formula

$$f(\phi(t), r(t), \tilde{w}, w) = \frac{\sum_{j=1}^{M} \psi_j(\phi(t), r(t)) \tilde{w}_j + \sum_{i=1}^{N} \zeta_i(\phi(t), r(t)) w_j}{\sum_{j=1}^{M} \psi_j(\phi(t), r(t)) + \sum_{i=1}^{N} \zeta_i(\phi(t), r(t))}, \quad (7.2)$$

where $\psi : \mathbb{R} \times \mathbb{R} \to \mathbb{R}$, and $\zeta : \mathbb{R} \times \mathbb{R} \to \mathbb{R}$ are the basis functions. While $\psi_j(\phi(t), r(t))$ are the basis functions encoding the transient part of the motion, the basis functions $\zeta_i(\phi(t), r(t))$ are 2π-periodic in the first argument, and encode the periodic pattern as described in Ref. 46.

Canonical System   The canonical system for a DMP that encodes both rhythmic and transient motions is an oscillator in the phase plane given by

$$
\begin{cases}
\dot{\phi}(t) & = \Omega, \qquad\qquad\qquad\qquad\qquad \phi(0) = \phi_0 \\
\dot{r}(t) & = \eta\left(\mu^\alpha - (r(t))^\alpha\right)(r(t))^\beta\ , \ r(0) = r_0
\end{cases}
\tag{7.3}
$$

where $r(t) \in \mathbb{R}$ is the distance from center of limit cycle, $\phi(t) \in \mathbb{R}$ is the phase, $\alpha \in \mathbb{R}^+$, $\beta \in \mathbb{R}^+$ are constants, $\eta \in \mathbb{R}^+$ is gain, $\Omega \in \mathbb{R}^+$ defined as $\Omega = 2\pi/p$ is the frequency of execution, $p \in \mathbb{R}^+$ is the period of rhythmic movement in seconds and $\mu \in \mathbb{R}^+$ is the radius of the limit cycle.

Basis Functions   The set of basis functions $\psi_j(\phi(t), r(t))$, $j = 1, 2, ..., M$ are used to encode the non-periodic transient behavior and another set of basis function $\zeta_i(\phi(t), r(t))$, $i = 1, 2, ...N$ are used to encode the periodic behavior. This means that in the beginning of the movement, the system should be only affected by $\psi_j(\phi(t), r(t))$ while in the long run their impact vanishes and $\zeta_i(\phi(t), r(t))$ smoothly begin to take over the control of the system. Therefore, $\psi_j(\phi(t), r(t))$ vanish close to the limit cycle, i.e., there exists a $\mu_1 \in \mathbb{R}^+$ such that $\mu_1 > \mu$ and $\psi_j(\phi(t), r(t))|_{\mathcal{R}\times(0,\mu_1)} = 0$. After passing the limit μ_1, the $\zeta_i(\phi(t), r(t))$ dominates the control of the system. Hence, the condition $\zeta_i(\phi(t), r(t))|_{\mathcal{R}\times(0,\mu_1)} = 1$ holds. The value of μ_1 is a constant that can be chosen arbitrarily.

Since the movement should be smooth, there has to be a region where the supports of the $\zeta_i(\phi(t), r(t))$ and the $\psi_j(\phi(t), r(t))$ overlap. The time needed for the canonical oscillator to pass that region is called transient fading time t_f. To create the fading region, μ_2 is set to be greater than μ_1, forcing the supports of $\zeta_i(\phi(t), r(t))$ and $\psi_j(\phi(t), r(t))$ to at most overlap for $r(t) \in (\mu_1, \mu_2)$. Here, $\mu_2 \in \mathbb{R}^+$ is chosen such that the transient fading time, which the oscillator needs to converge from μ_2 to μ_1, is equal to t_f.

Encoding Periodic Movement   The basis functions $\zeta_i(\phi(t), r(t))$ encode the periodic pattern and thus should vanish away from the limit cycle. Therefore, $\zeta_i(\phi(t), r(t)) = k(r(t))h_i(\phi(t))$ is composed of two functions, where, $h_i : \mathbb{R} \to \mathbb{R}$ is 2π-periodic and encodes the periodic pattern and the function $k : \mathbb{R} \to \mathbb{R}$ makes

$\zeta_i(\phi(t), r(t))$ vanish away from the limit cycle. The two functions are given by

$$h_i(\phi(t)) = \exp(v_i(\cos(\phi(t) - c_i) - 1)) \tag{7.4}$$

$$k(r(t)) = \begin{cases} 1 & r(t) < \mu_1 \\ \left(1 - \left(\frac{r(t)-\mu_1}{\mu_2-\mu_1}\right)^3\right)^3 & \mu_1 < r(t) < \mu_2 \\ 0 & r(t) > \mu_2 \end{cases} \tag{7.5}$$

where, $v_i \in \mathbb{R}^+$ is the variance and $c_i \in \mathbb{R}$ is the mean of the basis function.

Encoding Transient Movement The basis functions $\psi_j(\phi(t), r(t))$ are arranged on the phase plane away from the limit cycle. Similarly to the $\zeta_i(\phi(t), r(t))$, the basis functions $\psi_j(\phi(t), r(t))$ are composed of two functions: one for the actual encoding and another one for keeping them away from the limit cycle. Hence, in each function $\psi_j(\phi(t), r(t)) = a(r(t))b_j\left(\left\|\begin{bmatrix} r(t)\cos(\phi(t)) \\ r(t)\sin(\phi(t)) \end{bmatrix} - p_j\right\|_2\right)$ the function $a : \mathbb{R} \to \mathbb{R}$ ensures that the $\psi_j(\phi(t), r(t))$ are non-zero only away from the limit cycle.

The function $b : \mathbb{R} \to \mathbb{R}$ is a standard basis function which can be represented in the form of a Gaussian. Placing the norm difference into b_j leads to a radially symmetric function centered on $p_j \in \mathbb{R}^2$ on the phase plane with the variance $\tilde{v} \in \mathbb{R}$ given by

$$a(r(t)) = \begin{cases} 0 & r(t) < \mu_1 \\ (1 - (\frac{\mu_2-r(t)}{\mu_2-\mu_1})^3)^3 & \mu_1 < r(t) < \mu_2 \\ 1 & r(t) > \mu_2 \end{cases} \tag{7.6}$$

$$b_j(r(t)) = \exp\left(-\tilde{v}r(t)^2\right) \tag{7.7}$$

7.2.1.2 *Forcing term $f(\cdot)$ for discrete movements*

In order to obtain a merely point attractor dynamics, the following non-linear function $f : \mathbb{R} \times \mathbb{R} \times \mathbb{R}^M \to \mathbb{R}$.

$$f(x, v, \tilde{w}) = \frac{\sum_{i=1}^{M} \Psi_i \tilde{w}_i v}{\sum_{i=1}^{M} \Psi_i} \qquad \Psi_i = \exp(-h_i(x/g - c_i)^2) \tag{7.8}$$

can be used as a forcing term in (7.1) to generate the desired behavior, where M is the number of basis function encoding the discrete motion, $\tilde{w} \in \mathbb{R}^M$ are the weights of the basis functions, and x, v are derived from the following canonical dynamical system that is selected to be a second order dynamical system

$$\dot{v} = \Omega \alpha_v (\beta_v (g - x) - v) \qquad \dot{x} = \Omega v \qquad (7.9)$$

similar to (7.1) without the forcing term and thus its monotonic global convergence to g can be guaranteed with the proper choice of constant gains α_v, β_v Ref. 64. The high-level design parameters of the discrete system are Ω, the temporal scaling factor, and g the goal position. Depending on degrees of freedom associated with each manipulator, multiple DMPs are needed to represent the dynamics.

7.2.1.3 *Learning the forcing term*

The weights $\tilde{w}$, w are learned such that the system in (7.1) reproduces the demonstrated trajectory $y_{\text{demo}}(t)$. The required forcing term is computed by rearranging (7.1) as follows

$$f_{\text{target}}(t) = \frac{\ddot{y}_{\text{demo}}(t)}{\Omega^2} - \alpha_y \left(\beta_y (g - y_{\text{demo}}(t)) - \frac{\dot{y}_{\text{demo}}(t)}{\Omega} \right). \qquad (7.10)$$

The weights in the forcing term are learned using linear regression tools. Also, the attractor point for all the periodic parts is calculated as $g = \frac{1}{L - L_{\text{trans}}} \left(\sum_{L_{\text{trans}+1}}^{L} y_k(t) \right)$, where $L_{\text{trans}} \in \mathbb{R}^+$ is the time duration of transient motion and $L \in \mathbb{R}^+$ is time duration of the task.

7.2.2 *Brief Review of Contraction Analysis*

In this section, contraction analysis tool that is used to analyze the stability of the derived controller is reviewed. Consider a system of the form $\dot{x}(t) = f_{\text{dyn}}(x(t))$, where $f_{\text{dyn}} : \mathbb{R}^p \to \mathbb{R}^p$ is a nonlinear vector function and $x(t) \in \mathbb{R}^p$ is a state vector. Any trajectory which starts in a ball of constant radius centered about a given trajectory and contained at all times in a contraction region, remains in that ball and converges exponentially to this trajectory.[10] Also, a region of the state space is called a contraction region with respect to a symmetric and uniformly positive definite metric $M(x,t) = \Theta(x,t)^T \Theta(x,t)$, if

$$\forall x, \quad \left[\frac{\partial f_{\text{dyn}}^T}{\partial x} M(x,t) + M(x,t) \frac{\partial f_{\text{dyn}}}{\partial x} + \dot{M}(x,t) \right] \leq -\beta M(x,t) \qquad (7.11)$$

in that region, where $\beta \in \mathbb{R}^+$ is the contraction rate and $\Theta(x,t)$ is a square matrix.

Contraction analysis will be used in determining the gains of the closed-loop system of DMPs with feedback (discussed in later sections) such that the overall system is contracting.

Theorem 7.1. *(Theorem 3 of[65]) Synchronization in two way coupling configuration. Consider two coupled systems. If the dynamics equations verify $\dot{x}_1 - h(x_1,t) = \dot{x}_2 - h(x_2,t)$, where the function $h(\cdot)$ is contracting, then x_1 and x_2 will converge to each other exponentially, regardless of the initial conditions.*

Proof. See Ref. 65. □

7.3 Multi-agent System of Systems Modeling and Control Design

Let $q(t) \in \mathbb{R}^n$ be a state vector given by $q(t) = [y_1(t), y_2(t), \ldots y_n(t)]^T$, where the dynamics of each $y_i(t), i = 1, 2, .., n$ is represented using a single DMP. A set of six DMPs can be used to represent the end effector positions and the end effector orientations in the form of Euler angles or a set of 7 DMPs can be used to represent joint motion of a 7 degree of freedom (DoF) Baxter or ABB's YuMi robots.

For a given agent (e.g. Robot arm), there can be multiple DMPs each associated with a DOF. An agent with n - DMPs can be represented as follows

$$\ddot{y}_i(t) = -\Omega \alpha_{yi} \dot{y}_i(t) - \Omega^2 \alpha_{yi} \beta_{yi} y_i(t) + \Omega^2 \alpha_{yi} \beta_{yi} g_i$$
$$+ \Omega^2 f_i(\phi, r) + u_i(t), \quad i = 1, 2, .., n. \quad (7.12)$$

where $u_i(t) \in \mathbb{R}$ is the external control input. From (7.12), it can be inferred that in a system with m agents, an ith agent can be represented for $i = 1, 2 \cdots m$ as follows

$$\ddot{q}_i(t) = -K_a \dot{q}_i(t) - K_b q_i(t) + K_c + U_i(t), \quad (7.13)$$

where $K_a \in R^{n \times n}$, $K_b \in R^{n \times n}$, and $K_c \in \mathbb{R}^{n \times n}$ are given by

$$K_a = \begin{bmatrix} \Omega \alpha_{y1} & 0 & \cdots & 0 \\ 0 & \Omega \alpha_{y2} & & \vdots \\ \vdots & & \ddots & 0 \\ 0 & \cdots & 0 & \Omega \alpha_{yn} \end{bmatrix}, \quad K_c = \begin{bmatrix} \Omega^2 \alpha_{y1} \beta_{y1} g_1 + \Omega^2 f_1(\phi, r) \\ \Omega^2 \alpha_{y2} \beta_{y2} g_2 + \Omega^2 f_2(\phi, r) \\ \vdots \\ \Omega^2 \alpha_{yn} \beta_{yn} g_n + \Omega^2 f_n(\phi, r) \end{bmatrix}, \quad K_b =$$

$$\begin{bmatrix} \Omega^2 \alpha_{y1} \beta_{yn} & 0 & \cdots & 0 \\ 0 & \Omega^2 \alpha_{y2} \beta_{yn} & & \vdots \\ \vdots & & \ddots & 0 \\ 0 & \cdots & 0 & \Omega^2 \alpha_{yn} \beta_{yn} \end{bmatrix}, \text{ and } U_i(t) = \begin{bmatrix} u_{i1} & u_{i2} & \cdots & u_{in} \end{bmatrix}^T.$$

7.3.1 *Control Design*

The control input $U_i(t) \in \mathbb{R}^{n \times 1}$ is applied to an agent to alter its dynamics to achieve the requirements of tracking and synchronization. The control input in (7.13) is designed for $i = 1, 2 \cdots m$ as follows

$$U_i(t) = \ddot{q}_{i,r}(t) + K_a \dot{q}_{i,r}(t) + K_b q_i(t) + K_1 [\dot{q}_i(t) - \dot{q}_{i,r}(t)]$$
$$+ \sum_{j \in N(i)} K_2 [\dot{q}_j(t) - \dot{q}_{j,r}(t)] - K_c, \qquad (7.14)$$

where the gains $K_1 \in \mathbb{R}^{n \times n}$, $K_2 \in \mathbb{R}^{n \times n}$, and $D \in \mathbb{R}^{n \times n}$ are positive definite diagonal matrices, $N(i)$ represents the agents coupled with i^{th} agent in a system of m agents, and $\dot{q}_{i,r}(t) = \dot{q}_d(t) + D(q_d(t) - q_i(t))$ with $q_d(t)$ and $\dot{q}_d(t)$ representing the desired trajectory and its velocity term respectively. $q_d(t)$ is generated using the DMPs learned from the demonstration data.

After substituting (7.14) in (7.13), the resulting closed-loop dynamics of the system are given by

$$\ddot{q}_i(t) - \ddot{q}_{i,r}(t) = -K_a [\dot{q}_i(t) - \dot{q}_{i,r}(t)] + K_1 [\dot{q}_i(t) - \dot{q}_{i,r}(t)]$$
$$+ \sum_{j \in N(i)} K_2 [\dot{q}_j(t) - \dot{q}_{j,r}(t)]. \qquad (7.15)$$

In a system of m agents, let the tracking error $e_i \in \mathbb{R}^{n \times 1}$ of ith agent be defined as $e_i(t) = \dot{q}_i(t) - \dot{q}_{i,r}(t) = \dot{q}_i(t) - \dot{q}_d(t) + D[q_i(t) - q_d(t)]$. Based on (7.15), the error dynamics of the ith agent can be computed as follows

$$\dot{e}_i(t) = -K_a e_i(t) + K_1 e_i(t) + \sum_{j \in N(i)} K_2 e_j(t). \qquad (7.16)$$

7.4 Analysis of Multi-agent Tracking Control and Synchronization

In this section, gain designs for tracking control and synchronization of multi-agent systems with cyclic and all-to-all configurations are presented.

7.4.1 *Tracking Control Analysis*

Cyclic Configuration   For the system in (7.16) with cyclic configuration of coupling, the error dynamics are represented by

$$\dot{E}(t) = -L_c E(t), \qquad (7.17)$$

where $E(t) \in R^{mn \times 1}$ and $L_c \in \mathbb{R}^{mn \times mn}$ are given by $E(t) = \left[e_1(t), e_2(t), \ldots, e_m(t) \right]^T$ and

$$
L_c = \begin{bmatrix}
K_a - K_1 & -K_2 & 0 & . & 0 & -K_2 \\
-K_2 & K_a - K_1 & -K_2 & & & 0 \\
0 & & . & & & \\
. & & & . & & 0 \\
0 & & & -K_2 & K_a - K_1 & -K_2 \\
-K_2 & 0 & . & 0 & -K_2 & K_a - K_1
\end{bmatrix},
$$

respectively.

For the system in (7.17), $J = \frac{\partial(-L_c E(t))}{\partial E(t)} = -L_c$ and L_c is a symmetric matrix. With $J = -L_c$ and $J^T = -L_c$ and identity matrix as the positive definite metric $M(x)$, the condition in (7.11) can be written as $-L_c \leq -\frac{\beta I_{mn \times mn}}{2}$ which in turn yields

$$
L_c \geq \gamma I_{mn \times mn}, \tag{7.18}
$$

where $\gamma = \frac{\beta}{2}$. By satisfying the condition in (7.18), the system in (7.17) is contracting with the rate of β. Based on (7.18), the conditions for designing gains for $m = 2$ are derived first. Then, a generalized case with $m \geq 3$ is shown.

Systems with Two Agents

For a system in (7.17), with $m = 2$ agents, the error dynamics representation is as follows

$$
\begin{bmatrix} \dot{e}_1(t) \\ \dot{e}_2(t) \end{bmatrix} = - \begin{bmatrix} K_a - K_1 & -K_2 \\ -K_2 & K_a - K_1 \end{bmatrix} \begin{bmatrix} e_1(t) \\ e_2(t) \end{bmatrix}.
$$

Following the result of m agent system, $K_a - K_1 > 0$, and $K_2 > 0$, the conditions for selecting gains in this case are given by $K_a - K_1 + K_2 \geq \gamma_1 I_{n \times n}$ and $K_a - K_1 - K_2 \geq \gamma_1 I_{n \times n}$, where $\gamma_1 \in \mathbb{R}^+$ for the system in (7.17) with two agents to be contracting.

Systems with More than Two Agents

Given $K_a - K_1 > 0$ and $K_2 > 0$, it can be observed that for a system in (7.17) with $m \geq 3$ in order to satisfy the condition in (7.18), the smallest eigenvalue of matrix L_c should be greater than γ

$$
\lambda_{\min}(L_c) \geq \gamma. \tag{7.19}
$$

Therefore, by designing the gains $K_a, K_1,$ and K_2 such that $K_a - K_1 - 2K_2 \geq \gamma I_{n \times n}$ the condition in (7.19) is satisfied which in turn ensures that the system in (7.17) is contracting.

Example 7.1. ($m = 5$)

Similarly, for the system in (7.17) with five agents, the error dynamics representation is as follows

$$
\begin{bmatrix} \dot{e}_1 \\ \dot{e}_2 \\ \dot{e}_3 \\ \dot{e}_4 \\ \dot{e}_5 \end{bmatrix} = - \begin{bmatrix} K_a - K_1 & -K_2 & 0 & 0 & -K_2 \\ -K_2 & K_a - K_1 & -K_2 & 0 & 0 \\ 0 & -K_2 & K_a - K_1 & -K_2 & 0 \\ 0 & 0 & -K_2 & K_a - K_1 & -K_2 \\ -K_2 & 0 & 0 & -K_2 & K_a - K_1 \end{bmatrix} \begin{bmatrix} e_1 \\ e_2 \\ e_3 \\ e_4 \\ e_5 \end{bmatrix}
$$

In order to satisfy (7.19), the necessary conditions are given by $K_a - K_1 + 2K_2 \geq \gamma_2 I_{n \times n}$, $K_a - K_1 - \frac{K_2}{2} - \frac{\sqrt{5}K_2}{2} \geq \gamma_2 I_{n \times n}$, $K_a - K_1 - \frac{K_2}{2} - \frac{\sqrt{5}K_2}{2} \geq \gamma_2 I_{n \times n}$, $K_a - K_1 - \frac{K_2}{2} + \frac{\sqrt{5}K_2}{2} \geq \gamma_2 I_{n \times n}$, and $K_a - K_1 - \frac{K_2}{2} + \frac{\sqrt{5}K_2}{2} \geq \gamma_2 I_{n \times n}$, where $\gamma_2 \in \mathbb{R}^+$. It can be observed that designing gains such that $K_a - K_1 + K_2 \geq \gamma_2 I_{n \times n}$ is sufficient to satisfy the condition in (7.19).

All-to-all Configuration   Considering a system with m agents with each agent's error dynamics represented as in (7.16) and all-to-all configuration of coupling, its error dynamics are given by

$$
\dot{E}(t) = -L_a E(t), \tag{7.20}
$$

where $E(t) = [e_1(t), e_2(t), \ldots, e_m(t)]^T$ and

$$
L_a = \begin{bmatrix} K_a - K_1 & -K_2 & . & . & . & -K_2 \\ -K_2 & K_a - K_1 & -K_2 & & & . \\ . & & . & & & . \\ . & & & . & & . \\ . & & & -K_2 & K_a - K_1 & -K_2 \\ -K_2 & . & . & . & -K_2 & K_a - K_1 \end{bmatrix}.
$$

With $J = \frac{\partial(-L_a E(t))}{\partial E(t)} = -L_a$ and $J^T = -L_a$ and identity matrix as the positive definite metric $M(x)$, the condition in (7.11) can be written as $-L_a \leq -\frac{\beta I_{mn \times mn}}{2}$ which in turn yields

$$
L_a \geq \gamma I_{mn \times mn}. \tag{7.21}
$$

Given $K_a - K_1 > 0$ and $K_2 > 0$, it can be observed that for a system in (7.20) in order to satisfy the condition in (7.21), the smallest eigenvalue of matrix L_a should be greater than γ.

$$\lambda_{\min}(L_a) \geq \gamma \qquad (7.22)$$

Therefore, by designing the gains $K_a, K_1,$ and K_2 such that $K_a - K_1 - ((m - 1) \times K_2) \geq \gamma I_{n \times n}$ the condition in (7.22) is satisfied which in turn ensures that the system in (7.20) is contracting.

Example 7.2. $(m = 4)$

For the system in (7.20) with four agents, the error dynamics representation is as follows

$$\begin{bmatrix} \dot{e}_1 \\ \dot{e}_2 \\ \dot{e}_3 \\ \dot{e}_4 \end{bmatrix} = - \begin{bmatrix} K_a - K_1 & -K_2 & -K_2 & -K_2 \\ -K_2 & K_a - K_1 & -K_2 & -K_2 \\ -K_2 & -K_2 & K_a - K_1 & -K_2 \\ -K_2 & -K_2 & -K_2 & K_a - K_1 \end{bmatrix} \begin{bmatrix} e_1 \\ e_2 \\ e_3 \\ e_4 \end{bmatrix}.$$

In order to satisfy (7.22), the necessary conditions are given by $K_a - K_1 + K_2 \geq \gamma_3 I_{n \times n}$, $K_a - K_1 + K_2 \geq \gamma_3 I_{n \times n}$, $K_a - K_1 + K_2 \geq \gamma_3 I_{n \times n}$, and $K_a - K_1 - 3K_2 \geq \gamma_3 I_{n \times n}$, where $\gamma_3 \in \mathbb{R}^+$. It can be observed that designing gains such that $K_a - K_1 - 3K_2 \geq \gamma_3 I_{n \times n}$ is sufficient to satisfy the condition in (7.22).

7.4.2 *Synchronization Analysis*

Cyclic Configuration   Considering the system in (7.17) with $m = 2$ agents, the error dynamics of the first agent can be written as $\dot{e}_1(t) = -K_a e_1(t) + K_1 e_1(t) + K_2 e_2(t)$. By adding $K_2 e_1(t)$ on both sides, the error dynamics of the first agent can be reformulated as

$$\dot{e}_1(t) - h(e_1(t)) = g(e_1(t), e_2(t)), \qquad (7.23)$$

where $h(e_1(t)) = -(K_a - K_1 + K_2) e_1(t)$ and $g(e_1(t), e_2(t)) = K_2(e_1(t) + e_2(t))$. Similarly, the error dynamics for the second agent are given by

$$\dot{e}_2(t) - h(e_2(t)) = g(e_1(t), e_2(t)). \qquad (7.24)$$

Based on Theorem 3 of Ref. 65, (7.23), and (7.24), if $(K_a - K_1 + K_2) < 0$ the trajectories of the error dynamics of both the agents will always converge to each other exponentially, even under spatial perturbations. Similarly, for m = 3 agents, equations similar to (7.23) and (7.24) can be formulated to prove the synchronization. Note that for $m > 3$ agents, all the agents are no longer coupled with each other. The synchronization can be proved by using the matrix decomposition approach in Ref. 3.

All-to-all Configuration Considering the system in (7.20), the error dynamics of an ith agent can be written as $\dot{e}_i(t) = -K_a e_i(t) + K_1 e_i(t) + \sum_{j=1, j\neq i}^{m} K_2 e_j(t)$. By adding $K_2 e_i(t)$ on both sides, the error dynamics of the first agent can be reformulated as

$$\dot{e}_i(t) - h(e_i(t)) = g(e_1(t), e_2(t), ..., e_m(t)), \qquad (7.25)$$

where $h(e_i(t)) = -(K_a - K_1 + K_2)e_i(t)$ and $g(e_1(t), e_2(t), ..., e_m(t)) = K_2(\sum_{i=1}^{m} e_i(t))$. Similarly, the error dynamics for $i + 1^{th}$ agent are given by

$$\dot{e}_{i+1}(t) - h(e_{i+1}(t)) = g(e_1(t), e_2(t), ..., e_m(t)). \qquad (7.26)$$

Based on Theorem 3 of Ref. 65, (7.25), and (7.26), if $(K_a - K_1 + K_2) < 0$, then the trajectories of the error dynamics of any two agents will always converge to each other exponentially, even under spatial perturbations.

7.4.3 *Coordinate Transformation between Agents for Bimanual Manipulation*

The bimanual manipulation can be considered as the system with two agents (right and left arms). While implementing the learned bimanual task, such as transporting a box and moving it to a new goal location, learning the dynamics of one arm motion is sufficient. The synchronization and tracking control laws developed in previous section can be used to obtain the motion of two arms in task space. The desired trajectory for the second arm can be obtained by transforming the states of synchronized second arm's task space motion by a desired fixed or variable transformation.

Suppose that $^{\mathcal{R}}\xi_B(t)$ and $^{\mathcal{L}}\xi_B(t)$ are the task space poses of right arm and left arm end effectors with respect to the robot body reference frame at any given time t. Also, let $^{\mathcal{L}}\xi_{\mathcal{R}}(t)$ be the transformation of the right arm end effector with respect to left arm end effector, then the relationship between $^{\mathcal{R}}\xi_B(t)$ and $^{\mathcal{L}}\xi_B(t)$ is given by $^{\mathcal{L}}\xi_B(t) = {^{\mathcal{L}}\xi_{\mathcal{R}}(t)}\,{^{\mathcal{R}}\xi_B(t)}$. Additionally, if the object being manipulated is rigid, then the transformation between the two arms' end effectors is fixed, i.e., $^{\mathcal{L}}\xi_B(t) = {^{\mathcal{L}}\xi_{\mathcal{R}}}\,{^{\mathcal{R}}\xi_B(t)}$. In the case of rigid object manipulation, the constant transformation $^{\mathcal{L}}\xi_{\mathcal{R}}$ is chosen according to the experimental setup. If the object being manipulated is deformable, then the transformation between the two arms' end effectors is time varying, e.g., a mirror transformation for a two string pulling portion of knot tying operation.

Let $\Psi \subset \mathbb{R}^6$ be the space which satisfies the robot's end effector position and orientation restrictions, $q_{\mathcal{R}}(t) \in \Psi$ and $q_{\mathcal{L}}(t) \in \Psi$ represent the end effector positions and the end effector orientations in the form of Euler angles for right and left arms respectively. Let $f_{\text{trans}} : SE(3) \to \Psi$ be a function that computes the end effector position and orientation in the form of Euler angles given pose and $f_{\text{trans}}^{-1} :$ $\Psi \to SE(3)$ computes pose given end effector position and orientation. The right arm end effector dynamics are learned using DMPs with $q_R(t) = f_{\text{trans}}\left({}^{\mathcal{R}}\xi_{\mathcal{B}}(t)\right)$ as the states. Consider a virtual agent with pose ${}^{\mathcal{L}}\tilde{\xi}_{\mathcal{B}}(t)$ such that

$$ {}^{\mathcal{L}}\xi_{\mathcal{B}}(t) = {}^{\mathcal{L}}\xi_{\mathcal{R}}(t) \ {}^{\tilde{\mathcal{L}}}\xi_{\mathcal{B}}(t). \tag{7.27} $$

The virtual agent's dynamics are represented using the same learned DMPs with $q_{\tilde{L}}(t) = f_{\text{trans}}\left({}^{\mathcal{L}}\tilde{\xi}_{\mathcal{B}}(t)\right)$ as states. By designing the control law as described in Section 7.4, $q_R(t)$ and $q_{\tilde{L}}(t)$ will converge to each other and track the desired trajectory. The left arm end effector pose ${}^{\mathcal{L}}\xi_{\mathcal{B}}(t)$, is obtained by using ${}^{\mathcal{L}}\tilde{\xi}_{\mathcal{B}}(t) = f_{\text{trans}}^{-1}\left(q_{\tilde{L}}(t)\right)$ and (7.27).

Algorithm 1: Learning and Synchronization of Movement Primitives for Bimanual Manipulation Tasks

---

1 Obtain a joint angle measurements of the robot through kinesthetic demonstrations while user performing the task by guiding the robot arms;
2 Obtain the end effector pose from join angle measurements using DH-parameters of the robot;
3 Obtain the position, velocity, and acceleration estimates of the pose of the end effector using Kalman filter with constant acceleration model;
4 Define the gains of the DMP attractor system and the canonical system;
5 Learn the forcing terms for the single arm end effector pose and obtain the weights of the basis functions in the forcing term;
6 Determine the gains of the closed-loop system such that the overall system in (7.17) or (7.20) is contracting;
7 Obtain the second arm's end effector pose by transforming the second agent in the system as shown in (7.27) for implementation on the robot;

7.5   Experimental Results

Three experiments involving the bimanual manipulation tasks are performed using the learned DMPs and the control laws designed in Sections 7.4. The experiments are implemented using Robotics toolbox of Ref. 66 with MATLAB 2014b on a computer running a Intel i5 processor with 8 Gigabytes of memory. Kinesthetic demonstrations are obtained using the Baxter robot platform in order to learn the DMPs.

7.5.1 *Experiment 1*

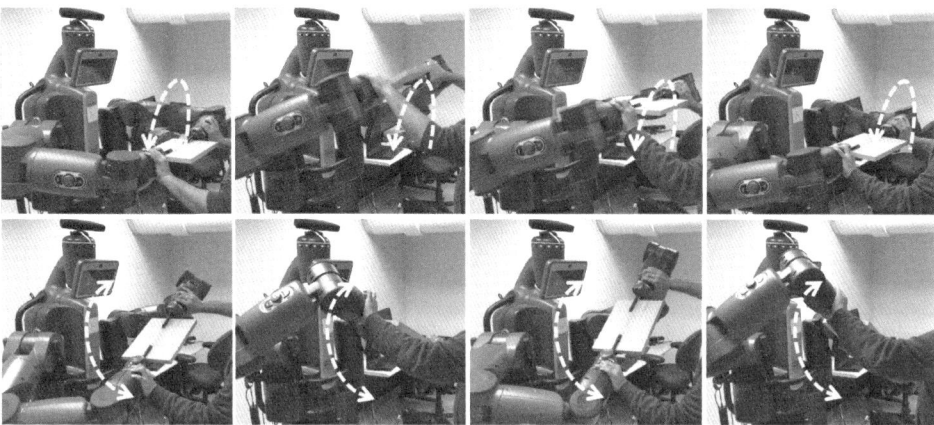

Fig. 7.1. Demonstrations obtained using the Baxter robot platform are shown in the figure. The pictures in the top row correspond to the transient motion at the beginning of the task and the pictures in the bottom row correspond to the subsequent periodic motion.

A single kinesthetic demonstration of a bimanual manipulation task with a solid object as shown in Fig. 7.1 is obtained using the 7 degrees of freedom Baxter robot. The DH-parameters of the robot are used to obtain the end effector pose (position and orientation) of the robot arms during the task. To test the robustness of the learned DMPs and the designed control laws, spatial perturbations are applied to one of the arms and the response of the system containing both the arms is observed. A DMP is learned in a single dimension, and due to the forward mapping between the joint-space ($\mathbb{R}^7$) and the end-effector space ($\mathbb{R}^6$), a set of 6 DMPs is used to learn the end-effector dynamics of one of the arms of the robot, as explained in Section 7.2.1. During the learning phase, the gains of the attractor system of each DMP are chosen to be $\alpha_y = 32$ and $\beta_y = 8$. The gains and constants used in canonical system are chosen to be $\alpha = \frac{1}{6}$, $\beta = \frac{1}{1000}$, $\eta = 35$, $\mu = 1$, $\mu_1 = 1.2$, and $\mu_2 = 1.4$. These gains are chosen such that the DMP can accurately reproduce the demonstrated data. Also, as the task requires the robot to use two arms (i.e., two agents in the system (7.17)), the gains K_1, K_2, and D are selected to be $K_1 = 5I_{6\times6}$, $K_2 = 45I_{6\times6}$ and $D = 10I_{6\times6}$ in order to satisfy the contraction condition given in (7.18). The DMPs are used to represent the task space motion of one of the arms of the robot, and then the other arm's dynamics are obtained by transforming the learned DMPs according to (7.27).

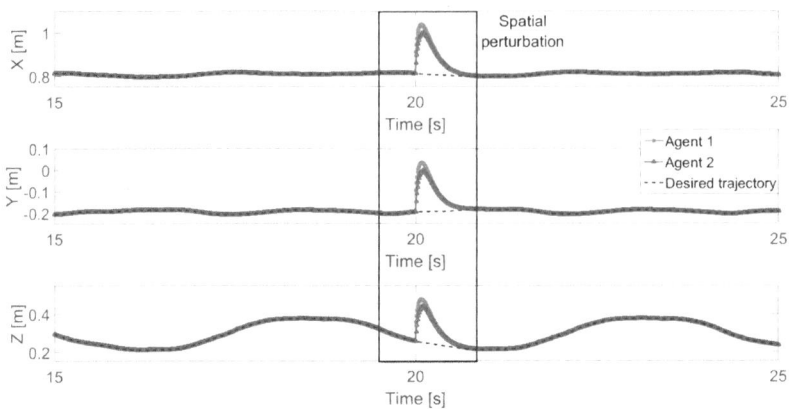

Fig. 7.2. Behaviors of both the arms when one of the arms is perturbed.

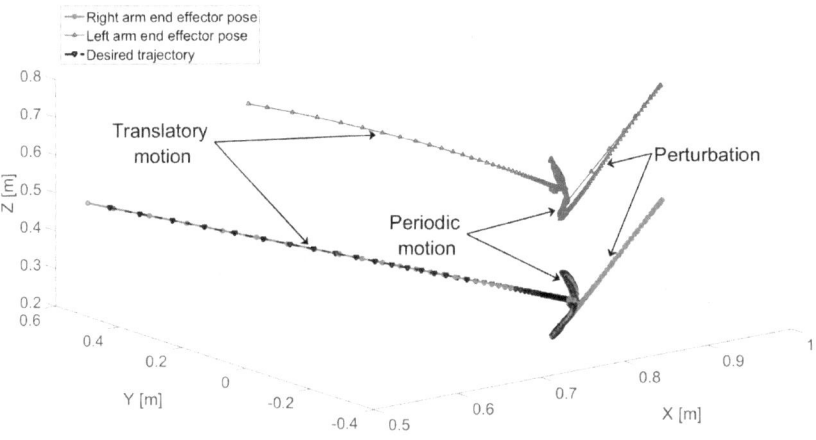

Fig. 7.3. 3D representation of the behaviors of both the arms when one of the arms is perturbed.

The response of the system to the perturbations is shown in Fig. 7.2. As one of the arms is perturbed, the other arm deviates from its desired trajectory in order to synchronize with the perturbed arm. It can be observed from Fig. 7.2 that the arms synchronize within 0.16 seconds and both the arms converge to the desired trajectory simultaneously. The 3D representation of both the arms' behaviors after the transformation is shown in Fig. 7.3.

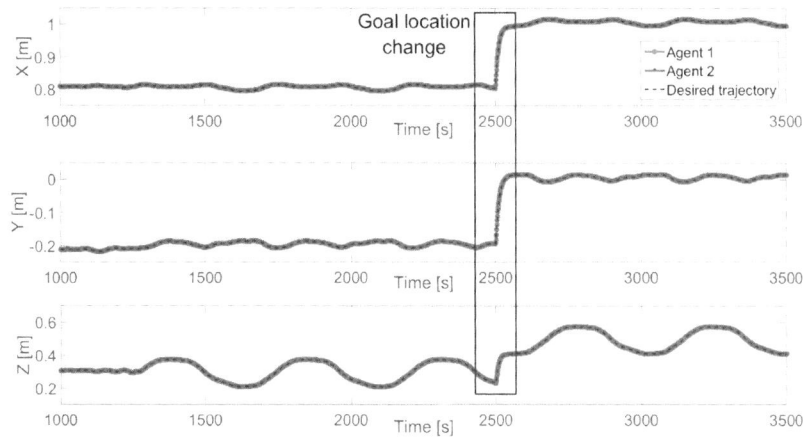

Fig. 7.4. Behaviors of both the arms when goal location is changed.

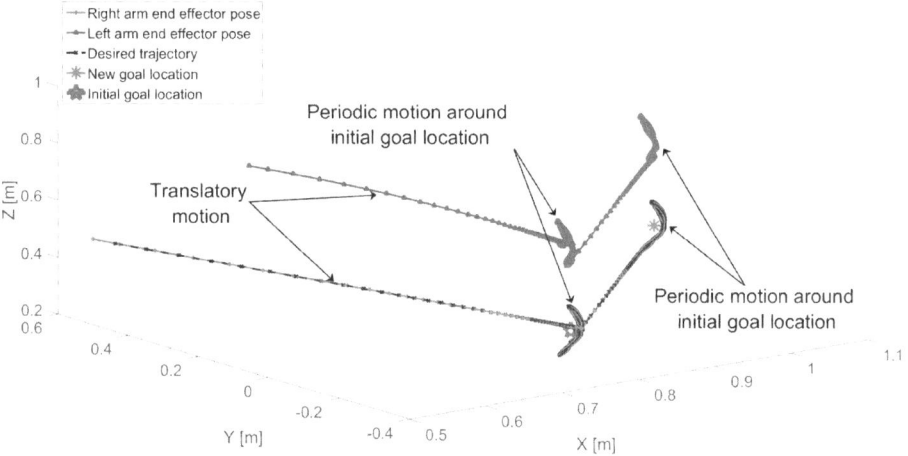

Fig. 7.5. 3D representation of the behaviors of both the arms when goal location is changed.

7.5.2 Experiment 2

In the second experiment, the adaption to the goal location changes while performing a task is demonstrated. The control gains are chosen to be of the same values as described in Experiment 1. The behaviors of the robot arms with the change in goal location are shown in Fig. 7.4. Both the arms are able to adapt to the change in goal location and carry out the task. The 3D representation of the behaviors of the arms is shown in Fig. 7.5.

7.5.3 *Experiment 3*

For the third experiment, tying an Overhand knot is considered. For simplicity, the two ends of a rope are assumed to be spliced together but not fully tightened. Baxter's two manipulators that are equipped with the parallel grippers are used to grasp the two ends and pull them simultaneously in the opposite directions to tighten the knot. A single kinesthetic demonstration of one of the Baxter's arm pulling on one end of a rope is obtained. During the demonstration, the joints' trajectory of the manipulator that takes the end effector to the location where the rope is at a fully tightened state (goal location) is recorded by guiding the associated arm to the maximum length of the rope. The recorded angular position and velocity measurements performing the rope pulling task are then used to obtain the end effector pose and ultimately the position, velocity, and acceleration estimates of the end effector pose. A set of 6 DMPs is used to learn the discrete movements of the rope pulling task using discrete movements as explained in 7.3. During the learning phase of the discrete movement, the gains of the attactor system of each DMP are chosen to be $\alpha_v = \alpha_y = 16$, $\beta_v = \beta_y = 8$. Also to satisfy the contraction condition in 7.11 the following gains are selected $K_1 = I_{6\times6}$, $K_2 = 0.5I_{6\times6}$ and $D = 10I_{6\times6}$. Once the DMPs of one arm are learned, the dynamics of the other arm are obtained by mirroring the points on the horizontal axis of the Baxter robot coordinate frames, namely y, by the vertical axis x while the other five dimensions (DMPs) remain fixed. The behaviors of the robot arms is depicted in Fig. 7.6, and can be observed that the arms synchronize and both converge to the goal location at the same time. Note that in Fig. 7.6 the trajectory of the second arm in y dimension is positive which implies that the second arm moves in the opposite direction from the first one.

Figure 7.7 shows the proposed method's ability to successfully learn the motion dynamics of the bimanual manipulation task of tightening of an Overhand knot. As it is shown in Fig. 7.7 Baxter holds the two ends and simultaneously pulls them in the opposite direction to tighten the knot.

7.6 Conclusion

Literature review shows that the bimanual manipulation is an important problem for many manufacturing applications. The control laws to achieve tracking and synchronization of dual arm manipulator performing bimanual manipulation tasks are developed. The designed control laws are robust to perturbations and instan-

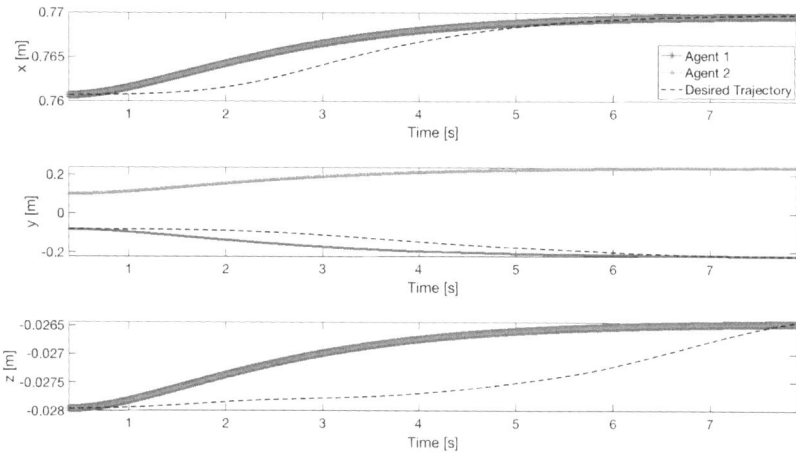

Fig. 7.6. Behavior of both the arms while tying an Overhand knot.

Fig. 7.7. Sequences of images showing the Baxter robot tying an Overhand knot using the tracking and synchronization controller.

taneously adapt to changes in the goal location. The experimental results suggest that the agents of the system in (7.17) are able to synchronize within 0.16 seconds. Experiments by implementation of the controller on a robot shows the usefulness of the controllers on a real system. In future, demonstration of the controllers for a real manufacturing application such as wire harness assembly will be shown.

Acknowledgments

The work was supported in part by Subaward No. ARM-17-QS-F-04 from the Advanced Robotics for Manufacturing (ARM) Institute under Agreement Number

W911NF-17-3-0004 sponsored by the Office of the Secretary of Defense. ARM Project Management was provided by Matthew S. Fischer. The views and conclusions contained in this document are those of the authors and should not be interpreted as representing the official policies, either expressed or implied, of either ARM or the Office of the Secretary of Defense of the U.S. Government. The U.S. Government is authorized to reproduce and distribute reprints for Government purposes, notwithstanding any copyright notation herein. The authors would like to thank Ryan Saltus for his help with the robot implementation.

References

1. C. Smith, Y. Karayiannidis, L. Nalpantidis, X. Gratal, P. Qi, D. V. Dimarogonas and D. Kragic, Dual arm manipulation - a survey, *Robotics and Autonomous Systems* **60**(10), 1340–1353 (2012).

2. J. D. Langsfeld, A. M. Kabir, K. N. Kaipa and S. K. Gupta, Robotic bimanual cleaning of deformable objects with online learning of part and tool models. In *IEEE International Conference on Automation Science and Engineering*, pp. 626–632 (2016).

3. S.-J. Chung and J.-J. E. Slotine, Cooperative robot control and concurrent synchronization of lagrangian systems, *IEEE Transactions on Robotics* **25**(3), 686–700 (2009).

4. S.-J. Chung, S. Bandyopadhyay, I. Chang and F. Y. Hadaegh, Phase synchronization control of complex networks of lagrangian systems on adaptive digraphs, *Automatica* **49**(5), 1148–1161 (2013).

5. A. P. Dani, N. R. Fischer and W. E. Dixon, Single camera structure and motion, *IEEE Transactions on Automatic Control* **57**(1), 238–243 (2012).

6. A. P. Dani and W. E. Dixon, Single camera structure and motion estimation. In *Visual Servoing via Advanced Numerical Methods*, G. Chesi and K. Hashimoto (eds). Springer (2010).

7. N. R. Gans, A. Dani and W. E. Dixon, Visual servoing to an arbitrary pose with respect to an object given a single known length. In *American Controls Conference*. pp. 1261–1267, Seattle, USA (2008).

8. J. Yang, A. Dani, S.-J. Chung and S. Hutchinson, Vision-based localization and robot-centric mapping in riverine environments, *Journal of Field Robotics* **34**(3), (2015).

9. D. Chwa, A. P. Dani and W. E. Dixon, Range and motion estimation of a monocular camera using static and moving objects, *IEEE Transactions on Control Systems Technology* **24**(4), 1174–1183 (2016), doi:10.1109/TCST.2015.2508001.

10. W. Lohmiller and J.-J. E. Slotine, On contraction analysis for non-linear systems, *Automatica* **34**(6), 683–696 (1998).

11. S. Bandyopadhyay, S.-J. Chung and F. Y. Hadaegh, Probabilistic and distributed control of a large-scale swarm of autonomous agents, *IEEE Transactions on Robotics* **33**(5), 1103–1123 (2017).

12. D. J. Balkcom and M. T. Mason, Robotic origami folding, *The International Journal of Robotics Research* **27**(5), 613–627 (2008).

13. A. Namiki and S. Yokosawa, Robotic origami folding with dynamic motion primitives, in *IEEE/RSJ International Conference on Intelligent Robots and Systems*. pp. 5623–5628 (2015).

14. X. Yun and V. R. Kumar, An approach to simultaneous control of trajectory and interaction forces in dual-arm configurations, *IEEE Transactions on Robotics and Automation* **7**(5), 618–625 (1991).

15. N. Sarkar, X. Yun and V. Kumar, Dynamic control of 3-D rolling contacts in two-arm manipulation, *IEEE Transactions on Robotics and Automation* **13**(3), 364–376 (1997).

16. Z. Doulgeri and A. Golfakis, Nonlinear manipulation control of a compliant object by dual fingers, *Journal of dynamic systems, measurement, and control* **128**(3), 473–481 (2006).

17. T. Watanabe, K. Harada, Z. Jiang and T. Yoshikawa, Object manipulation under hybrid active/passive closure. In *Proceedings of the 2005 IEEE International Conference on Robotics and Automation (ICRA 2005)*, IEEE, pp. 1013–1020 (2005).

18. R. Tinós, M. H. Terra and J. Y. Ishihara, Motion and force control of cooperative robotic manipulators with passive joints, *IEEE Transactions on Control Systems Technology* **14**(4), 725–734 (2006).

19. S. Erhart and S. Hirche, Adaptive force/velocity control for multi-robot cooperative manipulation under uncertain kinematic parameters. In *IEEE/RSJ International Conference on Intelligent Robots and Systems* pp. 307–314 (2013).

20. S. A. Schneider and R. H. Cannon, Object impedance control for cooperative manipulation: Theory and experimental results, *IEEE Transactions on Robotics and Automation* **8**(3), 383–394 (1992).

21. R. Bonitz and T. C. Hsia, Internal force-based impedance control for cooperating manipulators, *IEEE Transactions on Robotics and Automation* **12**(1), 78–89 (1996a).

22. R. G. Bonitz and T. C. Hsia, Robust dual-arm manipulation of rigid objects via palm grasping-theory and experiments. In *IEEE International Conference on Robotics and Automation,* Vol. 4, pp. 3047–3054 (1996b).

23. S. Erhart, D. Sieber and S. Hirche, An impedance-based control architecture for multi-robot cooperative dual-arm mobile manipulation. In *IEEE/RSJ International Conference on Intelligent Robots and Systems (IROS)*, pp. 315–322 (2013).

24. W. Gueaieb, F. Karray and S. Al-Sharhan, A robust hybrid intelligent position/force control scheme for cooperative manipulators, *IEEE/ASME Transactions on Mechatronics* **12**(2), 109–125 (2007).

25. Y. Zhao and C. C. Cheah, Neural network control of multifingered robot hands using visual feedback, *IEEE Transactions on Neural Networks* **20**(5), 758–767 (2009).

26. K.-Y. Lian, C.-S. Chiu and P. Liu, Semi-decentralized adaptive fuzzy control for cooperative multirobot systems with h/sup/spl infin//motion/internal force tracking performance, *IEEE Transactions on Systems, Man, and Cybernetics, Part B (Cybernetics)* **32**(3), 269–280 (2002).

27. Y. Kume, Y. Hirata and K. Kosuge, Coordinated motion control of multiple mobile manipulators handling a single object without using force/torque sensors. In *IEEE/RSJ International Conference on Intelligent Robots and Systems (IROS 2007)*, pp. 4077–4082 (2007).

28. D. Sun and J. K. Mills, Adaptive synchronized control for coordination of multirobot assembly tasks, *IEEE Transactions on Robotics and Automation* **18**(4), 498–510 (2002).

29. W.-H. Zhu, On adaptive synchronization control of coordinated multirobots with flexible/rigid constraints, *IEEE Transactions on Robotics* **21**(3), 520–525 (2005).

30. P. Dauchez, P. Fraisse and F. Pierrot, A vision/position/force control approach for performing assembly tasks with a humanoid robot. In *EEE-RAS International Conference on Humanoid Robots,* pp. 277–282 (2005).

31. K. Huebner, K. Welke, M. Przybylski, N. Vahrenkamp, T. Asfour, D. Kragic and R. Dillmann, Grasping known objects with humanoid robots: A box-based approach. In *International Conference on Advanced Robotics (ICAR 2009)*, pp. 1–6 (2009).

32. J. Maitin-Shepard, M. Cusumano-Towner, J. Lei and P. Abbeel, Cloth grasp point detection based on multiple-view geometric cues with application to robotic towel folding. In *2010 IEEE International Conference on Robotics and Automation (ICRA)*, pp. 2308–2315 (2010).

33. R. A. Knepper, T. Layton, J. Romanishin and D. Rus, Ikeabot: An autonomous multi-robot coordinated furniture assembly system. In *IEEE International Conference on Robotics and Automation*, pp. 855–862 (2013).

34. J. Barraquand and P. Ferbach, A penalty function method for constrained motion planning. In *Proceedings of the 1994 International Conference on Robotics and Automation*, pp. 1235–1242 (1994).

35. M. Dogar, A. Spielberg, S. Baker and D. Rus, Multi-robot grasp planning for sequential assembly operations. In *IEEE International Conference on Robotics and Automation*, pp. 193–200 (2015).

36. Z. Bien and J. Lee, A minimum-time trajectory planning method for two robots, *IEEE Transactions on Robotics and Automation* **8**(3), 414–418 (1992).

37. U. Sezgin, L. D. Seneviratne and S. Earles, Collision avoidance in multiple-redundant manipulators, *The International Journal of Robotics Research* **16**(5), 714–724 (1997).

38. K. Harada, T. Tsuji and J.-P. Laumond, A manipulation motion planner for dual-arm industrial manipulators. In *2014 IEEE International Conference on Robotics and Automation (ICRA)*, pp. 928–934 (2014).

39. F. Basile, F. Caccavale, P. Chiacchio, J. Coppola and C. Curatella, Task-oriented motion planning for multi-arm robotic systems, *Robotics and Computer-Integrated Manufacturing* **28**(5), 569–582 (2012).

40. Z. Li, S. S. Ge and Z. Wang, Robust adaptive control of coordinated multiple mobile manipulators, *Mechatronics* **18**(5-6), 239–250 (2008).

41. D. Sieber, F. Deroo and S. Hirche, Formation-based approach for multi-robot cooperative manipulation based on optimal control design. In *IEEE/RSJ International Conference on Intelligent Robots and Systems (IROS)*, pp. 5227–5233 (2013).

42. Y. Hirata, Y. Kume, Z.-D. Wang and K. Kosuge, Decentralized control of multiple mobile manipulators based on virtual 3-D caster motion for handling an object in cooperation with a human. In *IEEE International Conference on Robotics and Automation*, Vol. 1, pp. 938–943 (2003).

43. R. Zöllner, T. Asfour and R. Dillmann, Programming by demonstration: dual-arm manipulation tasks for humanoid robots. In *IEEE/RSJ International Conference on Intelligent Robots and Systems (IROS)*, pp. 479–484 (2004).

44. S. Calinon, F. D'halluin, E. L. Sauser, D. G. Caldwell and A. G. Billard, Learning and reproduction of gestures by imitation, *IEEE Robotics & Automation Magazine* **17**(2), 44–54 (2010).

45. A. J. Ijspeert, J. Nakanishi, H. Hoffmann, P. Pastor and S. Schaal, Dynamical movement primitives: learning attractor models for motor behaviors, *Neural Computation* **25**(2), 328–373 (2013).

46. J. Ernesti, L. Righetti, M. Do, T. Asfour and S. Schaal, Encoding of periodic and their transient motions by a single dynamic movement primitive. In *12th IEEE-RAS International Conference on Humanoid Robots (Humanoids)*, pp. 57–64 (2012).

47. D-H. Park, H. Hoffmann, P. Pastor, and S. Schaal, Movement reproduction and obstacle avoidance with dynamic movement primitives and potential fields. In *8th IEEE-RAS International Conference on Humanoid Robots (Humanoids)*, pp. 91–98 (2008).

48. M. Tamosiunaite, B. Nemec, A. Ude and F. Wörgötter, Learning to pour with a robot arm combining goal and shape learning for dynamic movement primitives, *Robotics and Autonomous Systems* **59**(11), 910–922 (2011).

49. S. Bitzer and S. Vijayakumar, Latent spaces for dynamic movement primitives. In *9th IEEE-RAS International Conference on Humanoid Robots (Humanoids)*, pp. 574–581 (2009).

50. T. Matsubara, S.-H. Hyon and J. Morimoto, Learning stylistic dynamic movement primitives from multiple demonstrations. In *2010 IEEE/RSJ International Conference on Intelligent Robots and Systems (IROS)*, pp. 1277–1283 (2010).

51. T. Matsubara, S.-H. Hyon and J. Morimoto, Learning parametric dynamic movement primitives from multiple demonstrations, *Neural Networks* **24**(5), 493–500 (2011).

52. B. Nemec and A. Ude, Action sequencing using dynamic movement primitives, *Robotica* **30**(5), 837–846 (2012).

53. T. Kulvicius, K. Ning, M. Tamosiunaite and F. Worgotter, Joining movement sequences: Modified dynamic movement primitives for robotics applications exemplified on handwriting, *IEEE Transactions on Robotics* **28**(1), 145–157 (2012).

54. J. Umlauft, D. Sieber and S. Hirche, Dynamic movement primitives for cooperative manipulation and synchronized motions. In *IEEE International Conference on Robotics and Automation*, pp. 766–771 (2014).

55. P. K. Thota, H. chaandar Ravichandar and A. P. Dani, Learning and synchronization of movement primitives for bimanual manipulation tasks. In *IEEE 55th Conference on Decision and Control*, pp. 945–950 (2016).

56. E. Gribovskaya, S. M. Khansari-Zadeh and A. Billard, Learning non-linear multivariate dynamics of motion in robotic manipulators, *The International Journal of Robotics Research* **30**(1), 80–117 (2010).

57. S. M. Khansari-Zadeh and A. Billard, Learning control Lyapunov function to ensure stability of dynamical system-based robot reaching motions, *Robotics and Autonomous Systems* **62**(6), 752–765 (2014).

58. H. Ravichandar and A. P. Dani, Learning contracting nonlinear dynamics from human demonstration for robot motion planning. In *ASME Dynamic Systems and Control Conference (DSCC)* (2015).

59. H. Ravichandar, I. Salehi and A. Dani, Learning partially contracting dynamical systems from demonstrations. In *Proceedings of the 1st Annual Conference on Robot Learning (PMLR)*, vol. 78, pp. 369–378 (2017).

60. H. Ravichandar and A. Dani, Learning pose dynamics from demonstrations via contraction analysis, *Autonomous Robots* **43**(4), 897–912 (2018). doi:https://doi.org/10.1007/s10514-018-9758-x.

61. H. Ravichandar, P. K. Thota and A. P. Dani, Learning periodic motions from human demonstrations using transverse contraction analysis. In *IEEE American Control Conference (ACC)* (2016).

62. J. Van Den Berg, S. Miller, D. Duckworth, H. Hu, A. Wan, X.-Y. Fu, K. Goldberg and P. Abbeel, Superhuman performance of surgical tasks by robots using iterative learning from human-guided demonstrations. In *2010 IEEE International Conference on Robotics and Automation*, pp. 2074–2081 (2010).

63. J. Schulman, J. Ho, C. Lee and P. Abbeel, Learning from demonstrations through the use of non-rigid registration. In *Robotics Research,* H.I. Christensen and O. Khatib (eds). Springer, (2016).
64. A. J. Ijspeert, J. Nakanishi and S. Schaal, Learning attractor landscapes for learning motor primitives. In *Proceedings of the 15th International Conference on Neural Information Processing Systems (NIPS'02),* pp. 1547–1554 (January 2002).
65. W. Wang and J.-J. E. Slotine, On partial contraction analysis for coupled nonlinear oscillators, *Biological Cybernetics* **92**(1), 38–53 (2005).
66. P. I. Corke, *Robotics, Vision & Control: Fundamental Algorithms in Matlab.* Springer (2011).

© 2020 World Scientific Publishing Company
https://doi.org/10.1142/9789811222849_0008

Chapter 8

Advances in Robot Technology Supporting Low-Volume/High-Mix Small Part Assembly Operations

Joe Falco, Karl Van Wyk, and Kenneth Kimble

8.1 Introduction

Recent advancements in robotic arms and end-effectors have the potential to accelerate the use of robotics for small parts assembly. The force sensing and compliance capabilities used in collaborative robots to prevent injuries and enable them to work safely alongside human workers in manufacturing environments lend themselves to robotic assembly tasks. Additionally, robotic hands are emerging as a next-generation end-effector technology with advanced force control and manipulation capabilities. These robotic components as well as advances in end-of-arm force sensing and compliance tooling, improved calibration methods, artificial intelligence techniques, simplified programming interfaces, and ease of reconfiguration are all contributing to new ways of tackling the small parts assembly field especially for low-volume, high-mix manufacturing operations.

Small parts assembly processes consist of insertions and fastening methods such as threading, snap fitting, and gear meshing using standard components including screws, nuts, washers, gears, and electrical connectors. Since the 1970s manufacturers had expectations that robots would be able to perform small parts assembly operations to alleviate humans from what were thought to be onerous, repetitive, and tedious tasks. While this seemed achievable in concept, robot technologies of the time could not cost-effectively support the tight tolerances and component variability associated with the assembly process. Despite many advancements in hardware and control software, the limitations encountered in the early days of attempting robotic assembly operations still persist after many decades. Due to their highly rigid designs and position-based control, most industrial robots require customized fixtures that are tailored to a particular assembly operation and component geometry in order to perform assembly tasks. These specialized fixtures introduce costs and add time to the setup of every new assembly job. Even more expensive and sophisticated approaches were conceived that compensated for motion errors using force sensing at the end-effector. These methods required 6-axis force-torque sensing at the tool point, low-level force feedback to the robot position or force controller, and the highly application specific algorithmic support for accomplishing assembly operations.

The International Federation of Robotics estimates that over 3 million industrial robots will be at work in 2020, representing an average annual growth rate of 14% between 2017 and 2020.[1] It is predicted that these new robots will especially play a key role in the productivity and competitiveness of small and medium-sized enterprises (SMEs). A Price Waterhouse (PwC) survey of 107 respondents, conducted in conjunction with the Manufacturing Institute, found that the most common task among US manufacturers was assembly (25%) followed by machining (21%), and the least common tasks were warehousing and performing dangerous tasks (both 6.5 %). The survey also indicates that assembly was the most common task that manufacturers planned to invest in robotic technology to support (27%).[2]

For robotic solutions to benefit SME-based manufacturing operations, where it is cost prohibitive to employ robotics experts, the robots must be used in existing previously human-only occupied work spaces. Moreover, they must be programmed by line operators and expediently deployed to support low volume, high mixture production runs. Recent progress in technologies for robotic arms and end-effectors holds potential to overcome the problems with robotic assembly. Some collaborative robots or Co-Bots are designed to safely contact humans working in close proximity in both manufacturing and service sectors.[3] Many of these robots are equipped with force sensing and/or compliance features in order to limit contact forces and prevent injury to humans working in their proximity. These capabilities inherently prove advantageous for facilitating assembly operations where force or compliance control is required. Some examples of these robots are shown in Fig. 8.1.[a]

Advanced robotic grippers and hands are also emerging as a next-generation end-effector technology with advanced force control and manipulation capabilities, attributes useful for assembly.[4] Some existing robotic-hand cutaneous sensors

---

[a]Certain commercial entities and items are identified in this chapter to foster understanding. Such identification does not imply recommendation or endorsement by the National Institute of Standards and Technology, nor does it imply that the materials or equipment identified are necessarily the best available for the purpose.

coupled with the latest advances in artificial intelligence are approaching and even exceeding the sensing capabilities of the human hand.[5,6] Moreover, the enhanced reconfigurability of robotic hands promises new ways of tackling the small parts assembly field for manufacturing operations.[7,8] Some examples of these robotic grippers are also shown in Fig. 8.1.

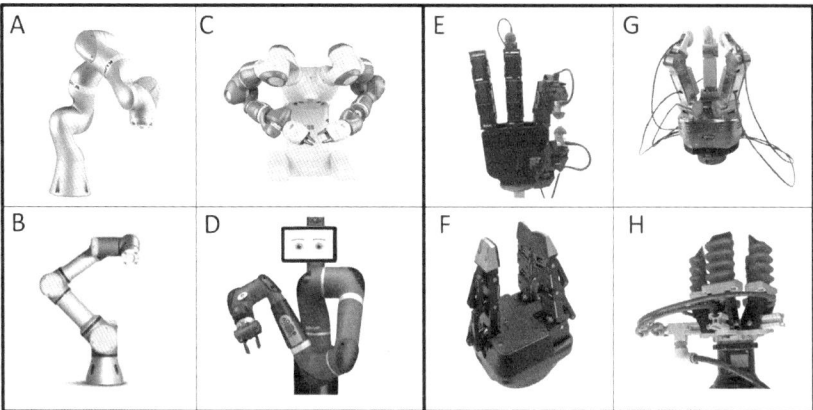

Fig. 8.1. Commercially available robotic arms (left) where: A) Kuka LBR IIWA incorporates strain gauges based force control; B) Universal Robots (UR) series of robots use motor current sensing; C) Asea Brown Boveri (ABB) YuMi uses motor current sensing; and D) Rethink Sawyer is designed with series elastic actuators in its joints for compliance. Commercially available robotic hands (right) where: E) Wonik Robotics Allegro Hand is retrofitted with six-axis force torque sensors for force control; F) Robotiq Adaptive Gripper with mechanical compliance and current-based force stopping; G) Schunk Dexterous Hand retrofitted with Syntouch Biotac sensors for force control; H) Soft robotics gripper with pneumatic compliance.

These progressing technological areas in robotic arms and hands are being used to develop new task-level force-control methods for robotic assembly. In addition, new developments in robot calibration, simplified programming interfaces, ease of reconfiguration, and artificial intelligence are technical areas contributing to robotic solutions for tackling the small parts assembly field. This is especially true for low-volume, high-mix manufacturing operations. This chapter presents recent advancements in robotic assembly towards reducing integration complexity, increasing production rates, and improving the process quality of small parts assembly operations.

Section 8.2 presents research in the area of task level force methods for assembly using end-effector compliance as well as active force control which can also provide a degree of compliance based on the control method used. The primary task used in the research is the peg-in-hole alignment and insertion operation. Section 8.3 describes methods of robot calibration and registration that support the increased need of re-tasking robots in SME environments. Section 8.4 presents methods of easier, faster, and more adaptable programming methods to support the re-tasking of robots in SME environments by workers who are not necessarily robotics experts. Section 8.5 is a brief look at the application of machine learning methods to support robotic assembly. Finally, Section 8.6 looks at the future direction of robotic assembly with respect to the research topics covered in this chapter.

8.2   Methods for Robotic Assembly

Position-controlled industrial robots cannot cost-effectively support the high tolerances and component variability associated with the assembly process despite the potential to alleviate humans from repetitive and tedious tasks. Due to their highly rigid designs and their implementation of position-based control, most industrial robots require customized fixtures that are tailored to a particular assembly operation and component geometry to perform a task. These specialized fixtures introduce cost and add time to the setup of every new assembly job. They are also cost prohibitive, especially in the case of small and medium sized manufacturers who regularly support low-volume, high-mix manufacturing operations. To attain these shortfalls, robotic assembly solutions are emerging that incorporate passive and active methods to overcome assembly tolerances using the forces and torques of the assembly-task interaction.

These methods include the use of passive-compliant devices and force-sensing end-effector tools as well as robots with built-in compliance mechanisms and force-sensing attributes of robots designed for collaborative operation in close proximity to humans. Most active robot force-control strategies are implemented using hybrid position control, force control, impedance control, and admittance control.[9] Non-contact object recognition and localization techniques such as visual servoing often lack the precision needed in the presence of high tolerances found in assembly operations. In these cases, perception systems are employed to resolve preliminary positions from which to start a force-control method used for final assembly.[10] The following are a selection of recent research and development activities in the field of force-based robotic assembly. Much of this work is based on the peg-in-hole task, a particularly relevant task for industrial robots since it accounts for over 35% of all assembly operations[11] followed by 27% for the installation of threaded fasteners. The threaded-fastener application space currently relies on special purpose fastening end-effectors and position controlled robots. Research in the area of force control of robotic hands and force based snap fitting is also identified.

8.2.1 *Passive Compliance*

Some position-controlled robots are deployed in assembly operations through the use of chamfers and passive compliant devices termed remote center of compliance (RCC) devices. The chamfers enable the robot to achieve the assembly tolerances by providing a larger target for preliminary insertion. RCC devices, attached to a robot arm tool flange, passively accommodate forces and torques to provide small adjustments to overcome nominal insertion pose errors. Figure 8.2 shows a peg-in-hole insertion process with a commercially available RCC device. This particular device has a pneumatic locking mechanism to disable compliant operation. While these fixed stiffness RCC devices have long been commercially available, new developments in this area are leading to RCC devices with expanded capabilities. Park et al.[12] developed a variable, passive-compliant RCC to better accommodate multiple assembly tasks. The device incorporates flexible, compliant materials into a mechanical transition structure that can theoretically achieve an exhaustive range of stiffness coefficients. The prototype reported had four stiffness settings at zero, 175N/mm, 350 N/mm, and 525N/mm with internal sensing to account for position variability internal to the device. Figure 8.3 shows the device design and the as-built prototype RCC device. To support the development of RCC devices, Vaschieri et al.[13] developed a modeling environment to support virtual prototyping of flexure-based RCC devices, where the properties of a set of flexural hinges can be simulated to achieve a maximum lateral and angular misalignment to support a given set of assembly tasks. In addition to RCC devices, some collaborative robot designs incorporate series elastic actuators to provide a level of compliance in order to reduce impact forces with humans during collaborative operations. The compliance in these arms can substitute the compliance provided by an RCC device provided that the positioning accuracy required to fall within a chamfer can be achieved. Similarly, active control methods such as impedance or admittance control can be tuned to provide a spring like compliance.

8.2.2 *Active Force Control*

Active force control strategies are also applied in assembly operations. For instance, Polverini et al.[14] apply admittance-based control to actively accomplish a peg-in-hole insertion task using a trajectory generator and constraint-based opti-

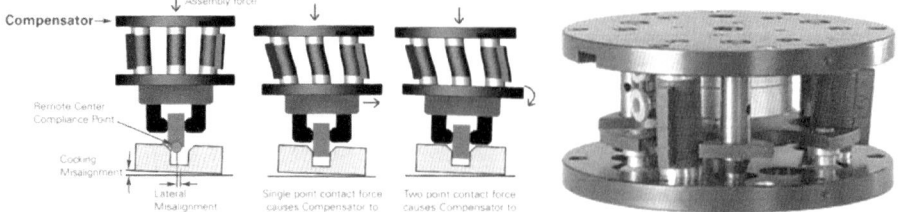

[ATI Industrial Automation- https://www.ati-ia.com/products/compliance/Compensator_product_desc.aspx]

Fig. 8.2. Commercially available remote center of compliance device. Reprinted with permission of ATI Industrial Automation.

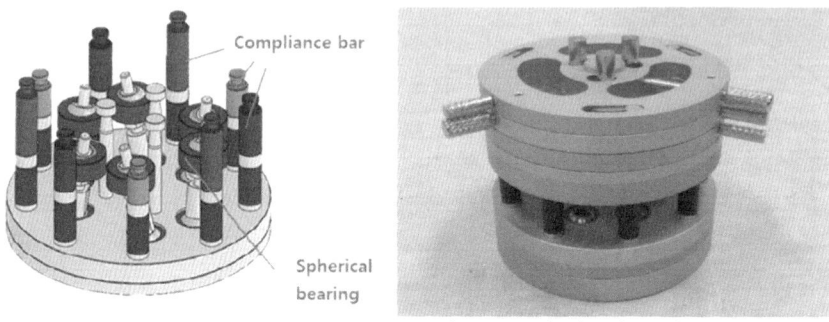

[Korea Institute of Machinery & Materials, Daejeon, Korea]

Fig. 8.3. Prototype passive remote center of compliance device. Reprinted with permission of the author.[12]

mization. The method is verified using a dual-arm robot manipulator where the peg is manipulated by one arm while the other supports the part with the receiving hole. The task is implemented utilizing velocity control along the peg axis (Z) and admittance control in the X and Y directions. Experimental results demonstrate insertion speeds comparable to human manual execution and in the presence of geometric uncertainty at 75 mm/s.

Park et al.[15] developed a peg-in-hole insertion strategy using a dual-armed robot and an admittance control scheme. The dual-arm robot consisted of two 8-DOF (degree of freedom) manipulators. The hole and the peg were attached to the right and left arms. The clearance between the hole and peg was 0.1 mm. To implement the peg-in-hole task with the compliant system, the authors used their previously developed intuitive peg-in-hole strategy.[16] The strategy generated a spiral-screw motion, and helped the peg move to the position for final insertion via active compliance.

Stolt et al.[17] developed a method for estimating the external forces acting on the end-effector of a robot based on control errors for the low-level joint-control loops. By disabling the integral action in the joint controllers, the joints behaved as virtual springs, and the deviation of each joint angle resulted in joint torques from which to calculate external force at the assembly contact point. To minimize joint errors due to friction and gravity, a small integral action was applied, which allowed for the detection of force transients and elimination of position errors. The method was experimentally verified in a small-part assembly task where a small plate is assembled on its major surface based on zeroing Cartesian forces at a single point of contact, allowing for the final seating process.

Tang et al.[18] presented an autonomous alignment method by force/torque measurement before the insertion phase to deal with large pose misalignment. Using a three-point contact model and an estimate of the peg-and-hole alignment via force and geometric analysis, the robot autonomously corrected misalignment before applying traditional assembly methods for insertion of a peg-in-hole assembly with 0.030 mm clearance. The test setup that utilized a six-axis force torque sensor is shown in Fig.8.4.

Abdullah et al.[19] presented a method for assembly using a force/torque sensor and a vision system. The vision system was used to guide the peg at an angle into the hole with a precision that only required the circumferences of both to overlap, which is useful if a vision system uncertainty is larger than a chamfer. Using forces and torques, the peg was then centered on the hole as the peg and hole axis converge for final insertion. Kim et al.[20] develop a hole-detection algorithm using force-based shape recognition, and validate with square peg-in-hole experiments using a 6-axis force-torque sensor and a robot under admittance control. Unlike circular peg-in-hole, an additional stage of the phase alignment was required to actively correct the angular error around the z axis. Jasim et al.[21] proposed a Gaussian-mixture model for the contact-state modeling in force-based assembly of flexible rubber parts. The method is evaluated using a peg-in-hole assembly processes for two rubber objects: an elastic peg of 30 durometer Shore A scale and an elastic peg of 6 Shore A.

Van Wyk et al.[22] utilized a four-fingered robotic hand with 16 independently controlled joints with rotary encoders and three 6-axis force-torque transducers at the fingertips with impedance control of the object via finger Cartesian force control (Fig. 8.5). The sensing suite includes a touch-based 6-DoF object pose estimation algorithm; 3-D fingertip force; 3-D fingertip normal force; and 3-D fingertip center of pressure. The peg is grasped and positioned angularly along its axis with respect to the hole axis to increase the likelihood of peg-and-hole edge collision as the

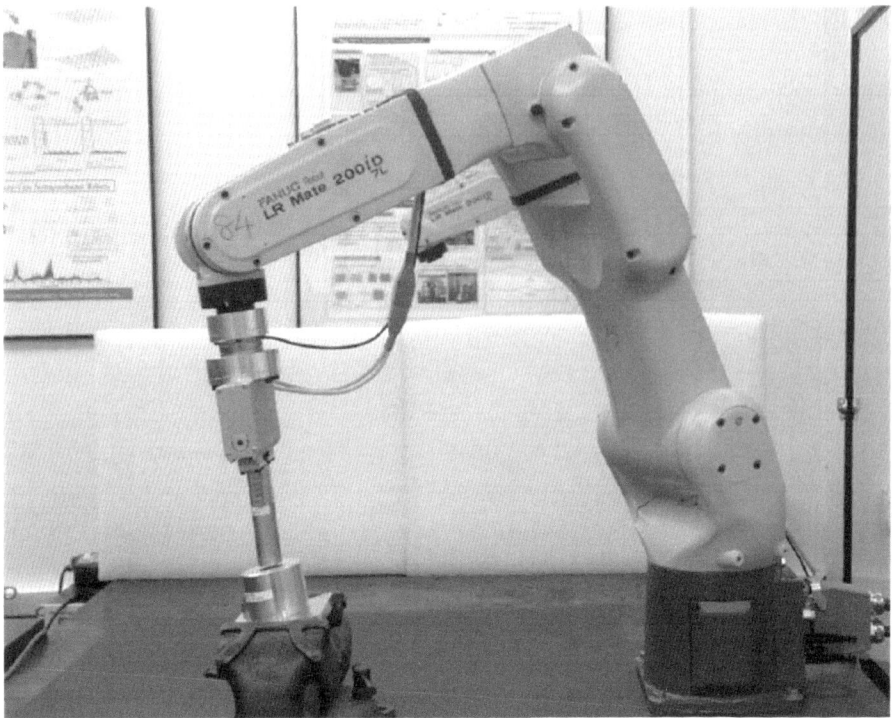

[Tang et al., University of California, Berkeley]

Fig. 8.4. Peg-Hole-Insertion Testbed with a FANUC LRMate-200iD/7L and a 6-axis force/torque sensor. The diameters of peg and hole are 25.370 mm and 25.400 mm respectively, with 0.030 mm clearance (H7h7 tolerance). Reprinted with permission of the author.[18]

position controlled robot translates the peg into the hole along the Z axis. The manipulation strategy monitors the resultant contact force and peg pose as position adjustments are made to zero the forces and the angular position of the peg relative to the insertion plane normal, similar to the method in Abdullah et al.[19]

Zheng et al.[23] developed a method using vision guidance and a robot incorporating a series of elastic actuators with low positioning accuracy to perform peg-and-hole assembly operations. A peg-in-hole assembly strategy based on vision/force guidance and dual-arm coordination is proposed. Vision guidance using a corner-detection algorithm is applied for rough adjustment and ensures a suitable dual-arm operating space. To realize precision placement, position and orientation adjustments are performed using a six-axis force/torque sensor. Master/slave operation is used between the two arms. The strategy can be applied to different shaped peg-in-hole assemblies: round, triangle, and square with experimental success at 0.5 mm clearances.

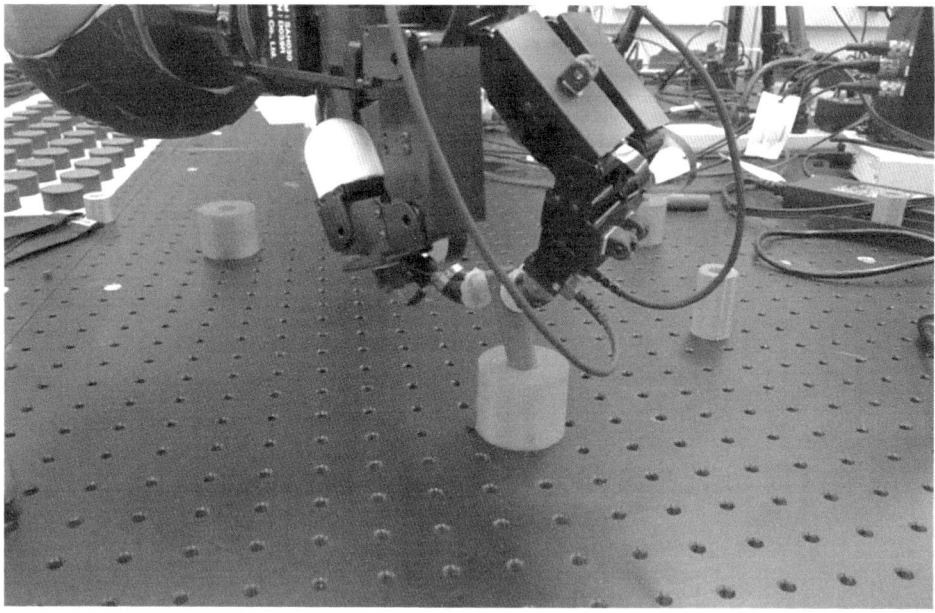

Fig. 8.5. Allegro hand retrofitted with 6-axis force/torque sensors performs a peg-in-hole insertion.

Koveos et al.[24] developed a fast robot deployment strategy for snap assembly operation using a wavelet-based pattern-recognition method to detect successful assembly. The method was characterized by multi-stiffness levels during insertion and by a lack of visual deformation of the internal locking mechanism associated with the single direction the snap fit operation. Experimental results produced successful snap fits for two assembly operations: seat-belt connect and electrical-plug insert. Results further demonstrated robustness of the proposed method to different robot velocities.

Ortega-Aranda et al.[25] realize the uncertainties of force-based assembly processes result in shortfalls when developing exact models. They observe successful full cycles during the assembly of an automotive-starter (Fig. 8.6), which was programmed using a point-based method via lead-through programming. However, as the repetitive tasks progressed over time, misalignment occurred with noticeable increases in assembly forces, which caused the assembly process to eventually fail. The authors propose to overcome these uncertainties using a Neural Network Classifier based on supervised learning. The demonstrated approach uses a dual-arm robot where each arm is equipped with a three-fingered gripper and a force/torque sensing capability. Several force patterns are generated and classified during the stages of the starter assembly. Three robot scenarios were considered for operations: moving both arms simultaneously, moving the right arm while keeping the left arm static, and vice versa. These contact states were generated using the robot and used to train an Artificial Neural Network (ANN). Results showed that manipulative forces could be recognized by the Neural Network Controller (NNC) so that a valid motion command can be issued to the robot arm favoring the assembly task.

This section has identified active force control methods that incorporate six axis force/torque sensors mounted at the tool interface plate of a robot arm in addition to a robotic hand force sensing implementation. Newer robot arm designs incorporate this force sensing internal to the robot, typically at the output of each joint. These measured forces can be used to resolve forces acting on any part of the robot arm to identify and minimize collision forces in collaborative applications. In addition, this joint level force sensing can be resolved to Cartesian force at the tool center point to support assembly operations similar to the assembly operations as described above. Examples of these robots include the KUKA LBR iiwa and the Franka Emika Panda robots. These new collaborative, force sensing robot designs have been shown by their manufacturers to accomplish active force control assembly operations as they make their way into the robotics industry.

8.3   Robot Calibration and Registration

Supporting small and medium-sized manufacturers requires the frequent re-tasking of robots within a facility. In an assembly environment, it is critical that this step include expedient methods to ensure that the robot maintains an expected Cartesian-positioning calibration.[26] Overall, there exist two primary categories for positioning calibration. First, intrinsic Cartesian calibration, also called "mastering", concerns the optimization of a robot's kinematic parameters such that its Cartesian-positioning accuracy is maximized. In contrast, extrinsic Cartesian calibration, also called "registration", concerns calculating the transformation or mapping from the robot's base coordinate system to an extrinsic coordinate system. The significance of methods for both intrinsic and extrinsic Cartesian calibration are subsequently discussed.

8.3.1   *Intrinsic Cartesian Calibration/Mastering*

The advancement of simulation-assisted robot programming, automation of high-tolerance assembly operations, and optimization of task-level performance can all benefit from improving the positioning accuracy of robots.[27–30] Despite quality

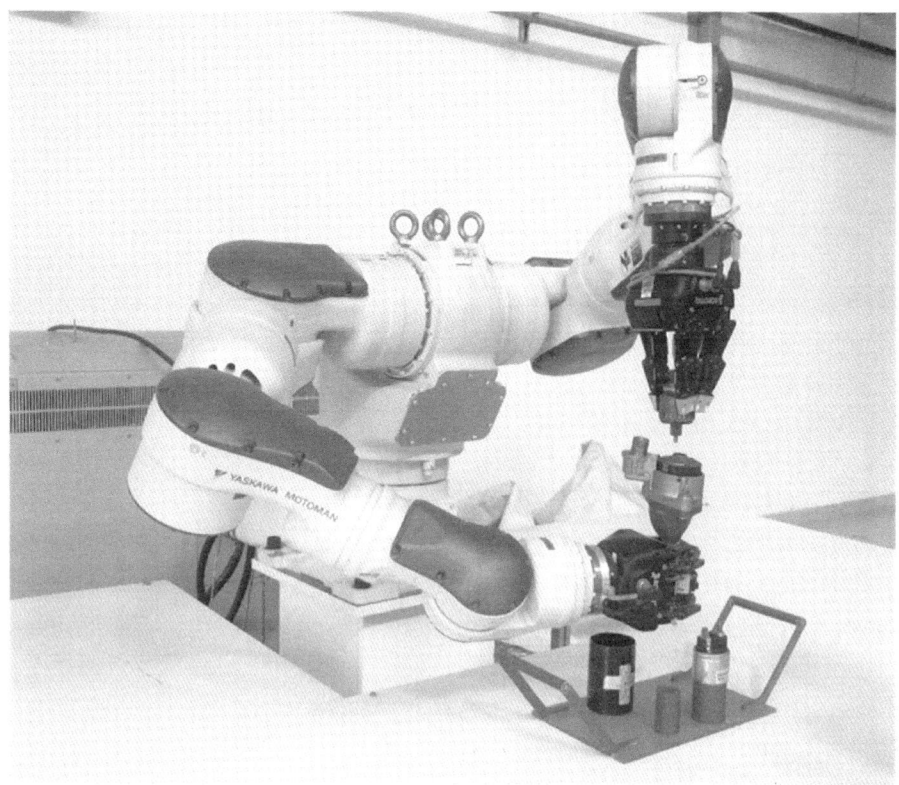

[Ortega et al., Center for Engineering and Industrial Development, CIDESI]

Fig. 8.6. Assembly of an automotive starter using a dual-arm robot. Reprinted with permission of the author.[25]

engineering, machining, and assembly, physical robots typically exhibit Cartesian positioning errors of several millimeters as reported in the following. The majority of this error can be removed and maintained with the periodic optimization of the robot's kinematic parameters, more specifically, its joint "zero-offsets". Fortunately, there exist many strategies for mastering robots to gain an order of magnitude improvement in the robot's Cartesian-positioning accuracy.

Many conventional robot mastering approaches leverage expensive laser trackers that serve as extremely high-fidelity, ground-truth, positioning systems. For example, Mustafa et al.[31] used the product-of-exponential (POE) formula and data collected by a laser tracker to reduce the average robot positioning error from 5.71 mm to 0.29 mm. Tao and Yang[32] extended this approach by coupling both POE modeling (for kinematic errors) and a neural network (for non-kinematic errors), reducing average positioning errors from over 1 mm to 0.34 mm.

Jiang et al.[33] sequentially applied an Extended Kalman Filter and particle algorithm to optimize all Denavit-Hartenberg (D-H) parameters of the robot from data collected by a laser tracker. The average robot positioning error was reduced to 0.26 mm from 3.14 mm.

More affordable sensor systems have also been used as ground truth systems for mastering robots that include laser pointers and position sensitive devices, or theodolites. Chen et al.[34] manually guided a robot along a laser line that centers on a pin hole at the robot end-effector and calculated zero-offset parameters such that the end-effector distances to the line are minimized. Robot positioning errors were reduced to 0.572 mm from over 3 cm. In several works,[35–38] leveraged a position-sensitive-detector (PSD) and laser pointer to automate the process of calculating zero-offset parameters through numerical optimization. The process involves aiming the laser lines loaded by the robot towards the center of the PSD surface from various robot positions and orientations. The intersections of each pair of laser lines converge to the same point after compensating the joint offsets. Some results showed reduction in positioning errors from over 3 cm to within 0.898 mm.

8.3.2 *Extrinsic Cartesian Calibration/Registration*

Rapid and persistent re-tasking of robots in high-mixture environments requires flexibility of robot configurations. In particular, a robot system may not be the most useful when fixed to a single station. Instead, freely repositioning robots throughout a variety of stations as needed could offer greater adaptability to ever-changing tasks. However, repositioning a robot immediately nullifies any lead-through programs or calibration to an extrinsic coordinate system (e.g., a workcell coordinate system) due to their dependency on the position of the robot's base. To overcome this issue, methods exist to easily perform robot registration, thereby providing direct measurement of the location of the robot's base coordinate system, re-establishing validity of past robot programs and extrinsic coordinate system transforms.

Several commercial, industrial robots include a multi-point registration process (e.g., Refs. 39,40) that is used to register the robot to an extrinsic coordinate system. Such implementations are both simple and effective, but offer relatively low accuracy considering the number of data points used for registration.[41] This strategy has also been adopted in robotic surgery where touch points are affixed to an object and manually probed for registration.[42,43]

Methods for improving the quality of registration have also been investigated.[44] Results indicated that the error in coordinate system mapping could be reduced through three primary mechanisms: 1) acquiring more position data points, 2) increasing the spacing among data points, and 3) applying machine learning algorithms like clustering or simulated annealing to refine the registration mapping. These mechanisms can significantly reduce the average and variance of registration error as well as attenuate the spatial correlation of registration error. Furthermore, an inverse correlation was established between the size of the registration error and the likelihood of successfully completing a one-shot peg-in-hole operation. This proved that quality registrations can have a positive effect on task-level assembly performance.

8.4 Programming Methods

SME's require programming techniques that are easier, faster, and more adaptable than ever before. High-level software engineers with a broad range of experience are otherwise required for any programming task using industrial robotic arms. Recent advancements in programming are allowing less experienced workers to learn, adapt, and apply robot programs with little understanding of software engineering.

Biggs and MacDonald[45] presented a survey of the current robot programming systems both manual and automatic. They offered a basic understanding of some of the programming methods available and examples of each. More detailed examples of recent technological advancements are provided below.

8.4.1 *Lead-through-programming*

Lead-through programming is the most common method used to program a robot. Using this method, an operator tele-operates the arm using a teach pendant to application-specific locations where joint positions or Cartesian pose (position and orientation) are recorded. This "teach mode" consists of a step-by-step approach that records multiple poses to establish the coarse points of a motion trajectory. A similar type of programming known as "kinesthetic teaching" uses the same method as previously mentioned with one exception: the operator making physical contact pulls the robot arm through the task motions. This method is more intuitive and faster than the teach-pendant, but requires direct contact with the robot arm.

In the 1999 patent for lead-through programming[46] described an invention where the operator could program a robot by attaching an end-effector model to the working end of the robot, and allow the operator to manipulate the working model to move the arm along a desired path.

Tang et al.[47] used one of the most common assembly based tasks, peg-in-hole, as a test for a kinesthetic teaching method involving the use of a "wrench" tool on the end-effector of a robot arm that is being physically guided by a human operator over many trials. They used a Dynamic Time Warping (DTW) algorithm to normalize the differences in the human data trials (Fig. 8.7). That algorithm factored out the difference in the time it takes for the human to do the task and then determined the optimal path.

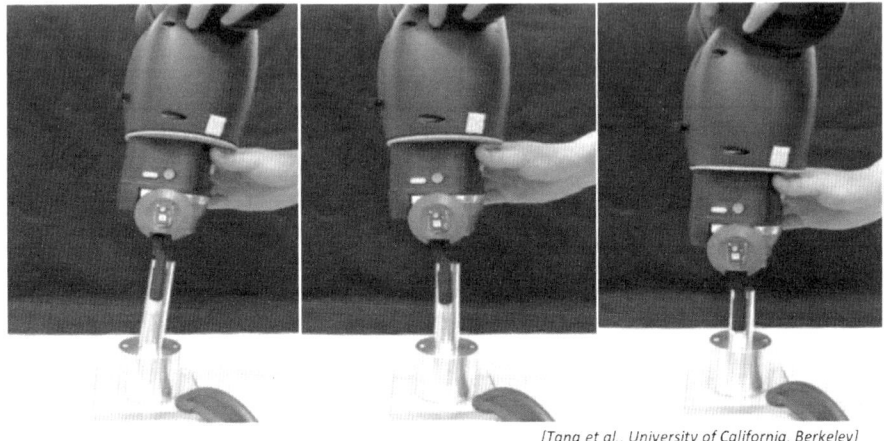

[Tang et al., University of California, Berkeley]

Fig. 8.7. Experimental setup of lead through programming for a peg-in-hole operation. Reprinted with permission of the author.[47]

Lee and Ott[48] present a method that combines programming with kinesthetic teaching. Similar to a "master-slave" approach, operators wore sensors on their head and/or extremities and moved their entire body in a desired path. The robot attempted to mimic the motions of the human by following the motion of the sensors. Afterwards, the operator corrected the robot's motions by using kinesthetic teaching to physically guide the robot through the desired motions.

8.4.2 *Software Engineering*

Another avenue for programming robots includes advancements made in software engineering. Recently, programming interfaces have been streamlined to help bridge the gap between experienced engineers and the average robot operator. For instance, visual block-based programming allows end-users to program robots without writing lines of code through a simple drag-and-drop experience.

Thomas et al.[49] recognized that text-based programming for multiple domains required specific domain experts, rendering programming intractable for others. More often than not, a factory worker lacks the expertise to program a robot for assembly operations and presented a new domain specific language (DSL), LightRocks, that allowed the average worker to use a visual interface to program the robot motions for a specific task. Moreover, they provided a framework through which the expert or robot could record a group of programmed commands as "skills" for rapid reuse when programming.

Hart et al.[50] recognized that LabVIEW, SCADE System, and ControlShell are all robot-focused Integrated Development Environments (IDE's) that served more general engineering needs. They offered more specific add-ons to serve the robotics community; however, they were not suited for high-level, application programming. They developed Robot Task Commander (RTC) as a tool to fill the niche that was not met by the previously mentioned systems. RTC was created by National Aeronautics and Space Administration (NASA) - Johnson Space Center in conjunction with General Motors. It used a Visual Programming Language (VPL) to allow less experienced developers to program by assembling "process nodes". Process nodes are blocks of code previously created by an expert-level programmer that can be dragged, dropped, and connected on a visual interface. Custom process nodes can also be created on-the-fly using the text editor if the developer is a more advanced user.

Another issue with programming robots is the need to communicate between multiple components using multiple languages. There have been many programs that offer a common solution to this problem, typically engineered as a middleware (software used to communicate between devices). With this software, the user does not have to intricately understand each of the devices they are working with in order to program, and can directly interface with the other devices in the system. Mohamed et al.[51] provided a survey of middleware products, and discusses the use, importance, and general feedback of existing middleware frameworks.

A prevalent middleware framework is the robot operating system (ROS) described in detail by Quigley et al.[52] ROS takes in multiple languages from different domains and translates the different syntax of code into a single usable language. It then translates this language back to the necessary language of each domain, thereby creating a bridge between different devices that normally do not communicate with one another. ROS communicates by managing code into software modules or "nodes" that publish messages such that subscribing nodes can retrieve the information when necessary. ROS was made to be an open-source and free product to encourage user improvements and overall usability.

This widely accepted framework has found strong use in industrial based robotics and robotic, assembly-based tasks through the ROS Industrial Project,[53] an open-source project that extends the advanced capabilities of ROS software to manufacturing. The ROS Industrial architecture is shown in Fig. 8.8. One activity within this project was the development of common messages containing the necessary parameters for setting impedance and force control parameters for robots. That project also defined an interface that allows a user to 1) set the necessary parameters for Cartesian impedance/force control and 2) interactively switch between control modes. These tools make developing force controlled applications more intuitive and independent to the robot's programming environment.

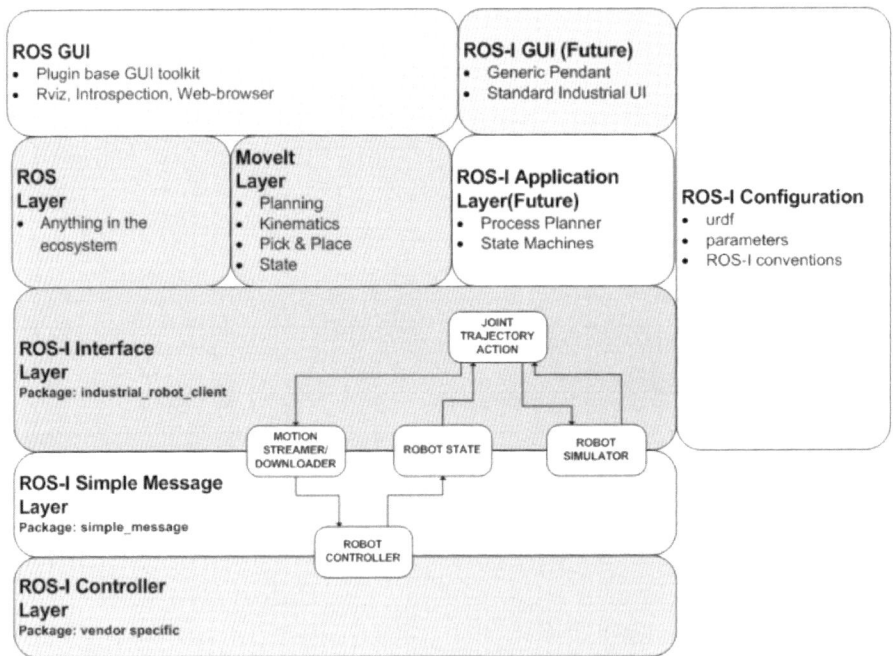

ROS-Industrial High Level Architecture - Rev 0.02.vsd

Fig. 8.8. ROS Industrial Architecture. Reprinted with permission of ROS Industrial.[53]

Wahrburg et al.[54] proposed a Robotic Assembly Skill (RAS) modeling framework. They describe an assembly skill as a primitive that encapsulates the capabilities to coordinate, control, and supervise an elementary robot task. To gain re-usability of a primitive in similar robot tasks, the primitives were represented as generic templates that were parameterized for each situation with data from an assembly specification. The authors represented skills in two ways, namely as a trajectory describing compliant motions in pose-wrench space and as a finite state machine. This approach comes with the potential to simplify robot programming and to improve robustness in robotic assembly due to inherent quality checking. The approach was implemented on an ABB YuMi robot performing the assembly of a programmable logic controller (PLC) input-output module as shown in Fig. 8.9.

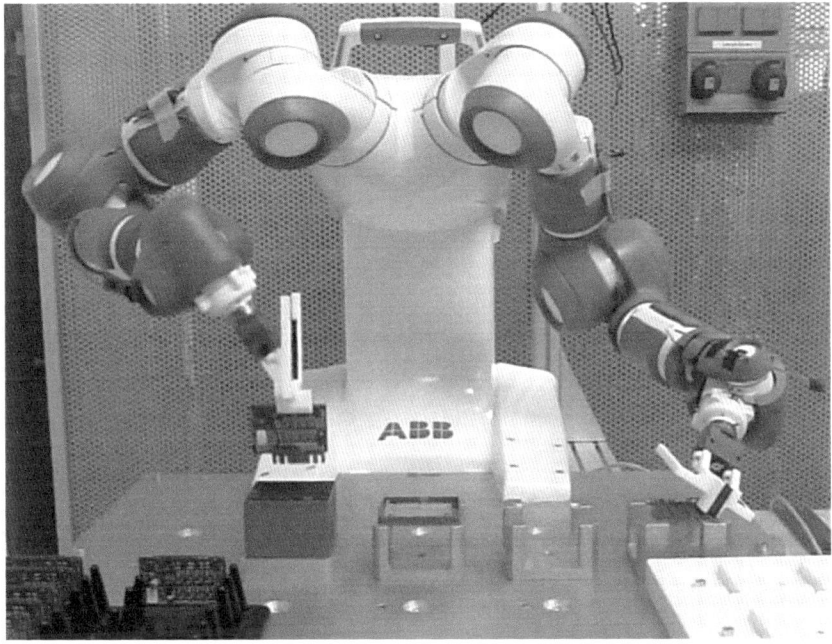

[Wahrburg et al., ABB Corporate Research Center, Germany]

Fig. 8.9. ABB YuMi, a dual-arm 7DOF manipulator, assembling a PLC I/O module employing the proposed RAS framework. Reprinted with permission of the author.[54]

8.5 Application of Artificial Intelligence

Within the last decade, significant advances have been made in artificial intelligence (AI) and its application towards real-world problems. Within the context of manufacturing and high-mixture environments, robots require two capabilities: rapid acquisition of new task-level sensorimotor policies and adaptation of existing skills to a variety of environmental and task conditions. Consequently, the emergence of a new paradigm for programming robots involves the automatic reconstruction of task-level solutions through the application of various machine-learning methods on task-specific datasets. This strategy is in stark contrast to the historical and ever-popular approach which involves hand-engineering software solutions for specific problems, a path that is often laborious, costly, and intractable depending on the difficulty of the task. Instead, modern algorithmic advances in supervised learning, imitation learning, and reinforcement learning have enabled efficient and robust, sensorimotor, skill acquisition in pick-and-place and insertion operations. The advancement in learning has also been facilitated through the generation and consumption of relevant datasets. Currently, a variety of data-generation mechanisms have been researched and developed for AI systems, allowing them to reconstruct their behavior from these experiences (data). These data-generation strategies include the use of simulation environments that mimic the real world, demonstrations from expert systems (humans, optimal control), and the self-exploration of physical systems. The following content reports some of the latest advances in the development of manufacturing-relevant, AI-powered robotic systems.

Only recently have attempts to train deep visuomotor neural networks on complex problem domains been successful. Levine et al.[55] used a model-based reinforcement-learning approach to train a deep visuomotor, neural network, end-to-end, that maps red-green-blue (RGB) camera inputs and robot proprioception to motor torques for solving a variety of manipulation tasks with a physical robot system. This research proved the generality of the learning approach and the ability to obtain high-performing neural network policies on a complex problem domain in the physical world with only raw sensory inputs.

Zhang et al.[56] streamlined the data-generation process of expert solutions for robot-object manipulation tasks and applied imitation learning to obtain a neural network that also solves the manipulation tasks. Specifically, the authors developed a teleoperated interface to a physical robot using a commercial, virtual reality headset and hand controllers. This interface allowed a human operator to both see from the robot's perspective as well as directly control its end-effector positions and gripper state. With this interface, a human could directly control a physical robot system in a more natural way to quickly solve a variety of manipulation tasks. Data generated during these trials were recorded for use in imitation learning. The imitation learning scheme leveraged supervised learning with a multi-priority cost function to train a deep convolutional neural network with image color and depth, end-effector positions as inputs, end-effector control velocities, and gripper state as outputs. With typically less than 200 human demonstrations, the robot was capable of completing a variety of manipulation tasks initialized with random object placement and achieving success rates above 90%. This work revealed that even a relatively small amount of training data could result in the learning of high-performing control policies.

Levine et al.[57] also demonstrated large-scale data collection with physical robots to automatically learn hand-eye coordination and grasping policies for cluttered bin picking. A series of robots pooled their experiences over two months to generate a database of over 800,000 grasp attempts. This data was leveraged to learn a grasp predictor and visuomotor policy for enabling automated pick-and-place operations in clutter. These policies were applied across all robot arms, grippers, and cameras, which intrinsically varied from manufacturing effects and mounting locations. Pick-and-place success rates of cluttered objects exceeded 80%, significantly outperforming three other documented strategies for cluttered bin picking.

Mahler et al.[58] investigated the possibility of learning grasp-planning skills completely from simulation, and transferring them to a real robot system. The simulation process generated a labeled dataset with over 6 million entries of point clouds, grasps, and the analytical grasp quality metric as the target label from thousands of 3-D objects placed in random poses on a table. A deep convolutional neural network used supervised training to predict 1) the likelihood of a successful grasp given a depth image and 2) a candidate pose of the gripper relative to its depth sensor. Results yielded a grasp-planning engine that is three times faster than a more conventional approach, while producing successful grasps with over 90 % success rates on adversarial, novel, rigid, and flexible objects. This research demonstrated a zero-shot transfer of simulation trained models to their physical counterparts with significant reduction in computational requirements.

Zhu et al.[59] demonstrated that the combination of imitation learning and reinforcement learning can enable the training of deep visuomotor networks to solve multi-stage manipulation tasks. Their pipeline started with the acquisition of human-demonstration data for solving the manipulation tasks. They then performed a multitude of trials in simulation and applied a hybrid reward function that encourages the search for high-performing policies near the demonstrated policies with reinforcement learning. Six manipulation tasks were robustly solved in simulation, and a zero-shot transfer to a real hardware system was fairly successful for picking and stacking tasks.

8.6 Conclusion

New robotic arms and end-effectors continue to emerge with advanced force sensing and compliance characteristics. In addition, improved calibration methods, artificial intelligence techniques, simplified programming interfaces, and ease of reconfiguration are all contributing to new ways of tackling the small parts assembly field. These advances as introduced in this chapter have the potential to accelerate the use of robotics for assembly, an untapped and fast growing robotics application area in all manufacturing sectors and show great promise in supporting small and medium sized manufacturing operations.

In parallel to these advancements in the field of assembly robotics, human/robot, collaborative, assembly application are beginning to emerge from research and development environments into real world applications. This transition is augmented by the recently released ISO/TS 15066:2016 Robots and robotic devices - Collaborative robots,[60–62] formal guidance to support development of safe collaborative robot applications. Villani et al.[63] reports on several examples of human-robot collaborative applications in the area of robotic assembly.

The development of community driven metrics and test methods for benchmarking the performance of robotic assembly systems as well as robotic assembly competitions are helping advance the use of new robotic technologies for assembly applications. Standardized performance testing has materialized as a necessary tool within the robotics community providing unbiased evaluation methods that assess how well a system performs a particular task. These performance evaluations can be used to assess a systemFLs individual components, as well as its system-level operation. In the case of robotic assembly, these benchmarking tools are being formalized at the elemental level to support the development of robotic hands[4,64] as well as at the robotic assembly application level.[65,66] Such research will eventually lead to a principled way of specifying robot system characteristics and will help manufacturers to determine which robot system components are best suited for their application space, including the small parts assembly space.[67]

References

1. The impact of robots on productivity, employment and jobs. Available at https://ifr.org/ifr-press-releases/news/position-paper (Accessed May 7, 2018).
2. The new hire: How a new generation of robots is transforming manufacturing, https://www.pwc.com/us/en/industrial-products/assets/industrial-robot-trends-in-manufacturing-report.pdf (Accessed May 7, 2018).

3. F. Tobe, Why co-bots will be a huge innovation and growth driver for robotics industry, *IEEE Spectrum* **December** (2015).

4. J. Falco, K. Van Wyk, S. Liu and S. Carpin, Grasping the performance: Facilitating replicable performance measures via benchmarking and standardized methodologies, *IEEE Robotics Automation Magazine* **22**(3), 32–35 (2015).

5. J. A. Fishel and G. E. Loeb, Sensing tactile microvibrations with the BioTac Comparison with human sensitivity. In *2012 4th IEEE RAS & EMBS International Conference on Biomedical Robotics and Biomechatronics (BioRob)*, pp. 1122–1127 (2012).

6. A. Saudabayev and H. A. Varol, Sensors for robotic hands: A survey of state of the art, *IEEE Access* **3**, 1765–1782 (2015).

7. Y. Hashimoto, D. Yatou, T. Yamada and H. Yamamoto, Fundamental study on robotic assembly of modular fixture parts by a low cost 4-finger 12 D.O.F hand. In *2015 IEEE/SICE International Symposium on System Integration (SII)*, pp. 930–935 (2015).

8. L. B. Bridgwater, C. Ihrke, M. A. Diftler, M. E. Abdallah, N. A. Radford, J. Rogers, S. Yayathi, R. S. Askew and D. M. Linn, The robonaut 2 hand-designed to do work with tools. In *2012 IEEE International Conference on Robotics and Automation (ICRA)*, pp. 3425–3430 (2012).

9. J. Marvel and J. Falco, Best practices and performance metrics using force control for robotic assembly, Tech. Rep., National Institute of Standards and Technology (NIST) (2012).

10. H. C. Song, M. C. Kim and J. B. Song, Usb assembly strategy based on visual servoing and impedance control. In *2015 12th International Conference on Ubiquitous Robots and Ambient Intelligence (URAI)*, pp. 114–117 (2015).

11. J. L. Nevins and D. E. Whitney, *Robot Assembly Research and Its Future Applications*. Springer (1979).

12. D. H. Park, H. Kim, C. Park, B. Kim, D. Kim and J. H. Kyung, Variable passive compliance device for the robotic assembly. In *2017 14th International Conference on Ubiquitous Robots and Ambient Intelligence (URAI)*, pp. 753–754 (2017).

13. V. Vaschieri, M. Gadaleta, P. Bilancia, G. Berselli and R. Razzoli, Virtual prototyping of a flexure-based RCC device for automated assembly, *Procedia Manufacturing* **11**, 380–388 (2017).

14. M. P. Polverini, A. M. Zanchettin, S. Castello and P. Rocco, Sensorless and constraint based peg-in-hole task execution with a dual-arm robot. In *2016 IEEE International Conference on Robotics and Automation (ICRA)*, pp. 415–420 (2016).

15. H. Park, P. K. Kim, J. H. Bae, J. H. Park, M. H. Baeg and J. Park, Dual arm peg-in-hole assembly with a programmed compliant system. In *2014 11th International Conference on Ubiquitous Robots and Ambient Intelligence (URAI)*, pp. 431–433 (2014).

16. H. Park, J.-H. Bae, J.-H. Park, M.-H. Baeg and J. Park, Intuitive peg-in-hole assembly strategy with a compliant manipulator. In *IEEE International Conference on Intelligence and Safety for Robotics (ISR 2013)*, pp. 1–5 (2013).

17. A. Stolt, M. Linderoth, A. Robertsson and R. Johansson, Force controlled robotic assembly without a force sensor. In *2012 IEEE International Conference on Robotics and Automation*, pp. 1538–1543 (2012).

18. T. Tang, H. C. Lin, Y. Zhao, W. Chen and M. Tomizuka, Autonomous alignment of peg and hole by force/torque measurement for robotic assembly. In *2016 IEEE International Conference on Automation Science and Engineering (CASE)*, pp. 162–167 (2016).

19. M. W. Abdullah, H. Roth, M. Weyrich and J. Wahrburg, An approach for peg-in-hole assembling using intuitive search algorithm based on human behavior and carried by sensors guided industrial robot, *IFAC-PapersOnLine* **48**(3), 1476–1481 (2015).

20. Y.-L. Kim, H.-C. Song and J.-B. Song, Hole detection algorithm for chamferless square peg-in-hole based on shape recognition using f/t sensor, *International Journal of Precision Engineering and Manufacturing* **15**(3), 425–432 (2014).

21. I. F. Jasim, P. W. Plapper and H. Voos, Contact-state modelling in force-controlled robotic peg-in-hole assembly processes of flexible objects using optimised gaussian mixtures, *Proceedings of the Institution of Mechanical Engineers, Part B: Journal of Engineering Manufacture* **231**(8), 1448–1463 (2017).

22. K. Van Wyk, M. Culleton, J. Falco and K. Kelly, Comparative peg-in-hole testing of a force-based manipulation controlled robotic hand, *IEEE Transactions on Robotics* **34**(2), 542–549 (2018).

23. Y. Zheng, X. Zhang, Y. Chen and Y. Huang, Peg-in-hole assembly based on hybrid vision/force guidance and dual-arm coordination. In *2017 IEEE International Conference on Robotics and Biomimetics (ROBIO)*, pp. 418–423 (2017).

24. Y. Koveos, D. Papageorgiou, S. Doltsinis and Z. Doulgeri, A fast robot deployment strategy for successful snap assembly. In *2016 IEEE International Symposium on Robotics and Intelligent Sensors (IRIS)*, pp. 80–85 (2016).

25. D. Ortega-Aranda, I. Lopez-Juarez, B. Nath-Saha, R. Osorio-Comparan, M. Peña-Cabrera and G. Lefranc, Towards learning contact states during peg-in-hole assembly with a dual-arm robot. In *2017 CHILEAN Conference on Electrical, Electronics Engineering, Information and Communication Technologies (CHILECON)*, pp. 1–6 (2017).

26. J. Marvel, E. Messina, B. Antonishek, K. V. Wyk and L. Fronczek, Tools for robotics in SME workcells: Challenges and approaches for calibration and registration, Tech. Rep., National Institute of Standards and Technology (NIST) (2015).

27. K. N. Kaipa, A. S. Kankanhalli-Nagendra, N. B. Kumbla, S. Shriyam, S. S. Thevendria-Karthic, J. A. Marvel and S. K. Gupta, Addressing perception uncertainty induced failure modes in robotic bin-picking, *Robotics and Computer-Integrated Manufacturing* **42**, 17–38 (2016).

28. K. Van Wyk, M. Culleton, J. Falco and K. Kelly, Comparative peg-in-hole testing of a force-based manipulation controlled robotic hand, *IEEE Transactions on Robotics* **34**(2), 542–549 (2018).

29. J. Mahler, F. T. Pokorny, B. Hou, M. Roderick, M. Laskey, M. Aubry, K. Kohlhoff, T. Kröger, J. Kuffner and K. Goldberg, Dex-net 1.0: A cloud-based network of 3d objects for robust grasp planning using a multi-armed bandit model with correlated rewards. In *2016 IEEE International Conference on Robotics and Automation (ICRA)*, pp. 1957–1964 (2016).

30. S. Liu and S. Carpin, Kinematic noise propagation and grasp quality evaluation. In *2016 IEEE International Conference on Automation Science and Engineering (CASE)*, pp. 1177–1183 (2016).

31. S. Mustafa, P. Tao, G. Yang and I. Chen, A geometrical approach for online error compensation of industrial manipulators. In *2010 IEEE/ASME International Conference on Advanced Inteligent Mechatronics*, pp. 738–743 (2010).

32. P. Tao and G. Yang, Calibration of industrial robots with product-of-exponential (POE) model and adaptive neural networks. In *2015 IEEE International Conference on Robotics and Automation (ICRA)*, pp. 1448–1454 (2015).

33. Z. Jiang, W. Zhou, H. Li, Y. Mo, W. Ni and Q. Huang, A new kind of accurate calibration method for robotic kinematic parameters based on extended kalman and particle filter algorithm, *IEEE Transactions on Industrial Electronics* **65**(4), 3337–3345 (2017).

34. H. Chen, T. Fuhlbrigge, S. Choi, J. Wang and X. Li, Practical industrial robot zero offset calibration. In *2008 IEEE International Conference on Automation Science and Engineering*, (2008).

35. Y. Liu, N. Xi, J. Zhao, E. Nieves-Rivera, y. Jia, B. Gao and J. Lu, Development and sensitivity analysis of a portable calibration system for joint offset of industrial robot. In *2009 IEEE/RSJ International Conference on Intelligent Robots and Systems* (October 2009).

36. Y. Liu, N. Xi, G. Zhang, X. Li, H. Chen, C. Zhang, M. Jeffery and T. Fuhlbrigge, An automated method to calibrate industrial robot joint offset using virtual line-based single-point constraint approach. In *2009 IEEE/RSJ International Conference on Intelligent Robots and Systems* (October 2009).

37. B. Gao, Y. Liu and Y. Shen, Developing an efficient calibration system for joint offset of industrial robots, *Journal of Applied Mathematics*, 1–9 (2014).

38. Y. Liu, D. Shi and J. Ding, An automated method to calibrate industrial robot kinematic parameters using spherical surface constraint approach. In *4th Annual IEEE International Conference on Cyber Technology in Automation, Control and Intelligent* (June 2014).

39. *KUKA System Software 5.6 lr: Operating and Programming Instructions for System Integrators*, KUKA Laboratories GmbH (2012).

40. *Operating Manual: IRC5 with FlexPendant*, ABB (2015).

41. J. A. Marvel and K. Van Wyk, Simplified framework for robot coordinate registration for manufacturing applications. In *2016 IEEE International Symposium on Assembly and Manufacturing (ISAM)*, pp. 56–63 (2016).

42. P. A. Woerdeman, P. W. A. Willems, H. J. Noordmans, C. A. F. Tulleken and J. W. B. van der Sprenkel, Application accuracy in frameless image-guided neurosurgery: A comparison study of three patient-to-image registration methods, *J. Neurosurgery* **106**(6), 1012–1016 (2007).

43. T. Haidegger, T. Xia and P. Kazanides, Accuracy improvement of a neurosurgical robot system. In *Proc. IEEE/RAS-EMBS Int. Conf. Biomed. Rob. Biomechatron,* pp. 836–841 (2008).

44. K. Van Wyk and J. A. Marvel, Strategies for improving and evaluating robot registration performance, *IEEE Transactions on Automation Science and Engineering* **15**(1), 320–328 (2018).

45. G. Biggs and B. MacDonald, A survey of robot programming systems. In *Proceedings of the Australasian Conference on Robotics and Automation*, pp. 1–3 (2003).

46. T. L. Graf, Lead-through robot programming system, (1999), US Patent 5,880,956.

47. T. Tang, H.-C. Lin and M. Tomizuka, A learning-based framework for robot peg-hole-insertion. In *ASME 2015 Dynamic Systems and Control Conference*. pp. V002T27A002–V002T27A002 (2015).

48. D. Lee and C. Ott, Incremental kinesthetic teaching of motion primitives using the motion refinement tube, *Autonomous Robots* **31**(2-3), pp. 115–131 (2011).

49. U. Thomas, G. Hirzinger, B. Rumpe, C. Schulze and A. Wortmann, A new skill based robot programming language using uml/p statecharts. In *2013 IEEE International Conference on Robotics and Automation (ICRA)*, pp. 461–466 (2013).

50. S. Hart, P. Dinh, J. D. Yamokoski, B. Wightman and N. Radford, Robot task commander: A framework and IDE for robot application development. In *2014 IEEE/RSJ International Conference on Intelligent Robots and Systems (IROS 2014)* pp. 1547–1554 (2014).

51. N. Mohamed, J. Al-Jaroodi and I. Jawhar, Middleware for robotics: A survey. In *2008 IEEE Conference on Robotics, Automation and Mechatronics*, pp. 736–742 (2008).

52. M. Quigley, B. Gerkey, K. Conley, J. Faust, T. Foote, J. Leibs, E. Berger, R. Wheeler and A. Ng, ROS: An open-source robot operating system (2009).

53. ROS industrial, https://rosindustrial.org/ (Accessed July 5, 2018).

54. A. Wahrburg, S. Zeiss, B. Matthias, J. Peters and H. Ding, Combined pose-wrench and state machine representation for modeling robotic assembly skills. In *2015 IEEE/RSJ International Conference on Intelligent Robots and Systems (IROS)*, pp. 852–857 (2015).

55. S. Levine, C. Finn, T. Darrell and P. Abbeel, End-to-end training of deep visuomotor policies, *The Journal of Machine Learning Research* **17**(1), 1334–1373 (2016).

56. T. Zhang, Z. McCarthy, O. Jow, D. Lee, K. Goldberg and P. Abbeel, Deep imitation learning for complex manipulation tasks from virtual reality teleoperation, *arXiv preprint arXiv:1710.04615* (2017).

57. S. Levine, P. Pastor, A. Krizhevsky and D. Quillen, Learning hand-eye coordination for robotic grasping with large-scale data collection. In *International Symposium on Experimental Robotics*. Springer, pp. 173–184 (2016).

58. J. Mahler, J. Liang, S. Niyaz, M. Laskey, R. Doan, X. Liu, J. A. Ojea and K. Goldberg, Dex-net 2.0: Deep learning to plan robust grasps with synthetic point clouds and analytic grasp metrics, *arXiv preprint arXiv:1703.09312* (2017).

59. Y. Zhu, Z. Wang, J. Merel, A. Rusu, T. Erez, S. Cabi, S. Tunyasuvunakool, J. Kramár, R. Hadsell, N. de Freitas, and N. Heess. Reinforcement and imitation learning for diverse visuomotor skills, *arXiv preprint arXiv:1802.09564* (2018).

60. *ISO/TS 15066:2016, Robots and Robotic Devices - Collaborative Robots*, ISO, Geneva, Switzerland (2016).

61. B. Matthias and T. Reisinger, Example application of iso/ts 15066 to a collaborative assembly scenario. In *Proceedings of ISR 2016: 47th International Symposium on Robotics*, pp. 1–5 (2016).

62. V. Gopinath and K. Johansen, Risk assessment process for collaborative assembly – A job safety analysis approach, *Procedia CIRP* **44**, 199 – 203 (2016).

63. V. Villani, F. Pini, F. Leali and C. Secchi, Survey on human–robot collaboration in industrial settings: Safety, intuitive interfaces and applications, *Mechatronics* (2018).

64. Performance metrics and benchmarks to advance the state of robotic grasping (Online). Available at https://www.nist.gov/programs-projects/performance-metrics-and-benchmarks-advance-state-robotic-grasping, (Acessed July 5, 2018).

65. J. Falco, J. Marvel, R. Norcross and K. Van Wyk, Benchmarking robot force control capabilities: Experimental results, Tech. Rep., National Institute of Standards and Technology (NIST), 100 Bureau Drive, Gaithersburg, MD 20899 (2016).

66. Performance metrics and benchmarks to advance the state of robotic assembly, (Online). Available at https://www.nist.gov/programs-projects/performance-metrics-and-benchmarks-advance-state-robotic-assembly (Accessed July 5, 2018).

67. S. Shneier, E. Messina, C. Schlenoff, F. Proctor, T. Kramer and J. Falco, Measuring and representing the performance of manufacturing assembly robots, Tech. Rep., National Institute of Standards and Technology (NIST) (2015).

© 2020 World Scientific Publishing Company
https://doi.org/10.1142/9789811222849_0009

Chapter 9

A Smart Companion Robot for Automotive Assembly

Jasprit Singh Gill, Yi Chen, Farbod Akhavan Niaki, Mark Tomaszewski, Weitian Wang, Laine Mears, Pierluigi Pisu, Yunyi Jia, and Venkat Krovi

9.1 Automotive Final Assembly: A New Playground for Human-Robot Collaboration

The global trends towards user-customized products have led to a significant increase in the number of product configurations / variants that ultimately need to be manufactured. Consequently, the manufacturing production systems have evolved to support the realization of high-volume high-mix (i.e. build to order) product portfolios by adoption of advanced automation paradigms. The automotive assembly plants are no exception. As an example, in BMW plants, it is estimated that customer selection of options can create 10^{13} possible unique product combinations for their vehicles. Over the decades, the automotive industry has seen significant incorporation of traditional automation and industrial robots in the low variation part of the manufacturing process such as *body shop* (e.g. to align and weld together various metal parts to create the body-in-white) and *paint shop* (e.g. to allow for high quality consistent painting). Fixed base manipulation robots dominate the deployment landscape working either in exclusive fenced zones or with a limited region for collaboration with humans.

However, automotive final assembly has been one arena that has not witnessed a significant adoption of robotics and automation due to inherent challenges. First, significant portion of the customization occurs in final assembly and hence disproportionally contributes to the variability (compared to the body shop). Human assembly line workers (referred to as associates in this chapter) now need to: (1) Understand the operation to be carried out for a specific vehicle; (2) Pick the appropriate parts; (3) Assemble them on the vehicle using a variety of tools and processes (e.g. bolting, gluing, clipping); and (4) Conduct quality checks on the operation.

This exposes the associates to two major loads: (1) Physical load: avoid repetitive strain injuries from handling (heavy) parts or conducting ergonomically challenging operations (e.g. overhead assembly); and (2) Cognitive load: understand which specific part and assembly operation is required for the next vehicle. Secondly, each vehicle spends only a few 10s of seconds at each assembly station making the assembly operations time sensitive. Thirdly, multiple dynamic elements like moving conveyors, stray carts, and human co-workers walking in and out to collect tools and parts to be assembled, contribute to a lack of structure at the auto-assembly station.

Automation approaches have not been able to provide the flexibility to support the timely high precision assembly of the right combination of parts with this unstructured environment to realize highly customized vehicles, hence, manual assembly remains the mainstay at this stage. While fixed-base/fenced robots may have proven to be too bulky and inflexible, a new class of mobile manipulators has emerged as a potentially viable alternative. These platforms possess greater versatility, increased workspace (due to mobility) and increased dexterity due to extra degrees-of-freedom (DOF). In the Smart Companion Robot (SCR) project, our efforts focus on augmenting this versatile mobile manipulator platform to realize human-robot collaboration both at the information level (*cognitive assist*) and physical level (*physical assist*). This chapter describes the science and technology challenges that exist from the automotive industry needs, identifies the technical requirements and specifications to meet the industry needs and shares some preliminary results observed as the project passes its first quarter of execution.

9.2 Project Overview

The SCR project aims to demonstrate the viability of an intelligent mobile manipulator robotic system to assist and augment human associates in automotive final assembly. Similar to R2D2 from the Star Wars saga, this self-contained SCR needs to exchange information with both the plant build-system and human associates seamlessly with minimal installed infrastructure support. The *physical assist* is provisioned in terms of helping transport medium-heavy parts from subassembly areas to reduce worker fatigue/repetitive injuries.

Our focus for coupling sensor intelligence to the mobile manipulator platform is directed along three tasks: Task 1: Situational awareness for up-to-date monitoring of obstacles and autonomous base navigation for obstacle avoidance; Task 2: autonomous arm motion planning for manipulation in cluttered environments; and

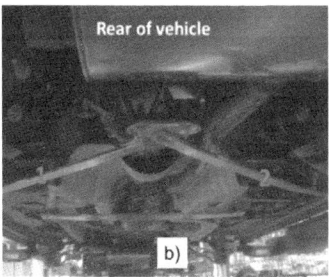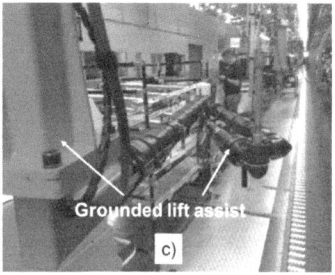

Fig. 9.1. a) Workers assembling the torsion bars under vehicle; b) Torsion bars under vehicle (marked 1, 2); c) Fixed-point/grounded lift assists to support the torque wrench to fasten the bolts.

Task 3: digital-twin/process-simulation for what-if analyses of human-robot collaborative scenarios. The overall build-system and operator orchestrate the process steps using shared and supervisory control.

The rest of the chapter is organized as follows. Section 9.3 discusses the technical approach taken by this project to address this need. Sections 9.4, 9.5 and 9.6 discuss some preliminary findings for the technical tasks identified for this project.

9.2.1 *Initial Use Case: Torsion Bar Overhead Assembly*

The overhead assembly operation of a torsion bar, exemplifies the physical and cognitive challenges in typical, real-life assembly operations, and hence was selected as the initial use case. Torsion bars need to be assembled underneath vehicles with panoramic roof windows to increase the body torsional stiffness and thereby handling of the vehicle. These solid steel bars are heavy and therefore awkward to install, see Fig. 9.1a, b. Currently two to three associates are needed to install these bars: one worker holds the bars in place while another worker aligns the bars and hand-starts threading the bolts. The bolts need to be tightened to exact specifications to be able to withstand the dynamic loading during driving of the vehicles. Therefore, a heavy torque-wrench is used to tighten the bolts. To lighten the load on the associates both from the weight of the wrench and from the jerk as it reaches peak torque, the wrench is mounted on a supporting lift assist Fig. 9.1c.

The goal of the project is to demonstrate self-contained robotic assistance for retrieval, transport, and alignment to support assembly of the torsion-bar (without relying on either hard tooling or alternatively, a second operator to achieve the needed assembly alignment). This use case will address the need for physical assist, with assembly of an unwieldy part (torsion-bar) in an ergonomically challenging setting (neck and shoulder stress due to overhead task performance),

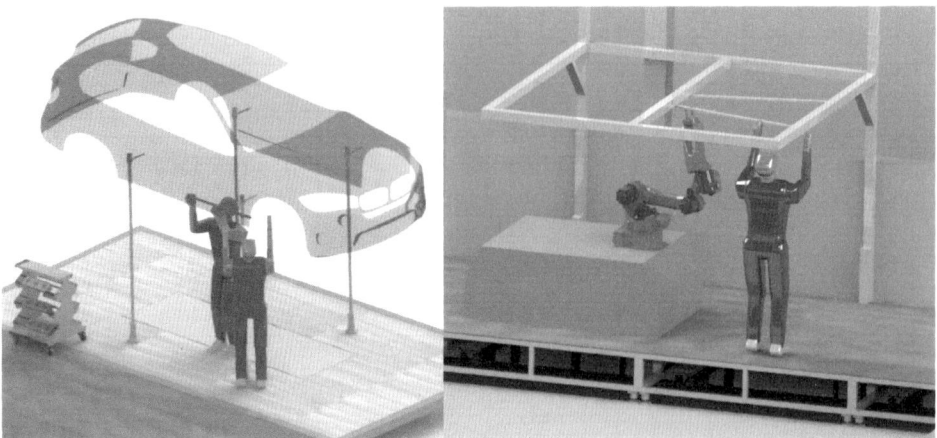

Fig. 9.2. a) Overhead assembly use-case for torsion bar installation; b) demonstration with an overhead fixture.

see Fig. 9.2a. Overhead operations in any assembly setting are particularly prone to creating ergonomic-stress impacting quality in the short term and resulting in workplace injury[a] (shoulder tendonitis, neurovascular compression) in the longer term. The SCR is intended to support the associate with the part/tool handling in this assembly operation as shown in Fig. 9.2b. Benefits to the operations will be three-fold: (1) ergonomic support for the workers, (2) productivity increase by eliminating the need for a second person and (3) flexibility increase by providing a mobile intelligent lift-assist solution. The latter benefit specifically results from eliminating a fixed lift assist which would otherwise constrain the rebalancing of the assembly line to adjust for monthly changes in model mix.

9.3 Implementation Scenario

The sensor enabled intelligence and physical assist capability of the SCR is intended to support automotive assembly workers for retrieving, manipulating, and presenting parts/tools. With the activities requiring Manufacturing Readiness Level (MRL)[b] 3-6, the focus was limited to mobile manipulators available within the commercial-off-the-shelf (COTS) marketplace for industrial applications (large payloads). Implicit in this choice of a COTS system is the incorporation of safety considerations for operation on the assembly line. See Chen et al.[1] for a brief survey of other COTS manipulators considered. Nevertheless, this off-the-shelf

---

[a] Gavriel Salvendy, Handbook of Human Factors and Ergonomics, Wiley, 2012, ISBN: 978-0-470-52838-
[b] https://www.darpa.mil/attachments/DARPATransitionGuideFinal2-26-16.pdf

Fig. 9.3. a) Yaskawa YMR12; b) YMR12 in the CUICAR ARMLAB as an initial instance of the SCR for torsion bar assembly.

solution still needs to be customized and evolved to service the needs of automotive final assembly, as exemplified in the Torsion-Bar Overhead Assembly use-case (Section 9.2.1).

Yaskawa YMR12 (Fig. 9.3(a)) was identified as the initial mobile manipulator platform instantiation of the SCR. YMR12 is comprised of Yaskawa-Motoman MH12 manipulator mounted on the Clearpath Robotics OTTO1500 mobile base. Reach range of 1440 mm, maximum payload of 12kg and a gripper that can have 5kg payload make MH12 a good fit for automotive assembly line. Programming in YMR12 is based on Robot Operating System (ROS). This enables development using various existing open-source components available in the ROS ecosystem. Further, the ROS framework facilitates portability of our research outcomes as well as merging simulation-based testing with other ROS enabled robots.

Using YMR12, an intelligent SCR will be realized that retrieves a torsion-bar from a floor-rack, travels underneath the vehicle, and supports the fastening of the bars by the assembly worker. Figure 9.3(b) demonstrates this with a YMR12 robot in the Automation, Robotics and Mechatronics Laboratory (ARMLAB)[c] at CUICAR. A passive compliance device at the SCR end-effector will allow for minor adjustments to the position of the bar for the associate, who will be responsible for bolting in the part. The process will be repeated for the other torsion-bar before the SCR moves to the next overhead vehicle. During this process, the SCR needs to be aware of its surroundings and will need to safely navigate through obstacles.

A reconfigurable automotive assembly line testbed (Fig. 9.4) is being developed at a 3,400-sq. ft. assembly center/collaboratory (between Clemson, BMW,

---

[c]https://sites.google.com/view/armlab-cuicar/

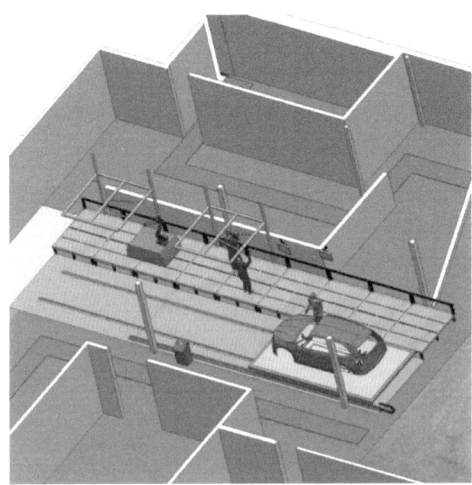

Fig. 9.4. Automotive assembly line test bed in CMI at Clemson University.

and Greenville Technical College). The Clemson University Vehicle Assembly Center (CVAC) is intended to serve as a realistic testbed for rapid exploration and integration of various advanced technologies into the automotive assembly process. A continuous conveyor line is emulated by a moving carrier (equipped with a scissor lift), which rectilinearly transports vehicle and associate among the 3 assembly stations (a.k.a TAKTs[d]). The carrier's scissor lift allows access to all the installation spaces of the vehicle including front, rear, side and overhead. Adjacent to the 3 stations is a static platform (same level as carrier) simulating the fixed plant floor with assorted tools and parts. Floor racks and moving carts serve to emulate the kitting area that provisions assembly parts/kits. A human associate or SCR can move on/off the static platform beside the carrier (for picking up parts or tools) or ride.

In the immediate short term, an assembly fixture serves to physically emulate the torsion bar assembly scenario. The project will be developed, refined, and demonstrated with the overhead structure and then transferred to the reconfigurable automotive assembly line testbed to be demonstrated in the fourth quarter of the project.

9.3.1 *Technical Tasks*

Technical activities for the project are aligned along three fundamental task-directions: two physical-robot oriented tasks (expanding the mobile manipula-

---

[d]https://en.wikipedia.org/wiki/Takt_time

tor intelligent-assist capabilities in two areas within a Robot Operating System-Industrial, i.e. ROS-I, framework) and one digital-twin oriented task (created using the SIEMENS Process Simulate).

- Task 1: Enhanced Perception and Navigation of Mobile Base (i.e. obstacle detection in immediate vicinity); in order to deliver parts to human associates, the mobile base needs to traverse the unstructured assembly shop floor environment. The goal of this task is to create and update the map of the automotive assembly environment while localizing the robot in it, and then generate a trajectory for the mobile base to move from its current configuration (i.e. position and orientation) to a goal configuration while avoiding collision with obstacles. An efficient framework to acquire and represent the map and robot location in unstructured and dynamic environments while navigating through it is a critical challenge.
- Task 2: Enhanced Manipulator Planning/Execution (i.e. dexterous end-effector motions, on-the-fly re-planning); the goal of this task is to generate manipulator trajectories to pick up and deliver the torsion bar. Two major challenges include: localizing the object to be grasped, and planning the manipulator joint trajectories in the presence of static obstacles.
- Task 3: Digital Twin (of the associate, the Smart Companion Robot and the 3-station assembly line together); the goal of this task is to develop and simulate various virtual models (of the plant, the associate, and the Smart Companion) to help improve manufacturing, shorten production time per unit and optimize return-on-tools investment.

The next sections elaborate the current progress of this project with regards to these three tasks described above.

9.4   Perception and Navigation of the Mobile Base

The goal of this task is to create and update the map of the automotive assembly environment as well as the robot location within the map while navigating through it so as to assist the manipulation task. The key component to the on-board perception of the SCR for this is the Simultaneous Localization and Mapping (SLAM) module. Fig. 9.5 visualizes the map of the CUICAR-ARMLAB, generated by the SLAM module of the YMR12, in the ROS rviz[e] tool. The YMR12 is represented by four spheres with the arrow indicating the heading direction. It is crucial to evaluate the existing SLAM implementations for the SCR against industry require-

---

[e]http://wiki.ros.org/rviz

Fig. 9.5. Automotive assembly line test bed in CMI at Clemson University.

ments. This section describes the various parameters against which the SLAM methods need to be evaluated for viability for deployment in an industrial setting.

9.4.1 *Related Work: Perception and Motion Planning Algorithms for Wheeled Mobile Base*

Cadena et al.[2] and the references therein provide an excellent survey of the developments in SLAM over the past three decades. In recent times, a number of reference implementations of state-of-the-art SLAM techniques have also been made publicly available via the ROS community portal[f]. Several implementations have also transitioned to commercial off the shelf products (vacuum robots, drones, warehouse robots, etc.) and are available for purchase and deployment. However, in such cases, they have been specialized and optimized for their specific domains of deployment.

While collectively referred to as SLAM algorithms, they switch between the following operational modes at any given time – *map-building, localization-only, re-localization* and *loop-closure detection. Map-building* is a mode in which the SLAM algorithm estimates the environment state while simultaneously estimating the ego-pose of the robot in that environment. The algorithms enter the *localization-only* mode when they have been provided with a pre-built map of the

---

[f] http://wiki.ros.org/

environment and their primary goal is to estimate just the ego-pose of the robot in it. When the robot is no longer aware of its current state due to some arbitrary event while the pre-built map is available the robot enters the *re-localization mode*. Finally, when building the map, when the robot enters an area that it has visited before, it enters a mode called *loop closure*.

There is a vast variety of SLAM implementations available working with different sensor configurations, with different representations of maps, and each implementation having its own strengths. To enable quantitative comparisons, we examine the extension of instrumentation theory concepts to the SLAM benchmarking problem, and cite the relevant literature where it exists. In particular, we explore the development of metrics – accuracy, consistency, performance, robustness and scalability – across all the above operating modes to facilitate cross-comparison of SLAM algorithms.

9.4.1.1 *Accuracy*

Two types of SLAM accuracy estimations abound in the literature – ego-robot localization and estimation of topology of the environment. Absolute Trajectory Error (ATE), and Relative Pose Error (RPE)[3] are popular quantitative measures for localization accuracy. Quantifying the topological accuracy of the environment poses a much greater challenge due to variability in feature definition, landmark selection and their map representation with different SLAM algorithms. Metric maps afford the possibility of benchmarking against ground truth data;[4] while successfully validated for 2D spaces, the extension to 3D spaces remains a challenge.

9.4.1.2 *Consistency*

Consistency of a SLAM algorithm can be measured with the following parameters – uniformity, stability, and repeatability. Uniformity is defined as the consistency of the error in the estimations over different maps or different areas of the maps. ATE measures of global consistency of the map, while RPE when measured over distance measures local consistency. Stability, the degree to which the system is consistent over time, is usually measured in terms of drift in the accuracy or error over a period of time, over multiple loops on the same map. RPE when measured over time, gives a measure of drift (or stability) of the algorithm. Repeatability is defined as a measure of the consistency of the algorithm every time the robot is subjected to similar initial conditions and provided similar inputs. For thorough measures of uniformity, the robot needs to be subjected to different initial conditions in the map and the measurements compared with each other. Repeatability of the system needs to be measured simply by checking the accuracy, uniformity and stability of the algorithm over multiple runs over similar trajectories and initial conditions. At the time of writing of this publication, the measurements for these metrics for different algorithms are not thorough in the literature.

9.4.1.3 *Performance*

The performance of the SLAM algorithm can be measured with following characteristics – computational resource usage and convergence. The computational resource usage can be defined as the CPU load as well as the memory consumption of the SLAM algorithm as measured in all the above four operating modes. The convergence on the other hand can be defined as the time it takes for the SLAM algorithm to minimize the localization error after a re-localization procedure. The metric for this can be a little challenging as the time required for convergence is a function of the environment that the robot is operating in, the navigation inputs that are provided to the robot to re-explore the environment and the function of the algorithm that it uses to re-localize itself. The relative comparison of the algorithms for above metrics requires running all the algorithms on the same hardware and subjecting them to the same initial conditions, environment, and navigational procedure.

9.4.1.4 *Robustness*

Robustness is defined as the ability of the system to cope with unexpected events / failures during operations. At a broad level, the failure events for SLAM can be classified as hardware-related or algorithmic. Cadena et al.[2] describe that hardware-related failures can be due to sensor or actuator degradation due to malfunction, aging, adverse operating conditions or a high degree of mismatch between the quality of measurements (noise) and the measurement model of the SLAM. Hardware-related failures can also occur due to unavailability of resources for the algorithm. Hence, the metric for robustness against hardware-related failures should measure – a) the effect on accuracy of the SLAM due to degraded sensors; b) the degree to which the algorithm detects the degraded sensor conditions and compensates for it; c) the degree to which it can handle conflicting information from different sensors; d) the degree to which the algorithm allows tuning of the sensor noise statistics in its model; e) the degree to which the algorithm adapts to the available resources (resource aware and resource adaptive). Currently, however,

Fig. 9.6. a) ASTM test workspace for testing navigation capabilities; b) Workspace simulated in Gazebo simulator with ASTM specifications; c) YMR12 in the CUICAR ARMLAB.

metrics for measuring robustness of the algorithms under the hardware failures do not exist and will need to be established.

Algorithmic failures on the other hand are due to the limitations of the SLAM algorithms under test. The main reason for such failures are incorrect data association.[2] The data association is a module in SLAM that matches every measurement to a portion of the states the measurement refers to (e.g. matching of visual feature in a visual SLAM with a specific landmark). There are specific cases related to them. First is handling of outliers in the measurement. Outliers are measurements that are inconsistent with the recent measurements due to sensor noise, adverse environment conditions or simply due to the presence of obstacles. Second is the case of perceptual aliasing, where two or more different locations on the map can appear to be the same to the robot. This may either lead to the kidnapped robot problem (a situation where the robot believes it is at a certain place but in reality, it is somewhere else), or it may lead to situations like wrong loop closures leading to incorrect maps. An effective SLAM algorithm should be fail-safe and failure aware, detecting failures, and able to recover from them. The metrics for measuring the robustness of the algorithms to data associations do not exist and will need to be established.

9.4.1.5 *Scalability*

Scalability, as applicable to SLAM, is the measure of how the algorithm scales up over: a) larger areas; and b) extended periods of time.[2] Most of the SLAM techniques have been demonstrated in either indoor or building scale environments and for short durations of time. However, for many applications (like industrial manufacturing, environmental monitoring or a long distant self-driving vehicle), the robot will have to work for extended times or over larger areas. This can make the size for its map representation grow really large resulting in a huge memory footprint and heavy computational resources. Metrics for measuring scalability of SLAM algorithm do not exist currently and need to be established.

9.4.2 *Ongoing Simulation Results*

The Gazebo simulator was chosen as the simulation environment for the SCR evaluation as it has a mature integration and interworking with the ROS framework. It uses the robot model defined in the standard Unified Robot Description Format (URDF) representation to simulate the kinematics and dynamics of the robot and provides the simulated sensor data from the model in the standard ROS sensor message formats. It also has the plugins available for extracting the ground truths for the pose of the robot and the 2D map of the environment enabling the rapid development of the benchmarking software for SLAM and navigation before moving to the hardware.

For our benchmarking effort, we adopt the ASTM F3244-17 standard[g] (created for evaluating autonomous navigation capabilities of the mobile robots). The standard defines different types of workspaces as well as their dimensions and constraints with respect to the footprint of the robot for the test. In addition, it specifies the test method for navigation, defining the success/failure criteria and methods to quantify (metrics/precision) the degree of the confidence of the result. An ASTM workspace with dual intersection (as specified in ASTM F3244-17 standard), shown in Fig. 9.6(a), was identified for this work. Using Gazebo, a simulated environment was created that meets the specifications of this workspace. Fig. 9.6(b) shows the aerial view of the developed workspace in gazebo juxtaposed against the visualization of the robot's perception using the ROS rviz tool. Rigorous testing is in progress using this environment. HectorSLAM, gmapping, KartoSLAM and Cartographer are the SLAM libraries available in ROS that are being evaluated in this workspace along with the available global and local planners in the ROS Navigation stack. A physical workspace to match the simulated environment is also being constructed to benchmark/validate the corresponding situational awareness and navigation performance with the physical YMR12 (Fig. 9.6(c)).

9.5 Motion Planning for Torsion Bar Manipulation

This task is mainly focused on the motion planning of the torsion bar assembly process; hence, the mobile base of the SCR robot is fixed. The manipulator needs

---

[g]https://www.astm.org/Standards/F3244.htm

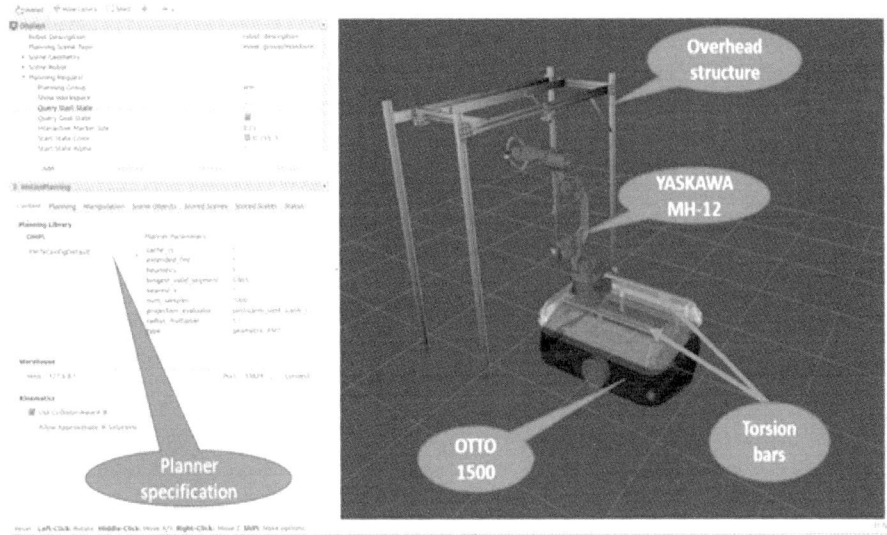

Fig. 9.7. The simulation environment for the SCR1.0a robot.

to pick up the torsion bars placed on the mobile base and align them to the correct assembly pose in sequence. The robot model and the robot kinematics used in this study were used with the ROS framework. The simulated robot model with the MH12 manipulator was acquired and modified to integrate MoveIt! motion planning framework (Fig. 9.7).

In the next three subsections, we first discuss some related works on motion planning algorithms and the MoveIt! motion planning framework. Three motion planning algorithms, probabilistic roadmap (PRM), rapidly exploring random trees (RRT) and faster marching tree (FMT), for torsion bar manipulation are then presented. Finally, the simulation based comparison of the three motion planning algorithms, for the torsion bar manipulation (based on MoveIt! motion planning framework) are presented.

9.5.1 *Related Work: Motion Planning Algorithms for Manipulator Arms*

In the past two decades, the probabilistic sampling-based algorithms have become popular and successful approaches for robotic motion planning problems especially in high-dimensional configuration spaces (e.g. the motion planning of high degree-of-freedom robots)[5] have been presented. Probabilistic sampling-based algorithms are commonly classified into two categories: single-query and multiple-query. Both the single-query and multiple-query path planning algorithms aim to explore the configuration space with a search which is a probabilistic-based sampling scheme while avoiding explicit construction of the configuration space.

The multiple-query approaches typically generate a roadmap, which is a topological graph that can be utilized by multiple initial-state/goal-state pairs. A classic example of this category is the probabilistic roadmap algorithm (PRM).[6] The given start-state/goal-state pairs are given as initial conditions of PRM algorithm, the roadmaps are established by randomly sampling points in configuration space and connecting nearby points if they can be reached from each other. The path from the start-state to the goal-state can then be found in the roadmap. The variants of PRM includes lazy PRM,[7] dynamic PRM[8] and PRM* algorithm.[9]

Instead of constructing a roadmap for the free configuration space, the single-query approaches keep searching for a path that connects the given single initial-state/goal-state pair until finding a solution or reporting an early failure. One classical example of this category is the rapidly exploring random trees algorithm (RRT).[10] This algorithm produces a randomly new state in each step, and then the state advancement is determined by either the collision detector or the distance between the current states to the goal state. The family of algorithms in this category also include the rapidly exploring dense trees algorithm[11] and RRT*.[9] The Fast Marching Trees (FMT),[12] which combines the features of both PRM and RRM, and grows a tree of trajectories like RRT, is designed to reduce the number of obstacle collision-checks and increase the efficiency in high-dimensional environments.

Besides the previous approaches, some other sampling based motion planning algorithms are also notable, such as sample-based roadmap of trees (SRT)[13]), the cross-entropy motion planning algorithm[14] and expensive space trees (EST).[15]

9.5.2 *MoveIt! Motion Planning Framework*

MoveIt! motion planning framework is a state-of-the-art software package for mobile manipulation that integrates motion planning, 3D perception, robot kinematics, control and navigation. The framework is based on the open motion planning library (OMPL)[16] and is integrated into ROS.[17] A ROS node called move_group is the primary node provided by MoveIt! which connects all the individual components and provides the programming interface for users. MoveIt! offers the C++ interface through the move_group_interface node, the Python interface through moveit_commander node, and the graphic user interface (GUI) though ROS Rviz plugin.

Table 9.1. Planners available in OMPL.

	Categories	
	Single-query	Multiple-query
Planners	PRM	RRT
	Lazy PRM	RRT Connect
	PRM*	RRT*
	Lazy PRM	Lower Bound Tree RRT
	SPArse Roadmap Spanner (SPARS)	Sparse Stable RRT
	SPARS2	EST
		FMT

The planners available in MoveIt! include the planners in open motion planning library (OMPL), the stochastic trajectory optimization for motion planning (STOMP),[18] the search-based planning library (SBPL)[19] and the covariant Hamiltonian optimization for motion planning (CHOMP).[20] The OMPL is fully supported by the MoveIt! motion planning framework and the planners available in OMPL are listed in Table 9.1.

9.5.3 *Ongoing Simulation Results and Analysis*

In this section, the simulation of the torsion bar assembly task is described. First the environment setup for the simulation based on ROS and MoveIt! motion planning framework is introduced. Three motion planning algorithms, PRM, RRT, and FMT, are implemented in the simulation. The simulation results and comparison are presented in the subsequent sub-section.

9.5.3.1 *Environment setup*

In order to utilize the MoveIt! motion planning framework for the SCR robot, the robot model was defined in Unified Robot Description Format, which is the standard ROS XML representation for all elements of a robot model including 3D meshes for visualization and collision, kinematics, dynamics, and sensors. MoveIt! was configured in the robot using the MoveIt! setup assistant. Figure 9.7 illustrates the MoveIt! configuration GUI for the SCR robot. Users can have various interactions with the robot model through the GUI, such as constructing the planning scene, specifying the motion planning algorithms and parameters, setting the start-state/goal-state for motion planning though the interaction marker, etc. Besides the

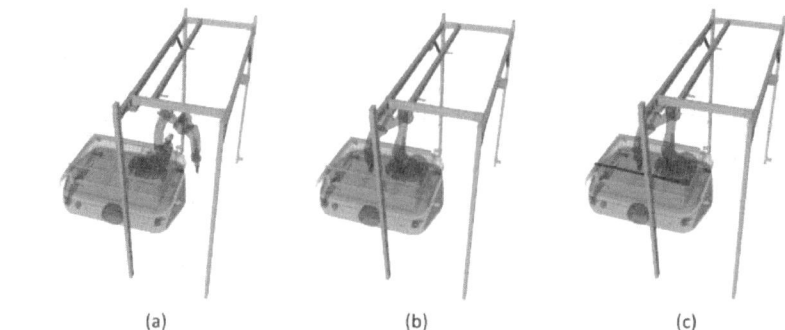

(a)   (b)   (c)

Fig. 9.8. Waypoints for picking up the torsion bar.

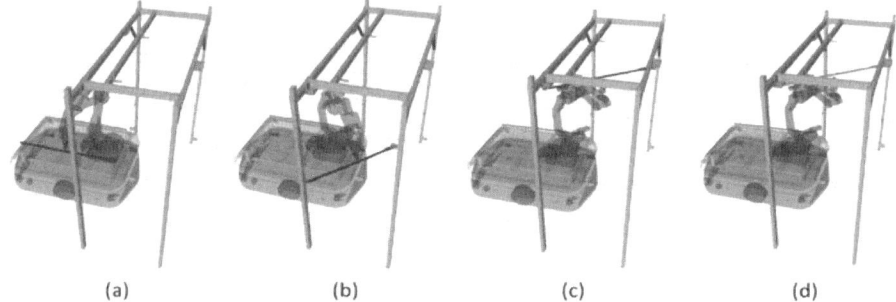

(a)   (b)   (c)   (d)

Fig. 9.9. Waypoints for placing the torsion bar.

SCR robot model, two torsion bars are added as manipulation objects and an overhead structure is imported as simulation scenario. Furthermore, a MoveIt! Python interface is developed to simulate the process of the torsion bar assembly; an independent ROS node is developed to abstract useful information from corresponding ROS topics and calculate the simulation results. Therefore, the simulation is visualized through the rviz package in ROS; the simulation results are printed by an independent ROS node; and the motion planners are specified through the MoveIt! GUI.

9.5.3.2   *Simulation results and analysis*

A completed process of the torsion bar assembly task is illustrated in Fig. 9.8(a) to (c) and Fig. 9.9(a) to (d). At the initial state, two torsion bars are located on the mobile base and the manipulator is located at its home position (Fig. 9.8(a)). The arm approaches the pick position for the left torsion bar (Fig. 9.8(b)) then moves in Z direction for about 3 cm to reach the exact pick position (Fig. 9.8(c)). After

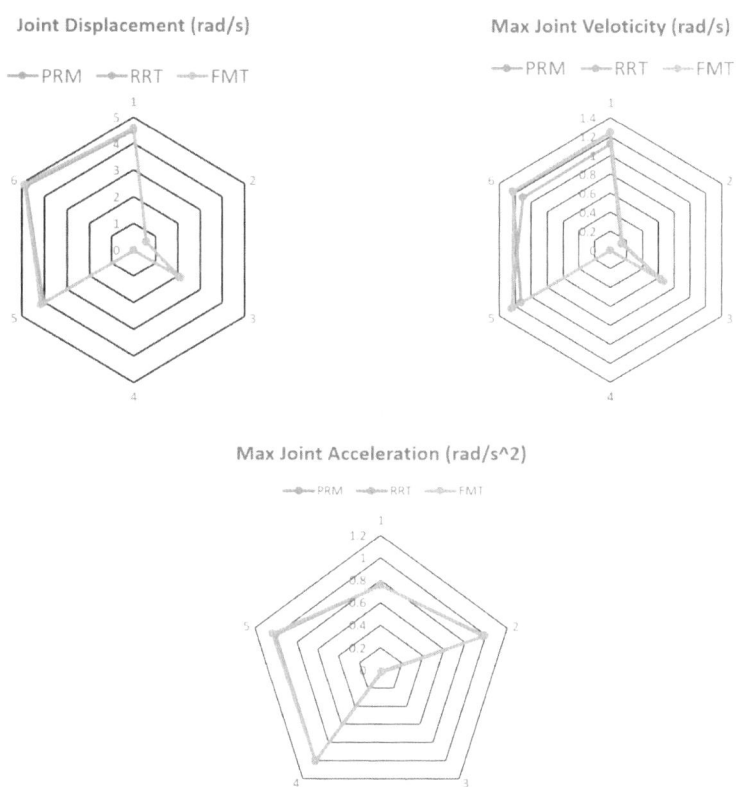

Fig. 9.10. Joint displacement, max velocity, and acceleration of the manipulator in left torsion bar assembly.

the torsion bar is attached to the gripper, the manipulator first lifts the torsion bar for about 3 cm (Fig. 9.9(a)), then transports the torsion bar to a waypoint in the middle which aligns the torsion bar to the assembly orientation (Fig. 9.9(b)). The manipulator then raises the torsion bar to approach the goal position in assembly (Fig. 9.9(c)) and finally aligns the corresponding screw holes on the torsion bar and overhead structure at the exact assembly position (Fig. 9.9(d)).

The PRM, RRT, and FMT algorithms discussed in previous sections are deployed in the simulation. Table 9.2 illustrates the statistic results in the task space. The results indicate that all the three planners can find the optimized collision-free path given the seven waypoints. The planners generate about 160-170 waypoints on average for the whole process. The differences on overall path length for different planners are less than 1 mm. The maximum accelerations and velocities of the end-effector are very similar to each other, which are around 2.3 m/s^2 and

Table 9.2. Task space evaluation for PRM, RRT, and FMT planners.

		Task Space Evaluation				
		Planned Waypoints	Path Length (m)	Max Acc. (m/s^2)	Max Vel. (m/s)	Exe. Time (s)
Planner	PRM	156	4.860	2.322	0.839	25.33
	RRT	168	4.860	2.292	0.843	25.77
	FMT	166	4.860	2.249	0.882	26.50

0.85 m/s. The overall execution time for the left torsion bar assembly is around 25 − 26 seconds.

From the simulation results, we first found that the waypoint in the middle (shown as Fig. 9.9(b)) of the torsion bar manipulation is a key waypoint in order to ensure that the planners can always find a constant trajectory successfully. Without this manually defined waypoint, all the three planners sometimes cannot find a solution or sometimes result in a very large-range and unpredictable motion.

With the waypoints in Fig. 9.8 and Fig. 9.9, the solutions of PRM, RRT, and FMT have the same overall path length (the errors between each test is less than 0.1 mm). RRT and FMT can automatically generate slightly more waypoints than the PRM. The PRM gets the shortest execution time as 25.33 s, while the FMT has the longest execution time as 26.50 s. In our test, each planner was run for three times and the average computed for the three runs. However, since all the three planners are probabilistic sampling based motion planning algorithms, the maximum acceleration, maximum velocity, and the execution time differed with each execution because of the randomness in sampling and searching of waypoints in the workspace.

For the joint space performance, the overall displacement, maximum velocity and maximum acceleration of each joint are evaluated. Fig. 9.10 illustrates the overall displacement (rad), maximum velocity (rad/s) and maximum acceleration (rad/s^2), for each joint in the left torsion manipulation process. The 1 to 6 in the charts refer to the 6 joints of the manipulator from its base to the end-effector. The results indicate that in the left torsion bar assembly, the 1st, 5th, and 6th joints mainly contribute the effort to transport, lift-up and align the torsion bar to the correct assembly position. The average displacements of these three joints are 4.55 rad, 4.08 rad and 4.86 rad. These three joints also have corresponding larger maximum velocities and accelerations than the other three joints.

9.6   Digital Twin – Process Simulate Based Model

The SCR is intended to enhance the human performance on the assembly line by handling tools and parts to the worker. There can be significant variability in assembly performance depending upon ergonomic factors such as individual variability of humans, geometric layout of the workspace, and rapidity of execution of the various tasks. Hence, significant efforts in the past have examined optimizing assembly performance by suitably adjusting all three factors. Optimized workplace ergonomics contribute not only to improved work comfort and employee health, but also to improved individual productivity and product quality. Process Simulate Human® software is an application within Tecnomatix® software – both from Siemens PLM Software – to help design human and human-machine workspaces. Jack is a digital human model that resides within a virtual 3D environment to simulate workplace scenarios and their impact on the human body. Basic analyses include reach distance, grip, visibility, and collision detection. More advanced features include biomechanical, ergonomic, and working motion analyses. The simulations with Process Simulate software are intended to allow "what-if" analyses completely in simulation and enable insights into adjusting the layout and enhancing human task performance. The combination of digital model of human and robot in the virtual environment provides the digital twin framework for simulation. The digital twin affords us ability to virtually perform various analyses (e.g. lower back analysis) and quantify various ergonomic measures (e.g. static loads etc.). This will serve as the baseline model to benchmark our proposed efforts for the human-robot collaboration.

9.6.1   *Human Digital Twin Strategic Framework for Simulation*

A three-stage process was adopted for creating the Process Simulate model: a) Torsion bar assembly operational details were collected (from live performance by human associates at the BMW plant); b) a workflow analysis was conducted to breakdown and identify the critical assembly subtasks; and c) the subtasks are systematically encoded within Process Simulate and customized to execute the simulation study. Our initial effort (reported here) is on developing a digital twin of human only performance of the torsion bar assembly.

9.6.1.1   *Stage 1: Data collection*

The torsion bar assembly operation was broken down into four tasks which are shown in Fig. 9.11. The process starts with the assembly line worker, picking up the left torsion bar and attaches its mid-connection point to the underbody frame of the vehicle using a nut (the mid-connection point is solely used for holding the torsion bar in place while the vehicle is moving from one assembly station to another). This is followed by the action of a second assembly line worker who picks up the right torsion bar and performs the same task. After this point, the first worker leaves the scene and the rest of assembly operation is carried out by the second worker only. In the next step, the head plate bolts which connect torsion bars to each other and also to the vehicle frame must be tightened. Next, the bolts on the other ends of both torsion bars (tail side) will be tightened, and after all these steps, the vehicle leaves the station and enters the next station where all the bolts are torqued to the required specifications. For better clarity, the geometric shapes of the left and right torsion bars are given in Fig. 9.12. Note that the left torsion bar is slightly different in geometry and weight in comparison to the right torsion bar.

Fig. 9.11. Four steps for torsion bar assembly in actual assembly plant.

9.6.1.2   *Stage 2: Storyboarding*

Based on the actual process break down, four steps for manual assembly operation were considered. For the discussion here, we focus on the process to model the assembly operation of the left torsion bar only. As shown in Fig. 9.13: 1) the human worker walks to pick up the left torsion bar from the stationary cart; 2) walks over to the overhead structure to connect the mid-connection point to the structure; 3) picks up the driver unit for fastening the head and tail plate bolts; and 4) tightens the bolts and places the driver unit back in the original location. Various observed real assembly operational details are recreated as closely as possible in the storyboarding process e.g. human body orientation when installing the torsion bar, structural height from the platform and human walking area, etc. After designing the fully manual operation, the robot collaboration scenario was created. Here, the robot picks up the torsion bar and holds the torsion bar for the human worker at the mid-connection point. When the human tightens the nut, the robot leaves the torsion bar, retracts its arm and moves away from the scene. The rest of the operation (steps 3 and 4 in Fig. 9.13) is carried out by human worker only. The storyboarding with collaborative robot was designed to allow for smooth and safe physical assist to the human worker.

9.6.1.3   *Stage 3: Simulation in virtual CVAC environment*

A 50th percentile male (with 1.75m of height, 79 kg weight) was used to down select other anthropometric parameters from the US Army Personnel anthropometric database (ANSUR standard). In addition, the head posture, distance to target, and field of view were calibrated carefully so objects (e.g. torsion bar, or driver unit) were reachable and observable for digital human model. Figure 9.14 shows an ex-

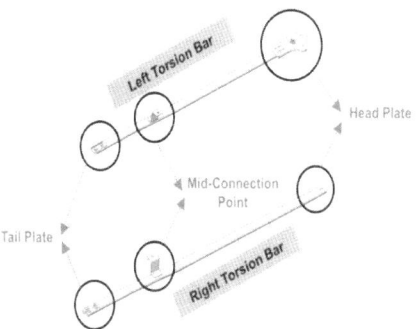

Fig. 9.12. Geometrical shape of left and right torsion bars.

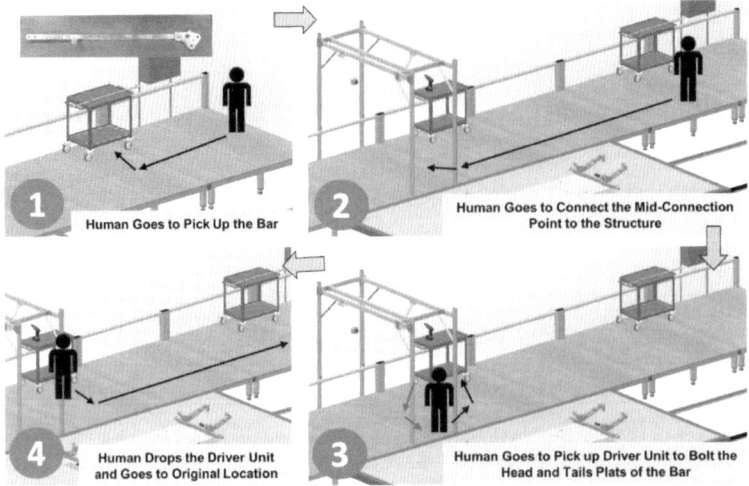

Fig. 9.13. Designed storyboard for manual assembly operation.

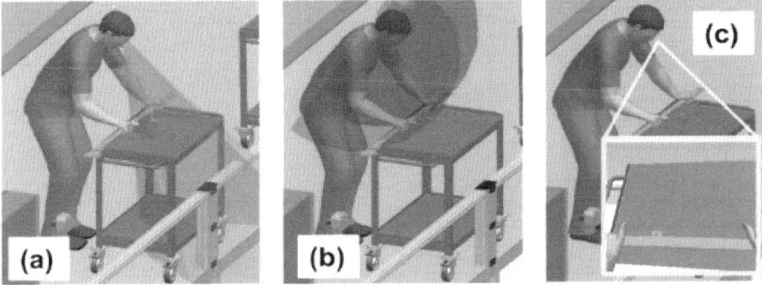

Fig. 9.14. Calibration check for human posture, (a) field of view, (b) reachability area, (c) mid-eye vision.

ample of each calibration steps when human digital model is picking up the torsion bar.

The postures of human in different stages of the assembly operation are given in Fig. 9.15. Process Simulate allows for static and real-time ergonomic analysis of the human model. Here, the lower back ergonomic analysis and joint static load analysis for the male model are given in Fig. 9.16 and Fig. 9.17.

As displayed in Fig. 9.16, each time the human performs a task that requires picking up or placing a part, a peak in forces and moments on the L4/L5 vertebral disks is observed. This peak reaches its maximum when the human bends to pick up the torsion bar from the cart in the first task. Furthermore, the detailed analysis of applied moments on every human joint is given in Fig. 9.17 where the column

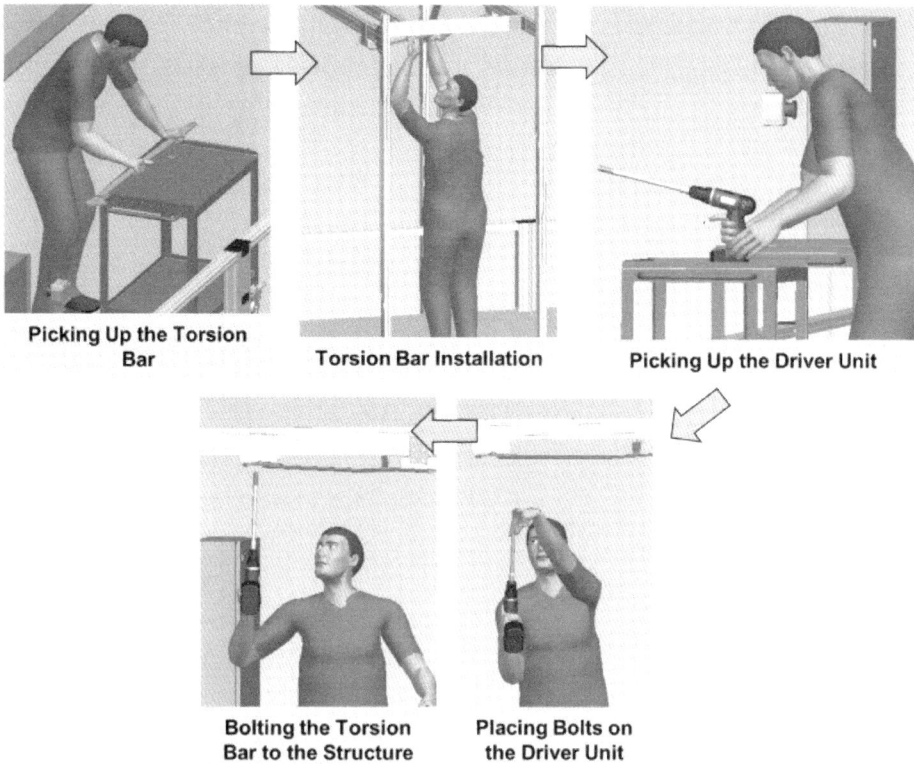

Fig. 9.15. Human body posture for each task.

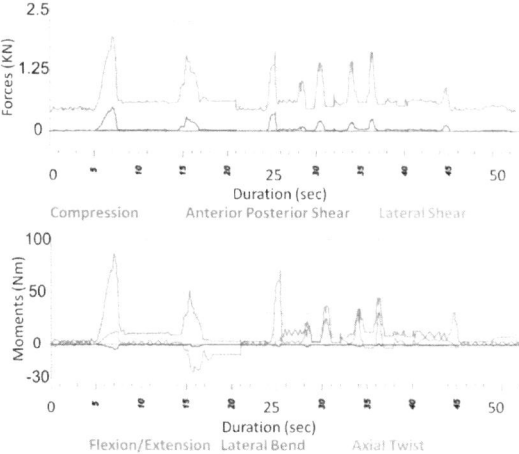

Fig. 9.16. In-process lower back analysis of the human model showing moments and forces on L4/L5 vertebral disks.

Capability Summary Chart										
		Left					Right			
		Moment (Nm)	Muscle Effect	Mean (Nm)	SD (Nm)	Cap (%)	Moment (Nm)	Muscle Effect	Mean (Nm)	SD (Nm)	Cap (%)
Wrist	Flex/Ext	1	EXT	5 8	1 9	99 5	0 9	EXT	8	2 6	99 7
	Rad/Ulnar dev	0	–	0	0	100	0	–	0	0	100
	Sup/Pro	0	–	0	0	100	0	–	0	0	100
	Elbow	-3 9	FLEXN	60 3	14 8	100	-6 3	FLEXN	73	17 9	100
	Abduc/Adduc	-8 7	ABDUCT	75 8	18 6	100	-6 3	ABDUCT	73 8	18 2	100
Shoulder	Rotation Bk/Fd	2 5	BACKWARD	74 2	21 7	100	-1 8	FORWARD	102 8	28 1	100
	Humeral Rot	-0 9	LATERAL	43 4	9 8	100	-1 2	LATERAL	41 1	9 3	100
	Flex/Ext	-86 5	EXTEN	324 4	102 2	99					
Trunk	Lateral Bending	11 8	LEFT	275 1	61 9	100					
	Rotation	-4 7	CW	94 6	25 3	100					
	Hip	-54 8	EXTEN	202 8	81 4	96 5	-41 7	EXTEN	202 7	81 4	97 6
	Knee	-11 6	FLEXN	124 8	36 8	99 9	-8	FLEXN	125	36 8	99 9
	Ankle	-49 4	EXTEN	153 5	50 8	98	-37	EXTEN	159 5	52 8	99

Fig. 9.17. Static load analysis and overall capabilities of the joints in the human model.

Summary	
Simulation duration	52 7 sec
Recovery Time	For the current task demands there is sufficient recovery time available to avoid an accumulation of muscle fatigue
Potential Next Steps	For completeness, you may choose to further evaluate this task using the other available ergonomic analysis tools

Fig. 9.18. Fatigue analysis results of the human model.

"Mean" and "SD" represents the average and standard deviation of the applied moments on each joint and the parameters "Cap", represents the capability of each joint to perform the operation (100% means a fully capable joint for performing the operation). According to this analysis, all the joints are more than 98% capable of performing the tasks.

The fatigue analysis was also conducted and results are shown in Fig. 9.18. According to this analysis, since enough recovery time is given to the human, throughout one full cycle of the operation, muscle fatigue is not a critical factor in this process. Results presented here are a representative sample of the types of analyses possible. Current efforts are focused on studying the effects of parametric variability (weight, height, gender) of anthropometric and workspace (layout geometry, cadence) on the task performance and ergonomic impacts on the workers.

9.7 Discussion and Future Directions

First, the need for intelligent industrial robots in the automotive final assembly was presented and the approach taken by the Smart Companion Robot (SCR) project was presented in this chapter.

Second, we presented some open gaps in the research for the benchmarking of SLAM for robots in the industrial environment. The benchmarking of modern SLAM algorithms is currently being done focusing primarily on accuracy and to a limited extent on consistency as the critical performance criteria. These are necessary measures for proving the performance of algorithms, however, they are not sufficient for mass deployment over long periods of operation. To trust the functionality for mass deployment in safety-critical and business-critical applications, the SLAM algorithms need to be benchmarked for robustness and scalability. For the future work, the metrics for robustness and scalability for benchmarking of situational awareness in industrial environments will be established.

Third, probabilistic sampling based motion planning approaches (both single-query and multiple-query) were discussed with examples. The PRM, RRT, and FMT algorithms are discussed in details and implemented in the torsion bar assembly task simulation based on an SCR. For the future work, the waypoints and the parameter configurations of the planners have potential to be optimized to get a shorter execution time with more automatically generated waypoints.

Lastly, the baseline results for testing different human models in terms of weight, height, gender, and various anthropometric standards were discussed. Using the ROS-Process Simulate interface, we plan to co-simulate the human/collaborative robot interactions (see Fig. 9.19) to provide physical assist for certain human tasks, i.e. picking up the torsion bar and holding it in the correct location. The changes in process time and any improvements in ergonomic performance of the human will need to be quantified and compared with the baseline scenario of manual assembly operation. Human-in-the-Loop (HIL) testing is the final stage in digital twin simulation where the human worker is repeating similar task as the digital human model and measurable process parameters will be

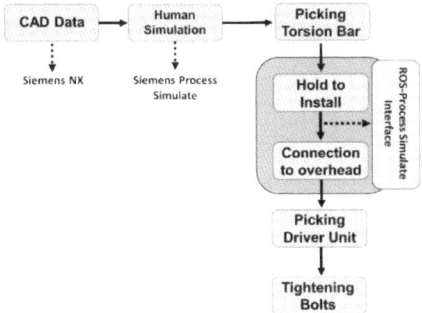

Fig. 9.19. ROS-Process Simulate interface for human-robot digital twin simulation.

compared to the digital twin simulation. We are also in the process of developing surveys and questionnaires for quantification of the human experience and real-life ergonomic difficulties during the HIL testing.

Acknowledgment

This work was supported in part by Subaward No. ARM-17-QS-F-02 from the Advanced Robotics for Manufacturing ("ARM") under Agreement Number W911NF-17-3-0004 sponsored by the Office of the Secretary of Defense. The views and conclusions contained in this document are those of the authors and should not be interpreted as representing the official policies, either expressed or implied, of either ARM or the Office of the Secretary of Defense of the U.S. Government. The U.S. Government is authorized to reproduce and distribute reprints for Government purposes notwithstanding any copyright notation herein.

References

1. Y. Chen, W. Wang, Z. Abdollahi, Z. Wang, J. Schulte, V. Krovi and Y. Jia, A robotic lift assister: a smart companion for heavy payload transport and manipulation in automotive assembly, *IEEE Robot. Autom. Mag. (USA)* **25**(2), 107–19 (2018), http://dx.doi.org/10.1109/MRA.2018.2815704.
2. C. Cadena, L. Carlone, H. Carrillo, Y. Latif, D. Scaramuzza, J. Neira, I. Reid and J. J. Leonard, Past, present, and future of simultaneous localization and mapping: Toward the robust-perception age, *IEEE Transactions on Robotics* **32**(6), 1309–1332 (2016).
3. J. Sturm, N. Engelhard, F. Endres, W. Burgard and D. Cremers, A benchmark for the evaluation of RGB-D SLAM systems. In *2012 IEEE/RSJ International Conference on Intelligent Robots and Systems (IROS)*, pp. 573–580 (2012).
4. J. M. Santos, D. Portugal and R. P. Rocha, An evaluation of 2D SLAM techniques available in robot operating system. In *2013 IEEE International Symposium on Safety, Security and Rescue Robotics (SSRR)*, pp. 1–6 (2013).
5. S. Thrun, W. Burgard and D. Fox, *Probabilistic Robotics*. MIT Press (2005).
6. L. Kavraki, P. Svestka, J.-C. Latombe and M. Overmars, Probabilistic roadmaps for path planning in high-dimensional configuration spaces, *IEEE Transactions on Robotics and Automation* **12**(4), 566–580 (1996), doi:10.1109/70.508439.
7. R. Bohlin and L. E. Kavraki, Path planning using lazy PRM. In *Proceedings of the 2000 IEEE International Conference on Robotics and Automation (ICRA'00)*, vol. 1, pp. 521–528 (2000).
8. L. Jaillet and T. Siméon, A PRM-based motion planner for dynamically changing environments. In *2004 IEEE/RSJ International Conference on Intelligent Robots and Systems (IROS 2004)*, pp. 1606–1611 (2004).
9. S. Karaman and E. Frazzoli, Sampling-based algorithms for optimal motion planning, *The International Journal of Robotics Research,* **30**(7), 846–894 (2011).

10. S. M. LaValle and J. J. Kuffner Jr, Randomized kinodynamic planning, *The International Journal of Robotics Research* **20**(5), 378–400 (2001).

11. S. M. LaValle, *Planning Algorithms*. Cambridge University Press (2006).

12. L. Janson, E. Schmerling, A. Clark and M. Pavone, Fast marching tree: A fast marching sampling-based method for optimal motion planning in many dimensions, *International Journal of Robotics Research* **34**(7), 883–921 (2015), doi:10.1177/0278364915577958.

13. E. Plaku, K. E. Bekris, B. Y. Chen, A. M. Ladd and L. E. Kavraki, Sampling-based roadmap of trees for parallel motion planning, *IEEE Transactions on Robotics* **21**(4), 597–608 (2005).

14. M. Kobilarov, Cross-entropy motion planning, *The International Journal of Robotics Research* **31**(7), 855–871 (2012).

15. J. M. Phillips, N. Bedrossian and L. E. Kavraki, Guided expansive spaces trees: A search strategy for motion-and cost-constrained state spaces. In *Proceedings of the 2004 IEEE International Conference on Robotics and Automation,* vol. 4, pp. 3968–3973 (2004).

16. I. A. Şucan, M. Moll and L. Kavraki, The open motion planning library, *IEEE Robotics and Automation Magazine* **19**(4), 72–82 (2012), doi:10.1109/MRA.2012.2205651.

17. M. Quigley, K. Conley, B. Gerkey, J. Faust, T. Foote, J. Leibs, R. Wheeler and A. Y. Ng, ROS: an open-source Robot Operating System. In *International Conference on Robotics and Automation (ICRA)* (2009).

18. M. Kalakrishnan, S. Chitta, E. Theodorou, P. Pastor and S. Schaal, STOMP: Stochastic trajectory optimization for motion planning. In *2011 IEEE International Conference on Robotics and Automation (ICRA),* pp. 4569–4574 (2011).

19. J. Butzke, K. Sapkota, K. Prasad, B. MacAllister, and M. Likhachev, State lattice with controllers: Augmenting lattice-based path planning with controller-based motion primitives. In *2014 IEEE/RSJ International Conference on Intelligent Robots and Systems,* pp. 258–265 (September 2014).

20. M. Zucker, N. Ratliff, A. D. Dragan, M. Pivtoraiko, M. Klingensmith, C. M. Dellin, J. A. Bagnell and S. S. Srinivasa, Chomp: Covariant hamiltonian optimization for motion planning, *The International Journal of Robotics Research* **32**(9–10), 1164–1193 (2013).

© 2020 World Scientific Publishing Company
https://doi.org/10.1142/9789811222849_0010

Chapter 10

Collaborative Robotics for Deformable Object Manipulation with Use Cases from Food Processing Industry

Philip Long, Philippe Martinet, and Taskın Padır

10.1   Introduction

The food industry in the U.S accounts for an estimated 12% of the total amount workers employed in manufacturing and 14% of the total value of shipments/receipts for services.[1] Moreover, according to the United Nations, food production will have to grow by 50% by 2050 in order to cope with the expected population increase.[2] While much of the packaging and sorting has been robotized, the bulk of the processing tasks are carried out using manual labor, where wages are roughly 80% national average in the U.S.[1] Existing robotic solutions have led to increased efficiency.[3] Hence, there is an enormous potential for robotization in the food industry worldwide,[4,5] however to do so several challenges must be overcome.

To understand the challenges the industry is facing, consider an illustrative example the Port of New Bedford, located 60 miles south of Boston, Massachusetts. This town is the largest fishing port in the United States with fish landings valued at $369 million and employs more than 4,500 workers. The port is viewed as New England's seafood hub, with more than 30 processors and distributors, ranging in size from high-volume international wholesale to small-scale local retail. As a testimony to New Bedford's vibrant economy based on fishing, each year, nearly 50 million pounds of sea scallops are processed, making New Bedford the most profitable port in the United States for the past 16 years. The port is the city's most critical asset to stimulate investment, attract new industry, create jobs and develop a healthy economy.

A recent report looks at "the future of work" in New Bedford's seafood manufacturing industry and acknowledges the need for automation in fish processing plants where workers wash, cut, inspect and pack more than 100 million pounds each year. In recent years, elaborate international supply chains became profitable due to cheap foreign labor and transport costs.[6] In 2016, the U.S. imported seafood worth about $20 billion, and a significant portion on this imported seafood is caught by American fishermen, exported overseas for processing and then re-imported.[7] For example, the salmon catch from Alaska is exported to China for processing and then imported back to the United States, to achieve a $2 per pound cheaper price tag in consumer markets. Massachusetts has the nation's most productive commercial fishing ports, and the industry is vital to economic growth in the state's coastal communities. There is an ever-increasing demand. For example, scallop processing lines at a local seafood processing plant have seen production increases from 2 million to 18 million scallops a year in 5 years. It is also believed that the impact will scale up nationwide, especially in seaport communities that rely on fishing as drivers of their economic development.

Even though there exists machinery to process fish products, their adoption by small businesses is limited due to the initial and operational costs, as well as design constraints of such machines resulting in inflexibility in operations. At a multi-million dollar price tag, it is simply not an option for the small and medium-size enterprises (SMEs). Furthermore, one size does not fit all. Two facilities the authors visited had a diverse range of operations from fresh to frozen, raw to cooked, and shelled to unshelled products. It is nearly impossible to automate all processes in seafood processing industry. Multi-use, low-cost robotics and automation solutions specifically developed for small fish processing plants will enhance the U.S. competitiveness in the global seafood economy. All stakeholders we talked to both during the site visits and through other channels confirmed that there is high demand for quality seafood products from the consumer side. In current operations, there are repetitive yet sufficiently challenging tasks for collaborative robots to perform in the same production line with humans. As a result, there is an end-user driven need and high-impact potential for developing adaptable, multi-use collaborative robots to perform dexterous manipulation tasks to inspect, handle, and grade fish in seafood manufacturing plants.

Fig. 10.1. Fish processing tasks at a fish processing plant visited by the authors. Robotization of the fish handling tasks is essential in order to meet growing demand.

10.2 Related Work

10.2.1 *Manipulation of Deformable Objects*

One of the principal differences between the food industry and classical manufacturing is that the target objects are typically deformable.[8] This means it is necessary to adapt classical methods for both perception[9] and manipulation.[10] In this chapter, recent advances in deformable object manipulation for food manufacturing industry are discussed.

Manipulation tasks concerning deformable objects can be divided by the object's geometric and material properties (for example articulated, flexible, cloth-like or Sanchez et al.,[11] Long et al.[12]). Alternatively, the classification can be based on the desired task properties. For instance, the deformation may be seen as a supplementary challenge of the manipulation task and the control is focused on eliminating or mitigating its effects.[12, 13] In contrast, the deformability may form an integral part of the task itself, sometimes referred to as shape control.[10, 14] In this scenario the objective is to control the internal object configuration variables such that they converge to a desired state. In both cases, both model based to sensors based approaches can be used.

For model based controllers an precise representation of the system deformation is required. Using this model to predict deformations the robot's controller can be adapted to ensure the minimization of deformations. Lumped parameter models, also known as mass spring damper models, respectively denoted as M, k and b, describe a deformable object by a set of discrete point masses. The masses are linked by springs and dampers. The main drawback of this system is the difficulty in accurately modeling realistic object behavior. The values of M, k and b must be carefully chosen, leading to parameter identification models. Mass-spring damper systems have been used to describe an object that is manipulated by a cooperative system, for instance in Refs. 15 and 16. Since the model of the manipulated object is not well known, the spring damper representation is sufficient when complemented with sensor or learning algorithms. An interesting wave based technique for regulation problems is proposed in Ref. 17. Vibration suppression is achieved by dividing the task into two phases. The deformation model is identified during the first phase and then used as a feedback during the second phase. In Ref. 18, the classical object impedance control for cooperative manipulators is extended to a class of deformable objects. The control law is constructed for objects that have less than 6 degrees of freedom (DOF). If this criteria is met, then a lumped parameter model of the object is created where the lumped parameters are controlled in the impedance law. In Ref. 15 a coarse planar object model is meshed then built using simple spring models. The position of the mesh points must be known. The mesh on the deformable object is discretized into three different point types: *manipulation* points where the robots apply forces, *positioned* points that must be positioned, and the rest *non-target* points. The objective is to apply forces to the *manipulation* point so that *positioned* points converge to a desired configuration. A similar work, which overcomes the requirement of having an estimation of the object model, is proposed by Ref. 19. The objective is to deform the object such that the extracted features reach a desired position. In Ref. 14, the shape of a mass spring damper type planar object is controlled by multiple manipulators. The shape of the object is described parametrically. The control scheme aims to change the shape of the object such that it converges to a desired curve.

10.2.2 *Modeling Separation of Deformable Objects*

In the food industry, manipulated objects must be frequently cut, sliced and separated to trim edges, homogenize portion sizes, remove waste matter and defects increasing task complexity. In order to achieve this, the cutting instrument must apply a sufficient force along a deformable contour while ensuring that global deformation, or *rupture*, is avoided. The separation of deformable objects encompasses a number of supplementary challenges with respect to classical contour following tasks. Firstly, in order to cut or sever the object, the tool must necessarily pass through the target contour. Secondly, the cutting force opposes the direction of motion, whereas, in the majority of contour following tasks, it is orthogonal to the motion allowing a convenient partition of control directions.[20] Finally, the target object is deformable and typically heterogeneous, thus both the contour shape and required cutting force varies throughout the task.

One method to approach this problem is to utilize an advanced object model whose properties are updated as the cutting progress. This problem has been extensively studied with respect to surgical applications,[21] where the objective is to mimic deformable body behavior. Thus the cutting force, if considered, is used as a haptic output rather than an input to a control system. For cutting tasks the reverse is desirable ie., an accurate object model which can be employed to obtain the deformation in response to the tool interaction. As expected, the accuracy of these models is largely dependent on computation time. The most accurate models are numerical models such as FEM (Finite element methods)[22] and BEM (Boundary element methods).[23] These models have the increased benefit of being able to handle extremely complex geometries relatively easily. However the computation time is a significant drawback as indeed is the intricacy in re-meshing the model to account for cutting. Discrete models or lumped parameter models, for instance mass-spring-damper systems, have a much lower complexity and thus have a lower computational load; they have been used successfully in the food separation tasks.[24] The primary limitation is the poor physical likeness of the model that can only be eliminated by individual parameter tuning.[25] If, as is often the case, the desired cutting volume is known, the system can be modeled as a set of deformable objects attached together. These methods are known as *regional models*[25] and combine realistic behavior with real time computation speeds.[26] A promising mesh-less approach based on displacing nodal coordinates is proposed in Ref. 27. Rather than try to completely characterize the material, empirical results may be used to update an initial model for example by recording cutting forces[28] or using learning techniques based on haptic feedback.[29]

Historically, robots have been successfully applied to tasks that require the separation of rigid objects such as milling or bone cutting. A desired cutting rate or *feed* is defined for a given object based on material properties. For deformable objects, such an approach is impractical as the properties can vary with different fixations, ambient conditions and in particular with structural changes during cutting. To avoid global deformations and rupture, it is desirable to minimize cutting forces. One method of achieving this is to apply a shearing force. Intuitively, it is obvious that the cutting force can be reduced when shearing or slicing is applied. This means that instead of a force purely orthogonal to the cutting surface, a force parallel to the surface is simultaneously applied. This is known as the *pressing* and *slicing* approach[30] (as the knife is pressed into the material it is simultaneously drawn across its exposed face). There are several ways to explain the apparent reduction in cutting forces, for instance by studying the stress concentration at the contact area[31, 32] or by treating the cutting action as a crack propagation problem,[33] or as in the following using an energy balance formulation.[30]

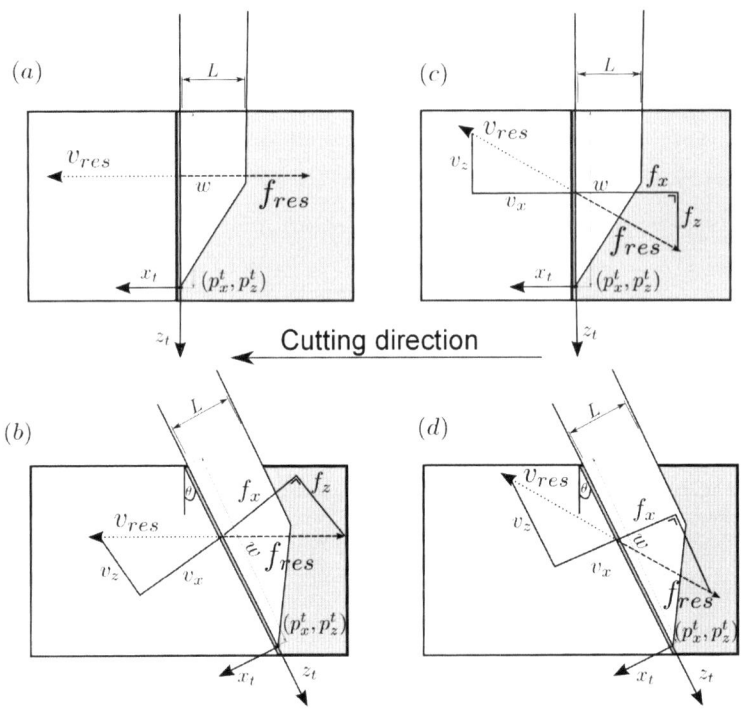

Fig. 10.2. Cutting cases: (a) cutting angle zero pure pressing, (b) cutting angle θ pure pressing, (c) cutting angle zero, pressing and slicing, (d) cutting angle θ, pressing and slicing.

As shown in Fig.10.2, the shearing force can be engendered when a *slicing* velocity is added to the tool velocity or alternatively by positioning the tool at an angle to the material.[34] In Fig.10.2, to cut the material the knife must along the x-axis of the tool. A displacement of Δx_t means the knife must overcome a resistive force, denoted as $^t f_x$, hence the work done by the cutting tool is written as

$$^t f_x \Delta x_t = K_c w \Delta x_t, \tag{10.1}$$

where K_c is the material's fracture toughness while w is the width of the blade in contact with the material. If a shearing motion is added, the work required to cut the material is now a product of the work done in both the *pressing* and *slicing* directions:

$$^t f_x \Delta x_t + {}^t f_z \Delta z_t = K_c w \Delta x_t. \tag{10.2}$$

The resultant tool force and displacement are given respectively as ${}^t f_r = \sqrt{({}^t f_x^2 + {}^t f_z^2)}$ and $\Delta p_t = \sqrt{(\Delta x_t^2 + \Delta z_t^2)}$. Therefore assuming the resultant forces are used purely to cut the material, the energy balance can also be written as

$${}^t f_r \Delta p_t = K_c w \Delta x_t, \tag{10.3}$$

$$\xi = \frac{\Delta z_t}{\Delta x_t}. \tag{10.4}$$

By introducing the *slice/push* ratio, given in (10.4), into (10.2) and (10.3), the authors derive the following relation

$$\frac{{}^t f_r}{K_c w} = \sqrt{\frac{1}{1 + \xi^2}}. \tag{10.5}$$

The above expression demonstrates how an increase in ξ reduces the resultant forces provided K_c is constant.

Hence three areas of research are particularly pertinent to this task, the use of exteroceptive sensors to allow greater flexibility when dealing with unknown objects, the simulation of deformable objects and a mathematical model of cutting.

10.3 Case Study: Modeling and Control of Robotic Meat Cutting Cell

10.3.1 *Overview*

In this section, we describe recent work into the separation of beef meat muscles within the framework of the ARMS project.[a] The ARMS research project *A multi-arms Robotic System for Muscle Separation*, funded by the, national French research institution, ANR (Agence Nationale de la Recherche), reference ANR-10-SEGI-000, aims to contribute to the separation of beef rounds (hindquarters) by an autonomous robotic cell.

In France meat processing accounts for over 25% of the food industry's total employees and includes over 2,000 companies. The robotization of meat cutting tasks is of increasing importance for several reasons. The unsocial working hours (typically night shifts) along with the strenuous, uncomfortable working conditions have created a shortage of skilled labor at a time when competition from low cost labor regions, notably from the *Southern Common Market* (MERCOSUR) countries, is growing. Furthermore the physical tasks involved in the work lead to a high rate of musculoskeletal injuries.[35] The robotization of the meat processing industry has been the focus of several works worldwide. A general overview of the role of robots in the meat processing industry is outlined in Ref. 36, 37. The

---

[a] http://www.agence-nationale-recherche.fr/Project-ANR-10-SEGI-0008

Danish pig slaughter industry is an example of a successful robotization of a manual process. The automation process has improved both hygiene and accuracy in the manufacturing environment.[38] In Refs. 39, 40, a specific robotic meat cutting cell is analyzed from the point of view of the cutting parameters, while using bones as a positional guide. In Japan, robots have been widely introduced in poultry cutting operations.[41] The previous works deal with highly repeatable scenarios in controlled environments, often aiming to optimize a well known existing process.

In contrast, the objective of the ARMS project is to enable the robotic system to autonomously separate highly variable beef rounds. An example separation preformed by a skilled operator is shown in Fig.10.3. A multi-arm system is proposed in order to deal with key challenges such as the irregularity of the target object and its deformable nature. This cell comprises three serial robots, two 6-DOF ADEPT Viper robots and a 7-DOF Kuka lwr. In addition to this a holding system for the meat muscles is devised with 2-DOF in order to allow greater access to the meat.

The robotic system must complete the same tasks as the human worker i.e. the first arm carries a knife and executes the cutting task while the second arm grasps the object and by applying force attempts to open up the cutting valley, finally the third robot carries the perception system that is used to obtain the cutting trajectory and update this trajectory as the object deforms. An advanced object model is created to predict object deformation and generate control signals for the multi-arm system. Therefore the project spans research domains such as cooperative robot motion, robot cell design, mechanical modeling of soft materials, force/vision control and visual tracking of deformable bodies.

The proposed robotic cell consists of a multi-arm system equipped with an array of exteroceptive sensors, notably force and vision sensors. The proposed control approach is first presented in a dynamic simulation environment before validation on an experimental cell.

10.3.2 *Simulation of Robotic Meat Cutting Cell*

The *Kuka lwr* is the robotic platform for both simulation and experimental validation, while MSC Adams is used as the simulation environment as shown in Fig. 10.4. [42] The Modified Denavit-Hartenberg (MDH) notation[43] is used to parameterize the kinematics of the system. For each robot $i = c, p, v$, the tool location is obtained as

$$^{0}\mathbf{T}_{i} = \begin{bmatrix} ^{0}\mathbf{R}_{i} & ^{0}\mathbf{p}_{i} \\ 0\,0\,0 & 1 \end{bmatrix}. \tag{10.6}$$

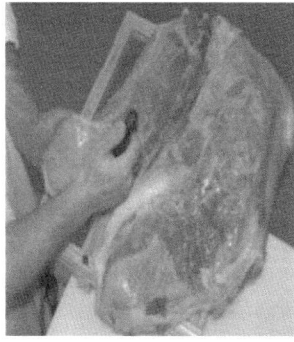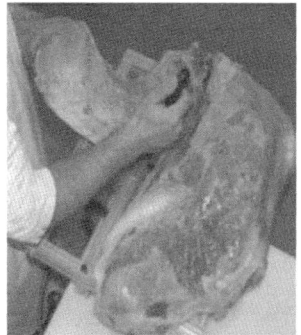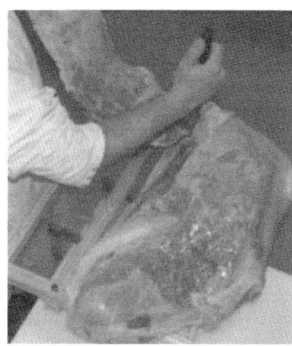

Fig. 10.3. Separation steps of the round and shank of beef muscles, targeted application of the ARMS project.[24]

$^0\mathbf{T}_i$ is the 4×4 homogeneous transformation matrix composed of $\mathbf{R}_i$ the 3×3 orthogonal rotation matrix and $\mathbf{p}_i$ the position of the task frame of robot i with respect to its base frame. Using the angle axis representation for orientation, the Cartesian position, kinematic screw and acceleration of the ith robot are given as

$$\mathbf{x}_i = \begin{bmatrix} \mathbf{p}_i \\ \mathbf{u}\psi_i \end{bmatrix}, \qquad \mathbf{V}_i = \mathbf{J}_i\dot{\mathbf{q}}_i, \qquad \dot{\mathbf{V}}_i = \mathbf{J}_i\ddot{\mathbf{q}}_i + \dot{\mathbf{J}}_i\dot{\mathbf{q}}_i. \qquad (10.7)$$

The dynamic model of each robot can be written as:

$$\boldsymbol{\tau}_i = \mathbf{A}_i\ddot{\mathbf{q}}_i + \mathbf{c}_i + \mathbf{J}_i^T\mathbf{h}_i. \qquad (10.8)$$

$\mathbf{V}_i$ is the kinematic twist, $\mathbf{J}_i$ is the kinematic Jacobian matrix and $\mathbf{q}_i$ the vector of joint coordinates while $\dot{\mathbf{q}}$ and $\ddot{\mathbf{q}}$ are the velocities and accelerations respectively. The inertial parameters are taken from the equivalent CAD model. The inertia matrix and the matrix of centrifugal, Coriolis and gravity torques are denoted as $\mathbf{A}_i$, and $\mathbf{c}_i$. The Cartesian wrench is denoted as $\mathbf{h}_i$ while $\boldsymbol{\tau}_i$ is the joint torque.

The deformable object is modeled using the *regional models* approach, i.e. the cutting is restricted to an a priori defined region. Hence two distinct types of deformable model are generated, a model that represent the meat muscles and a second model that represents the aponeurosis, similar to tendons, which act as links between muscles.

The meat muscles are modeled using a finite element model approach as shown in Fig. 10.5. Firstly, a visual scan of a generic beef round is obtained after separation and converted into a 3D-geometry. The two muscles are reconstructed and the exact cutting surface is extracted. Since the area of interest for the simulation is the cutting region, the muscles can be simplified thereby reducing the computational

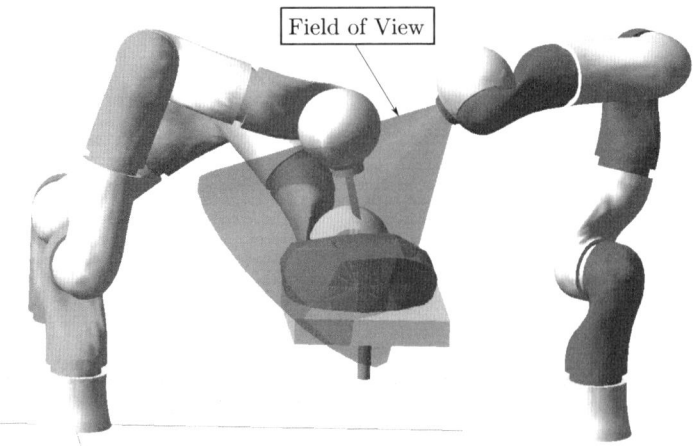

Fig. 10.4. Simulated robotic cell using MSC Adams. The system is composed of three Kuka LWR robots, a cutting robot, a pulling robot and a vision robot. The meat muscles are attached using a set of detachable spring dampers.

cost. On the other hand, the exact cutting surface is used to mirror the intricacies of the separation procedure.

The models are discretized volumetrically and nodes are generated on the cutting surface of each muscle. For each node on the cutting surface of one muscle, there exists a corresponding attachment point on the other muscle, which is coincident at the beginning of the simulation. These nodes can transmit forces from one muscle to the other. A modal analysis is performed for each muscle and the resulting system is imported into the simulation environment. This file contains the object geometry, the orthonormalization of the Craig-Bampton modes and the generalized mass and stiffness for the mode shapes.

The aponeurosis are modeled as the second deformable object located in an intermediate layer in the beef shoulder. The aponeurosis can store elastic energy, then recoil when unloaded, thus an appropriate representation is spring damper systems which are then fixed to partner nodes on the cutting surfaces as shown in Fig. 10.6. The simulation commences at the equilibrium condition, i.e., when the muscles are perfectly mated and net spring foce is zero.

During the simulation experiments, if the line segment representing the knife intersects the line segment representing the aponeurosis, the corresponding spring damper system is deactivated. Thus the link is severed between the nodal attachment points.

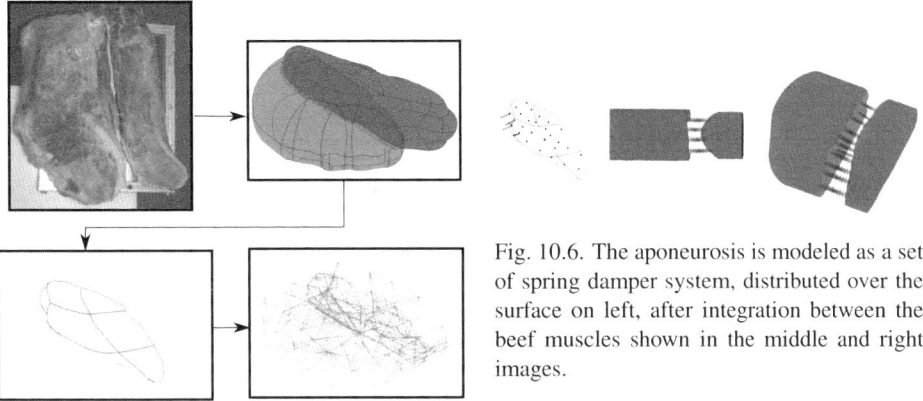

Fig. 10.6. The aponeurosis is modeled as a set of spring damper system, distributed over the surface on left, after integration between the beef muscles shown in the middle and right images.

Fig. 10.5. From 3D scan to finite element mesh.

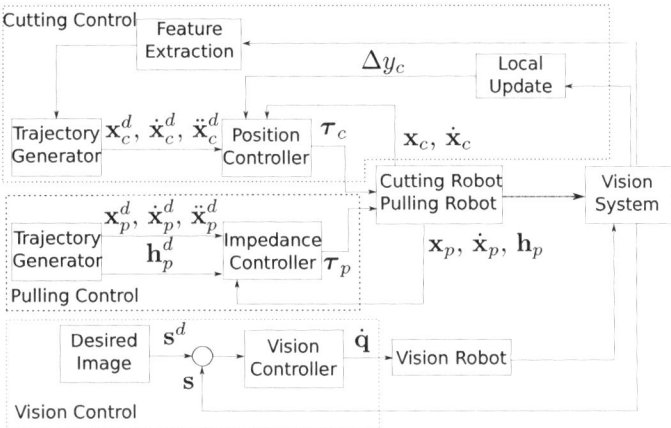

Fig. 10.7. Global control scheme for the robot meat cutting simulator, showing the controller for the cutting, pulling and vision robot.

10.3.2.1 *Global controller*

A global decentralized control scheme is employed to separate the muscles as shown in Fig. 10.7. The cutting robot follows an off-line generated trajectory based on the object model. The reference trajectory is modified on-line using the output of vision system to compensate for the object deformation. To track the desired variables, a computed torque controller is used, therefore the desired Cartesian acceleration, $\mathbf{w}_c$, is defined as

$$\mathbf{w}_c = \dot{\mathbf{V}}^d + \mathbf{K}_d\left(\Delta\mathbf{V}\right) + \mathbf{K}_p\left(\Delta\mathbf{x}\right) - \dot{\mathbf{J}}_c\dot{\mathbf{q}}, \qquad (10.9)$$

where $\mathbf{K}_d$ $\mathbf{K}_p$ are positive gains. $\mathbf{w}_c$ is then transformed to the joint space, and a new desired acceleration is defined as

$$\ddot{\mathbf{q}}^d = \mathbf{J}_c^+ \left(\mathbf{w}_c + \mathbf{P}_c \, \mathbf{z} \right). \tag{10.10}$$

$\mathbf{z}$ is a secondary criterion used to shift the solution away from joint limits, and $\mathbf{P}$ projects $\mathbf{z}$ into the null space of the primary solution. Finally, a joint torque realizing this acceleration is obtained as

$$\tau_c = \mathbf{A}_c \ddot{\mathbf{q}}^d + \mathbf{c}_c + \mathbf{J}_i^T \mathbf{h}_c. \tag{10.11}$$

The on-line update is computed by using y_g, the exact position of the guide line extracted from the visual primitive. y^d is updated as:

$$y^{*d}(t) = y^d(t) + \Delta y \tag{10.12}$$

$$\Delta y = y_g - y_c. \tag{10.13}$$

Equation (10.9) is modified to create an impedance relationship[44] between the desired position and empirically learned pulling froce that is necessary to aid the separation and allow greater access for the vision system. The desired cartesian acceleration is given as

$$\mathbf{w}_p = \dot{\mathbf{V}} + \lambda \left(\mathbf{K}_d \left(\Delta \mathbf{V} \right) + \mathbf{K}_p \left(\Delta \mathbf{x} \right) - \mathbf{K}_f (\Delta \mathbf{h}) \right) - \dot{\mathbf{J}}_p \dot{\mathbf{q}}, \tag{10.14}$$

where λ is the inverse of the desired inertial behavior.

Finally, the global controller guides the vision robot to maintain the cutting surfaces within its field of view. To do so, the robot is controlled in image space, by minimizing the error between a desired image denoted by the feature vector $\mathbf{s}_d$ and the current camera image $\mathbf{s}_{im}$

$$\dot{\mathbf{q}}_v^d = -\mathbf{K}_p \left(\mathbf{L}_s \mathbf{J}_v \right)^+ \left(\mathbf{s}_d - \mathbf{s}_{im} \right), \tag{10.15}$$

where $\mathbf{L}_s$ is known as the interaction matrix.[45]

10.3.2.2   *Simulation results*

In order to fully separate the muscles the knife must cut a distance of 80mm. This is achieved by repeatably cutting along the surface of separation with the knife. An overview of the resulting behavior can be seen in Fig.10.8. This image is split into six panes. Each pane gives two separate views of the simulator. By examining the image, the evolution of the system can be seen as the cutting progresses. Fig.10.9 and Fig.10.10 show the results of the cutting task with and without the local vision update. In both cases, large changes in the cutting profile (guide line) are noted as the aponeurosis are severed due to the applied pulling forces. The local vision system compensates for these change by simultaneously applied a corrective translational and angular velocity.

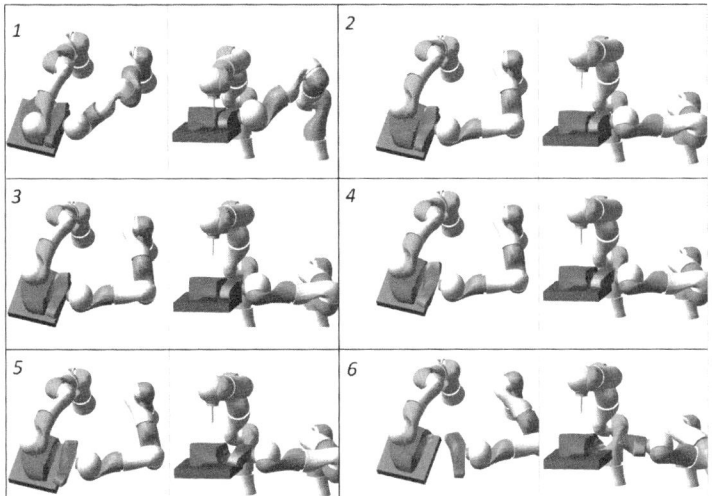

Fig. 10.8. Snapshot of separation process.

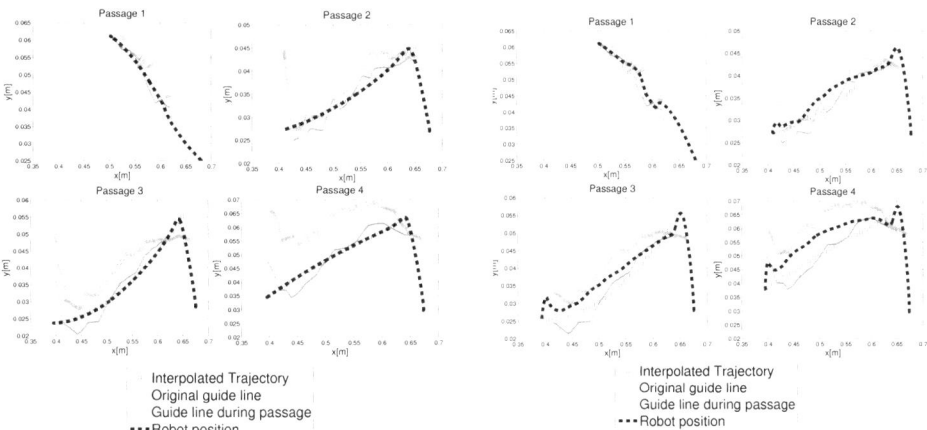

Fig. 10.9. Robot trajectory for each passage, using off-line trajectory planner based on model data.

Fig. 10.10. Robot trajectory for each passage, using off-line model-based trajectory modified by visual feedback.

10.3.3 *Modeling Separation of Deformable Objects*

In the food industry, manipulated objects must be frequently cut, sliced and separated to trim edges, homogenize portion sizes, remove waste matter and defects increasing task complexity. In order to achieve this, the cutting instrument must apply a sufficient force along a deformable contour while ensuring that global deformation or *rupture* is avoided. The separation of deformable objects encompasses a number of supplementary challenges with respect to classical contour following tasks. Firstly, in order to cut or sever the object the tool must necessarily pass through the target contour. Secondly, the cutting force opposes the direction of motion, whereas in the majority of contour following tasks, it is orthogonal to the motion allowing a convenient partition of control directions.[20] Finally, the target object is deformable and typically heterogeneous, thus both the contour shape and required cutting force varies throughout the task.

One method to approach this problem is to utilize an advanced object model whose properties are updated as the cutting progress. This problem has been extensively studied with respect to surgical applications,[21] where the objective is to mimic deformable body behavior. Thus the cutting force, if considered, is used as a haptic output rather than an input to a control system. For cutting tasks the reverse is desirable ie., an accurate object model which can be emploted to obtain the deformation in response to the tool interaction. As expected, the accuracy of these models is largely dependent on computation time. The most accurate models are numerical models such as FEM (finite element methods)[22] and BEM (boundary element methods).[23] These models have the increased benefit of being able to handle extremely complex geometries relatively easily. However the computation time is a significant drawback as indeed is the intricacy in re-meshing the model to account for cutting. Discrete models or lumped parameter models, for instance mass-spring-damper systems, have a much lower complexity and thus have a lower computational load. They have been used successfully in the food separation tasks.[24] The primary limitation is the poor physical likeness of the model that can only be eliminated by individual parameter tuning.[25] If, as is often the case, the desired cutting volume is known, the system can be modeled as a set of deformable objects attached together. These methods are known as *regional models*[25] and combine realistic behavior with a real time computation speeds.[26] A promising mesh-less approaches based on displacing nodal coordinates is proposed in Ref. 27. Rather than try to completely characterize the material, emprical results may be used to update an initial model for example by recording cutting forces[28] or using learning techniques based on haptic feedback.[29]

Historically, robots have been successfully applied to tasks that require the separation of rigid objects such as milling or bone cutting. A desired cutting rate or *feed* is defined for a given object based on material properties. For deformable objects, such an approach is impractical as the properties can vary with different fixations, ambient conditions and in particular with structural changes during cutting. To avoid global deformations and rupture, it is desirable to minimize cutting forces. One method of achieving this is to apply a shearing force. Intuitively, it is obvious that the cutting force can be reduced when shearing or slicing is applied. This means that instead of a force purely orthogonal to the cutting surface, a force parallel to the surface is simultaneously applied. This is known as the *pressing* and *slicing* approach[30] (as the knife is pressed into the material it is simultaneously drawn across its exposed face). There are several ways to explain the apparent reduction in cutting forces, for instance by studying the stress concentration at the contact area[31,32] or by treating the cutting action as a crack propagation problem,[33] or as in the following using an energy balance formulation.[30]

10.3.4 *Experimental Validation of Robotic Meat Cutting Cell*

The proposed meat cutting cell is transferred to an experimental setup.[46] There are several supplementary difficulties for the experimental validation absent in the simulations. Firstly, the vision system can no longer be considered as ideal and in order to get a precise view of the cutting zone it is more expedient to replace the cutting robot by an *eye-in-hand* system that focuses on local deformation. Secondly, the force control must be modified to consider the resistive force during the cut. In the following the proposed force controller is examined in detail.

10.3.4.1 *Novel cutting force controller*

When cutting deformable objects it is desirable to minimize the generated cutting force at the tool frame for two reasons. Firstly, a large cutting force can induce global deformation rather than rupture, leading to the clustering of material around the cutting tool. This global deformation reduces the product quality. Secondly, a smaller cutting force reduces the energy input of the system whereas a larger cutting force may be outside the capabilities of the tool. This is particularly important when using precisely machined blades.

Equation (10.16) describes the cutting process, where W_r is the work done by the cutting tool, defined as the sum of W_c, the energy required to cut the material; W_f, the work done in overcoming the frictional effects on the blade and U, the strain energy due to global deformation of the soft material.

$$W_r = W_c + W_f + U. \tag{10.16}$$

During a pure cutting motion, it is assumed that the global deformation caused by the cutting tool is negligible, $U = 0$, therefore $W_r = W_c + W_f$. One method of decreasing the energy required to generate rupture is to reduce the effects of friction. The friction is due to shear as the soft material rubs against the sides of the blade. The work required to overcome the friction is defined as:[30]

$$W_f = 2Lw\tau_f \Delta_x \qquad (10.17)$$

where τ_f is a shear stress acting over length L. A force denoted as $\mathbf{f}_p$ is applied by the pulling robot. This pulling force opens the cutting valley meaning that contact between the cutting tool and the material is reduced, albeit increasing in the lateral deformation of the object, notably the cutting trajectory.

Assuming, the opening of the cutting valley renders frictional effects negligible, the work done by the robot is used purely to cut the material, hence (10.16) becomes $W_r = W_c$. The energy required to initialize a crack can be reduced by adding a shear element to the cutting motion. From examination of (10.16) we propose to modify the ratio ξ, from (10.5) in response to the presence of resistive forces. ξ can be increased by changing the cutting angle or by generating a velocity parallel to the cutting surface. It is undesirable to alter the cutting angle during the trajectory due to both the practical difficulties and the reduction in material feed. Therefore the *slicing* velocity is linked to the resistive cutting force by an impedance controller.

In this case the impedance controller is defined at the tool frame to generate the force correction term $^{ob}d\mathbf{X}_t^f$. However in contrast to the standard force controllers, for the cutting task the impedance controller is designed such that the resistive force creates a change in position in an orthogonal axis. As shown in Fig. 10.2, the z axis is defined as parallel to the cutting surface, while $^t f_c$ is defined as the resistive force of the cut, therefore the change in position is generated as

$$\Delta z_t = \min \left(0, \ k_z \, ^t f_c \right) \qquad (10.18)$$

where k_z is a positive gain. From (10.4) and (10.18), it is obvious that the controller will increase the *slice/press* ratio in response to a resistive force thereby reducing the resistive forces and allowing the cutting to continue without deforming the material. By using the min function the positive values of (10.18) are rejected. These values are due to noisy force sensor measurements and would cause the knife to enter deeper into the material.

To validate the proposed force controller, a set of experiments are carried out in a simple cutting scenario where the target object is soft foam known as Bultex©. For each experiment the robot followed a straight line cutting trajectory with a constant velocity. This trajectory is defined by a linear interpolation from point to point. The control law is given as:

$$
{}^t\mathbf{V}_t = {}^t\mathbf{S}_{ob}\left(\mathbf{k}_p d\mathbf{X} + \mathbf{k}_v \mathbf{V}^d\right) + \begin{bmatrix} 0 \\ 0 \\ k_z^t f_c \\ 0 \\ 0 \\ 0 \end{bmatrix}
\tag{10.19}
$$

$$
\dot{\mathbf{q}} = {}^t\mathbf{J}^+\,{}^t\mathbf{V}_t
\tag{10.20}
$$

where $d\mathbf{X}$ is the position error in the object frame, $\mathbf{V}^d$ is the desired cutting velocity and ${}^t\mathbf{S}_{ob}$ is the screw transformation matrix. When the knife exits the media, due to the slicing effect of the controller, the robot returns to the initial position to restart the passage. The behavior of the force controller is investigated with respect to changes in the cutting angle, θ as shown in Fig.10.2, and the gain k_z^t.

In total twelve experiments are carried out. The test matrix and the quality of the cut for each test is shown in Table 10.1. The quality of the cut, which depends on the level of global deformation and rupture in the object, is judged visually. An example of three cases is shown in Fig.10.14. These cases are described as:

- Good: No global deformation, an extremely clean cut
- Medium: Slight global deformation, in the cutting region
- Poor: Large global deformation and permanent damage to surrounding area

Table 10.1. Test matrix for force controller.

	$k_z = 0.0$	$k_z = 0.001$	$k_z = 0.005$	$k_z = 0.01$
$\theta = \dfrac{\pi}{12}$	Poor*	Medium	Good	Good
$\theta = \dfrac{\pi}{6}$	Poor	Medium	Good	Good
$\theta = \dfrac{\pi}{4}$	Poor	Good	Good	Good

The table shows that the quality of the cut can be increased either by changing the cutting angle or by increasing the force gain. It should be noted that for the experiment $k_z = 0.0$, $\theta = \frac{\pi}{12}$, the knife deformed the object without any cutting. This resulted in a constant increase in force until the experiment was stopped, to prevent damage to the robot and the tool. The increase in force can been seen in Fig.10.11.

The graphical results for $\theta = \frac{\pi}{12}$, $\theta = \frac{\pi}{6}$ and $\theta = \frac{\pi}{4}$ are shown in Fig.10.11, Fig.10.12 and Fig.10.13, respectively. Each figure consists of six sub-figures arranged in two rows and three columns. The top row shows the cutting forces as the cutting distance is increased. The bottom row shows the corresponding cutting depth as the cutting distance is increased. Each of the three columns shows the results of a particular passages. Although in the case of $k_z = 0.0$, the robot completes is only one passage since there is no slicing action.

For each cutting angle, it can be seen that by increasing the value of k_z, the resulting resistive force is reduced. Furthermore for each value of $k_z > 0$, the results show a decrease in the cutting forces as the controller begins the slicing phase. This generates a n-shaped for the force response and thus shows the effectiveness of the proposed controller. In contrast, the position controller $k_z = 0.0$, results not only in a poor quality, as shown in Table 10.1, but also high forces on the cutting tool reaching up to 32 Newtons in Fig.10.11.

However, a drawback of increasing the force gain is the reduction in cutting distance. For example Fig.10.13, the control law with $k_z = 0.001$ has cut a distance of over $200mm$ at the end of the third passage whereas $k_z = 0.001$ has cut less than half this distance.

By increasing the cutting angle, the force on the blade is decreased for all tests. This is expected since the cutting angle also increases the *slice/press* ratio. For this set of experiments, the cutting depth was constant, however in practice by increasing the cutting angle, the possible cutting depth and therefore cutting feed is reduced.

10.3.4.2 *Experimental validation of force/vision controller*

The proposed force controller is coupled with a visual feedback to cut a 200mm × 200mm × 100mm block of foam known as Bultex © as shown in Fig.10.15. Visual feedback is essential to cope with complex deformation behaviors.[47] In this work, a series of dots, serving as the visual markers, are attached to the foam. The cutting trajectory is offset from these dots by a small distance to ensure the knife does not cut the visual marker. The cutting robot is fitted with a ATI gamma 6-axis force sensor, a marlin 1394 camera and a razor blade, whereas the pulling robot is equipped with a set of hooks to grasp the soft object.

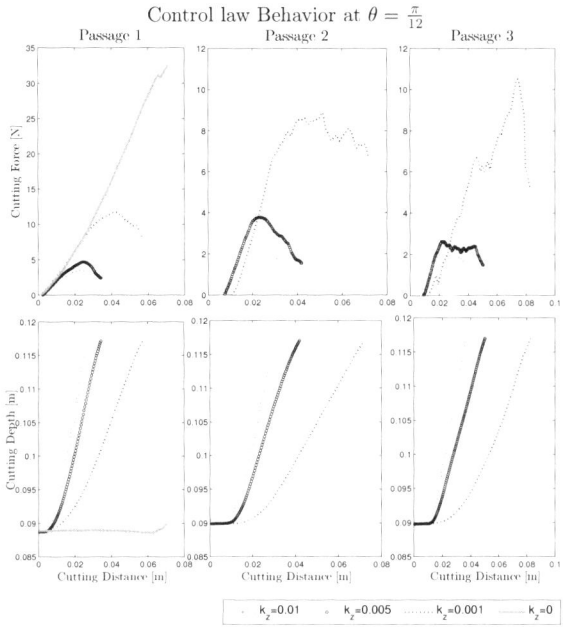

Fig. 10.11. Cutting force versus displacement with $\theta = \frac{\pi}{12}$. The cutting forces versus cutting distance are shown on the top row. The cutting depth versus cutting distance are shown on the bottom row. Each column represents a passage.

The desired pose is updated using vision and force. The controller generates a Cartesian velocity that is transformed into a joint velocity, by firstly representing the kinematic Jacobian matrix in the object frame and then obtaining the pseudoinverse of this matrix, denoted as $^{ob}\mathbf{J}^{+}$. The joint velocity is transformed into a joint torque using the Kuka's internal controller before being sent to the motors. The pulling robot is used to both hold the object in place and to open up the cutting valley to reduce friction. The resulting global controller is shown in Fig.10.16.

The cutting robot follows a polynomial curve, $\mathcal{C}$ defined in the object frame $\mathcal{R}_{ob}$ in the form $y = a_n x^n + a_{n-1} x^{n-1} + \ldots a^0$. At any instant the knife's desired location, defined by the 4×4 homogenous transformation matrix in the object frame is given as $^{ob}\mathbf{T}_t^d = {}^{ob}\mathbf{T}_c \, {}^{c}\mathbf{T}_t(\theta)$, where $^{c}\mathbf{T}_t(\theta.)$ is used to make the trajectory consistent with the cutting angle θ. The position of $^{ob}\mathbf{T}_c$, denoted $^{ob}\mathbf{p}_c$, is defined as:

$$\mathbf{p} = \begin{bmatrix} p_x^d & p_y^d & p_z^d \end{bmatrix}^T. \tag{10.21}$$

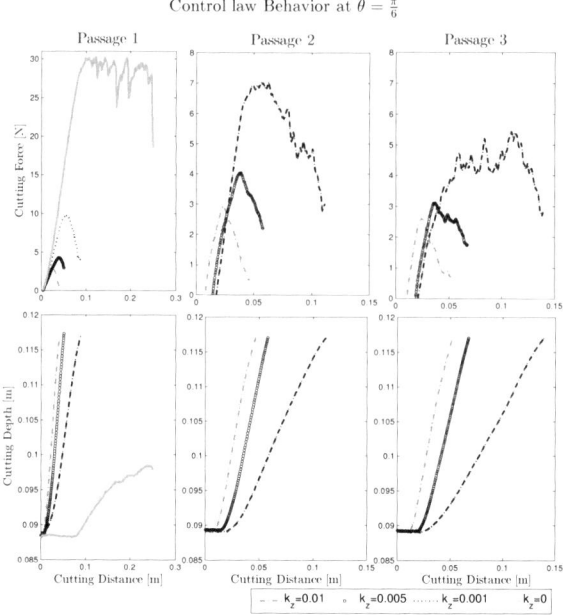

Fig. 10.12. The cutting forces versus cutting distance are shown on the top row. The cutting depth versus cutting distance are shown on the bottom row. Each column represents a passage.

The orientation of $^{ob}\mathbf{T}_c$, denoted $^{ob}\mathbf{R}_c$, is defined as:

$$^{ob}\mathbf{R}_c = \begin{bmatrix} \mathbf{t} & \mathbf{n} & \mathbf{a} \end{bmatrix}$$

$$\mathbf{t} = \left[\frac{1}{\sqrt{\left(1 + \frac{\partial y}{\partial x}^2\right)}}, \frac{\frac{\partial y}{\partial x}}{\sqrt{\left(1 + \frac{\partial y}{\partial x}^2\right)}}, 0 \right]^T \tag{10.22}$$

$$\mathbf{n} = \left[\frac{-\frac{\partial y}{\partial x}}{\sqrt{\left(1 + \frac{\partial y}{\partial x}^2\right)}}, \frac{1}{\sqrt{\left(1 + \frac{\partial y}{\partial x}^2\right)}}, 0 \right]^T \tag{10.23}$$

$$\mathbf{a} = \begin{bmatrix} 0, & 0, & -1 \end{bmatrix}^T, \tag{10.24}$$

where $\mathbf{t}$ is the desired cutting direction, which is tangential to $\mathcal{C}$. $\mathbf{a}$ is the axis normal to the object's surface while $\mathbf{n}$ is the remaining orthogonal axis of the frame. $\frac{\partial y}{\partial x}$ is the value of $\frac{\partial y}{\partial x}$ evaluated at p_x^d.

The vision controller updates the $^{ob}\mathbf{T}_t^d$ in response to on-line deformations by creating a positional deviation, denoted as $^{ob}d\mathbf{X}_t^v$. The vision system extracts the image coordinates of the trajectory adhered to the block, obtaining (u_i, v_i), (u_j, v_j) and (u_k, v_k), which constitute a series of points ahead of the image projection of

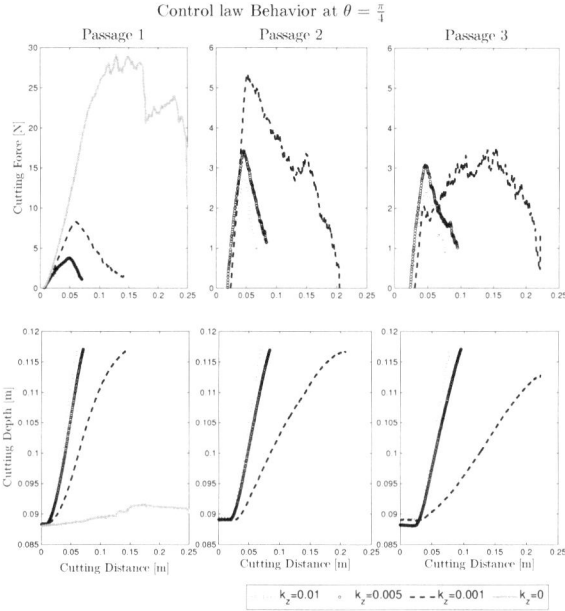

Fig. 10.13. The cutting forces versus cutting distance are shown on the top row. The cutting depth versus cutting distance are shown on the bottom row. Each column represents a passage.

tool point. The normalized position of a point i is reconstructed using the intrinsic camera parameters, $\mathbf{C}$, which relate the image coordinates to the coordinates in the perspective plane i.e.,

$$
\begin{bmatrix}
\dfrac{p_{xi}^v}{p_{zi}^v} \\
\dfrac{p_{yi}^v}{p_{zi}^v} \\
1
\end{bmatrix}
= \mathbf{C}
\begin{bmatrix}
u_i \\
v_i \\
1
\end{bmatrix}.
\tag{10.25}
$$

The depth of a point, p_{zi}^v, is estimated using the material height and the tool position, the depth estimation allows the reconstruction of the 3D position of the point. Since the camera gives a local view of the trajectory, the curvature within this window is quite small and can be approximated by a straight line. By fitting this line to the Cartesian position of points i, j and k the vectors $\mathbf{t}$ and then $\mathbf{n}$ are obtained. The use of the reconstructed position in the control is generally known as position based visual servoing.[48] In order to generate an error vector, the curve $\mathcal{C}$ is evaluated at p_{xi} allowing a desired matrix $^{ob}\mathbf{T}_i^d$ to be obtained. This in turn is used to calculate the vision generated deviation which acts in one translational direction and three

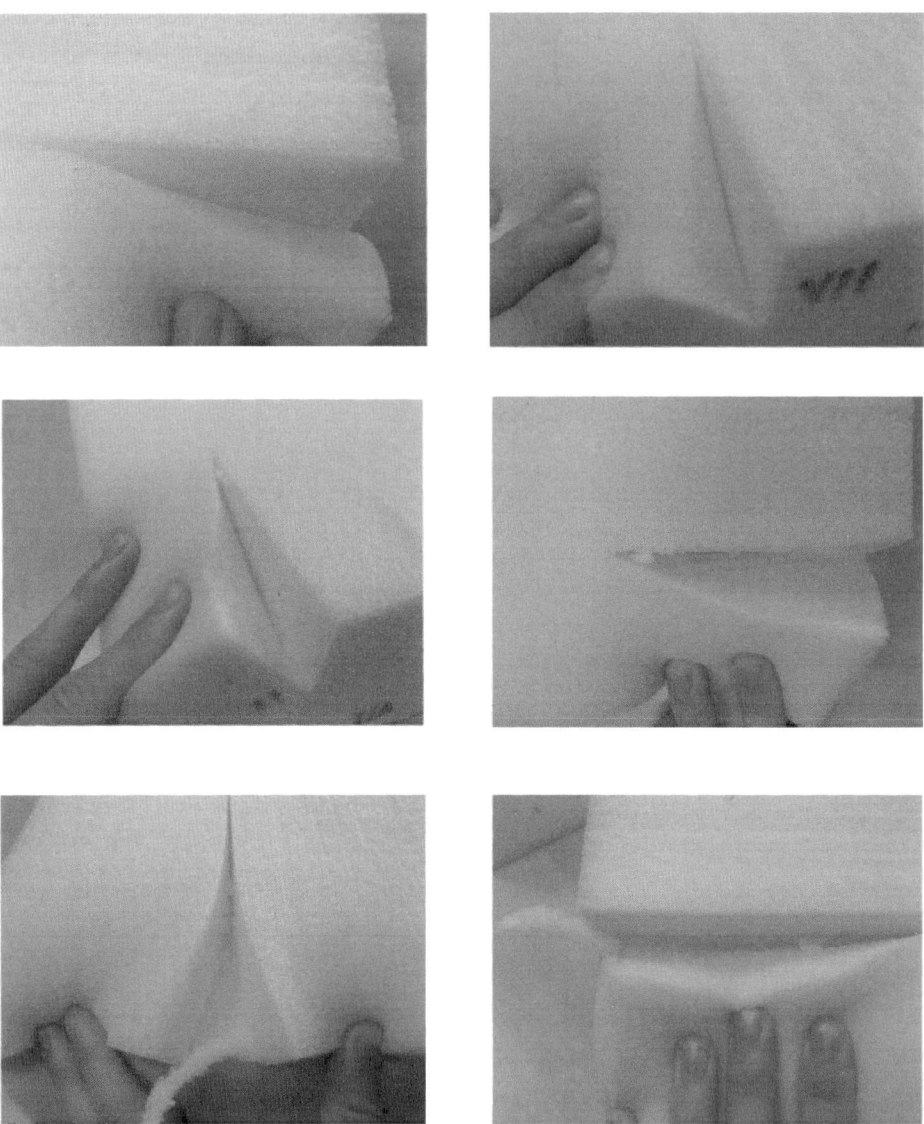

Fig. 10.14. Comparison of cut quality for the proposed force controller, (top) A good quality cut with no global deformations, where the force gain $k_z = 0.01$ and the cutting angle $\theta = \frac{\pi}{4}$, (middle) A medium quality with some small deformations where the force gain $k_z = 0.001$ and the cutting angle $\theta = \frac{\pi}{12}$, (bottom) Poor quality with large global deformations where the force gain $k_z = 0.0$ and the cutting angle $\theta = \frac{\pi}{4}$.

rotational directions:

$$\Delta p_{yi} = p_{yi}^d - p_{yi}^v \tag{10.26}$$

$$\Delta^{ob}\mathbf{R}_i = {}^{ob}\mathbf{R}_i^d \left({}^{ob}\mathbf{R}_i^v\right)^T. \tag{10.27}$$

10.3.4.3 *Experimental results*

Each passage allows the robot to cut further and further along the trajectory. If the knife leaves the material due to the slicing action the controller returns the system to its initial position. The gradual rupture of the material allows the system to progress over several passages as seen in Fig.10.17, Fig.10.18 and Fig.10.19.

In Fig.10.17, the off-line estimation of the curve, the visually extracted curve and the robot position are shown. This graph shows that the desired trajectory is

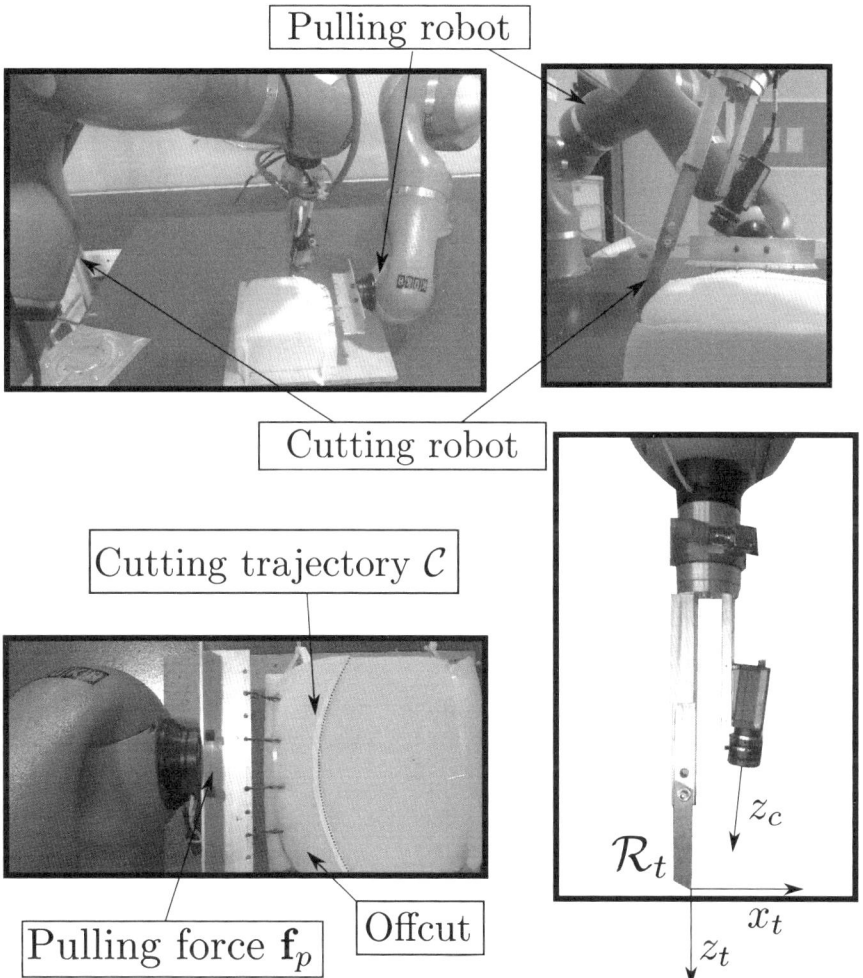

Fig. 10.15. Experimental platform for separation of soft objects. Top left global view of experimental platform. Top right cutting tool at initial position. Bottom left, pulling robot at initial position. Bottom right, cutting tool, camera and tool frame.

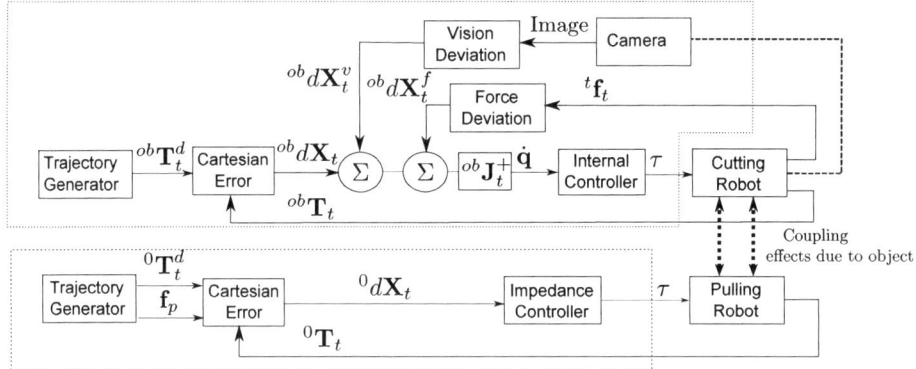

Fig. 10.16. Global control scheme.

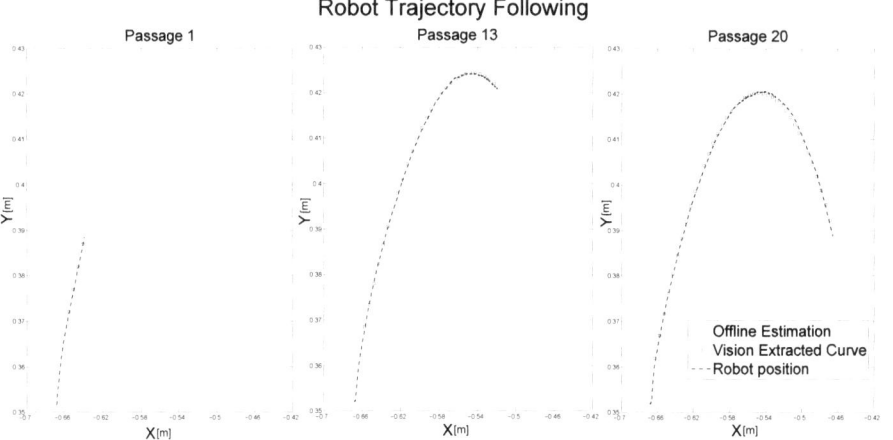

Fig. 10.17. Displacement in the x-y plane of the object.

deformed due to the force applied by the pulling robot. The vision controller allows the robot to cut along the new trajectory. In Fig.10.17, Passage 20 shows that the cutting trajectory begins to resemble the initial estimation as the separation reaches its end. This is expected since $\mathbf{f}_p$ at this moment is applied to the offcut. Therefore as the cutting proceeds, the deformation effect due to $\mathbf{f}_p$ on the main part of the object is reduced, meaning the cutting trajectory returns to its original undeformed shape.

Figures 10.18 and 10.19 show the cutting force in the tool frame and the z position of the tool versus the progress along the curve during the crack initialization and propagation phase respectively. In Fig.10.18 the increase in the resistive cutting force causes the controller to create a slicing action which in turn results in a decrease of the force. During the crack propagation phase the magnitude of the

Cutting Force & Displacement

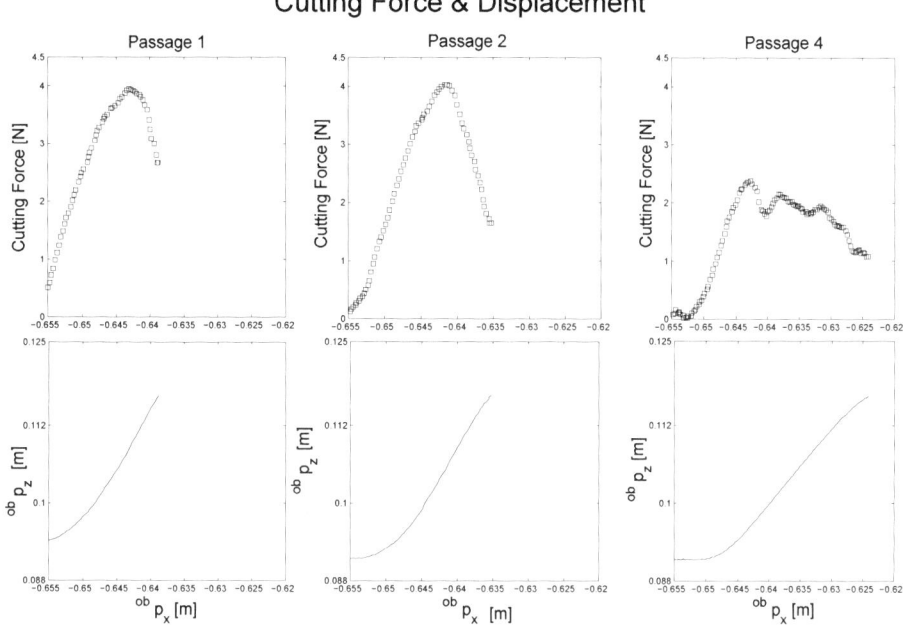

Fig. 10.18. Cutting force and the displacement along the x and z axes during the initial cutting phase.

Cutting Force & Displacement
Passage 13

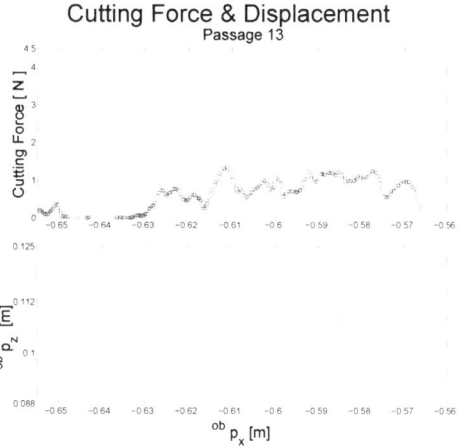

Fig. 10.19. Cutting forces and displacement along the x and z axes during the cutting propagation phase.

resistive force has decreased. Finally in Fig.10.19, for the phases where cutting has taken place, the sensed force is close to zero demonstrating the absence of frictional forces due to the pulling robot.

10.4 Conclusion

In this chapter the modeling, simulation and control of a robotic meat cutting cell is described. The modeling process for the robot, the meat, visual primitives and the interaction between muscles is outlined. A control scheme is proposed using visual and force data to deal with uncertainties about the object behavior. The presented results show how both local and global visual primitives can be used to compensate for object deformations during the separation procedure. In particular, it is shown that large deformations require a fast local system in order to re-adjust the robot's motion on-line.

An innovative force controller is outlined and validated for the separation of deformable objects. This force controller creates an impedance relationship between two orthogonal directions to minimize global deformation. Hence increased resistive forces generate a slicing motion, thus avoiding any rupture. A series of experiments have been carried out to evaluate the performance of this controller. In summary, these tests prove that the proposed force controller performs much better compared with a position controller. It would be possible, by changing the cutting angle and velocities, to construct an effective cutting controller without a force feedback as shown by the increase in performance of all control laws as θ increases. Indeed, previous researchers have focused on optimizing cutting parameters for specific materials. Improving upon these methods, the current work demonstrates that by using the resistive force as an input to induce a slicing motion, this costly step can be avoided. This controller is combined with a visual servoing system, to allow the robotic system to cut along deformable trajectories. This position based visual servoing system can perform clean and efficient cutting operations in spite of un-modeled object deformations. Furthermore a desired cutting velocity can be set off-line allowing for a very accurate force control with a reasonable cutting speed. However the position based visual servoing scheme requires an estimate of the trajectory. This estimate allows the calculation of the curve parameters and thus the formulation of a trajectory that results in a constant cutting speed. Furthermore information about the material such as the height and surface profile are required. The controller needs knowledge of the material height in order to reset the trajectory once the knife has left the material. This requirement could be eliminated by using a more precise force controller. Finally, it should be noted that the scheme is very sensitive to calibration errors and thus requires a painstaking and precise calibration of intrinsic and extrinsic camera parameters, this can be mitigated by transforming the controller into the image space.[49]

While robots are widely used in the food industry, they have not been as prevalent as their counterparts in other industries, for instance in automotive manufacturing. A contributing factor is the challenge of manipulating and separating parts which are both deformable and non-standard, as discussed in this chapter. There are however other significant challenges which are limiting robot deployment. For example hygiene standards are extremely rigorous and require systems to be thoroughly cleaned to avoid germ transmission. Worker safety is another critical aspect due to the presence of dangerous tools and the necessary proximity between workers and robots. On the other hand, an integrated robotic system would help with quality control and reduce work related injuries. Whilst there remains several challenges to overcome, recent research efforts and promising results indicate a future wave of robot deployment in the food industry, increasing productivity, food hygiene and improving operator safety.

Acknowledgments

This chapter describes work carried out in the framework of the ARMS project, a project funded by the ANR (Agence Nationale de la Recherche), reference ANR-10-SEGI-000. Parts of the equipment used here were funded by the project ROBO-TEX, reference ANR-10-EQPX-44-01. Additionally, research was sponsored by the Office of the Secretary of Defense and was accomplished under Agreement Number W911NF-17-3-0004. The views and conclusions contained in this chapter are those of the authors and should not be interpreted as representing the official policies, either expressed or implied, of the Office of the Secretary of Defense or the U.S. Government. The U.S. Government is authorized to reproduce and distribute reprints for Government purposes notwithstanding any copyright notation herein.

References

1. U.S. Census Bureau, The 2016 annual survey of manufactures, annual survey of manufactures: General statistics: Statistics for industry groups and industries: 2016 and 2015, Tech. Rep., U.S. Federal Statistical System (2017).
2. Food and Agriculture Organization of the United Nations., Faostat statistics database. Tech. Rep., United Nations (2017).
3. R. Gebbers and V. I. Adamchuk, Precision agriculture and food security, *Science* **327**(5967), 828–831 (2010).
4. G. A. Nayik, K. Muzaffar and A. Gull. Robotics and food technology: A mini review, *Journal of Nutrition & Food Sciences* **5**(4), 1–11 (2015).

5. J. Iqbal, Z. H. Khan and A. Khalid, Prospects of robotics in food industry, *Food Science and Technology,* **37**(2), 159–165 (2017).

6. J. Mussman, Documentary. Rotten: Cod is dead, Zero Point Zero Production Inc. (2018).

7. National Oceanic and Atmospheric Administration, Fisheries of the United States, 2016 report, Tech. Rep., U.S Department of Commerce (2018).

8. R. Masey, J. Gray, T. Dodd and D. Caldwell, Guidelines for the design of low-cost robots for the food industry, *Industrial Robot: An International Journal* **37**(6), 509–517 (2010).

9. A. Petit, V. Lippiello, G. A. Fontanelli and B. Siciliano, Tracking elastic deformable objects with an RGB-D sensor for a pizza chef robot, *Robotics and Autonomous Systems* **88**, 187–201 (2017).

10. D. Navarro-Alarcon, H. M. Yip, Z. Wang, Y.-H. Liu, F. Zhong, T. Zhang and P. Li, Automatic 3-D manipulation of soft objects by robotic arms with an adaptive deformation model, *IEEE Transactions on Robotics* **32**(2), 429–441 (2016).

11. J. Sanchez, J.-A. Corrales, B.-C. Bouzgarrou and Y. Mezouar, Robotic manipulation and sensing of deformable objects in domestic and industrial applications: A survey, *The International Journal of Robotics Research* **37**(7), 688-716(2018).

12. P. Long, W. Khalil and P. Martinet, Dynamic modeling of cooperative robots holding flexible objects. In *Proceedings of the 2015 International Conference on Advanced Robotics (ICAR),* pp. 182–187 (2015).

13. P. Long, W. Khalil and P. Martinet, Dynamic modeling of parallel robots with flexible platforms, *Mechanism and Machine Theory* **81**, 21–35 (2014).

14. J. Das and N. Sarkar, Autonomous shape control of a deformable object by multiple manipulators, *Journal of Intelligent & Robotic Systems* **62**(1), 3–27 (2011).

15. T. Wada, S. Hirai, S. Kawamura and N. Kamiji, Robust manipulation of deformable objects by a simple pid feedback. In *Proceedings of the 2001 IEEE International Conference on Robotics and Automation (ICRA)*, vol. 1, pp. 85–90 (2001).

16. X. Delebarre, E. Dégoulange, P. Dauchez and Y. Bouffard-Vercelli, Force control of a two-arm robot manipulating a deformable object. In *Experimental Robotics II, R. Chatila and G. Hirzinger (eds).*, Springer (1993).

17. W. O'Connor, Control of flexible mechanical systems: Wave-based techniques. In *American Control Conference, 2007. ACC '07*, pp. 4192–4202 (2007), doi:10.1109/ACC.2007.4283157.

18. D. Weer and S. Rock, Experiments in object impedance control for flexible objects. In *Proceedings of the 1994 IEEE International Conference on Robotics and Automation (ICRA)*, vol. 2, pp. 1222–1227 (1994).

19. D. Navarro-Alarcon, Y. hui Liu, J. Romero and P. Li, Model-free visually servoed deformation control of elastic objects by robot manipulators, *IEEE Transactions on Robotics* **29**(6), 1457–1468 (2013), doi:10.1109/TRO.2013.2275651.

20. V. Lippiello, B. Siciliano and L. Villani, Robot interaction control using force and vision. In *Proceedings of the 2006 IEEE/RSJ International Conference on Intelligent Robots and Systems (IROS)*, pp. 1470–1475 (2006).

21. S. Misra, K. Ramesh and A. M. Okamura, Modeling of tool-tissue interactions for computer-based surgical simulation: A literature review, *Presence: Teleoperators and Virtual Environments* **17**(5), 463–491 (2008).

22. C. Mendoza and C. Laugier, Simulating soft tissue cutting using finite element models. In *Proceedings of the 2003 IEEE International Conference on Robotics and Automation (ICRA)*, Vol. 1, pp. 1109–1114 (2003).

23. U. Meier, O. López, C. Monserrat, M. C. Juan and M. Alcaniz, Real-time deformable models for surgery simulation: A survey, *Computer Methods and Programs in Biomedicine* **77**(3), 183–197 (2005).
24. E. Nabil, B. Belhassen-Chedli and G. Grigore, Soft material modeling for robotic task formulation and control in the muscle separation process, *Robotics and Computer-Integrated Manufacturing* **32**, 37–53 (2015).
25. H. Delingette, S. Cotin and N. Ayache, A hybrid elastic model allowing real-time cutting, deformations and force-feedback for surgery training and simulation. In *1999 Proceedings of Computer Animation.* pp. 70–81 (1999).
26. L. M. Vigneron, J. G. Verly and S. K. Warfield, On extended finite element method (xfem) for modelling of organ deformations associated with surgical cuts. In *Medical Simulation*, Springer, (2004).
27. X. Jin, G. R. Joldes, K. Miller, K. H. Yang and A. Wittek, Meshless algorithm for soft tissue cutting in surgical simulation, *Computer Methods in Biomechanics and Biomedical Engineering* **17**(7), 800–811 (2014).
28. T. Chanthasopeephan, J. P. Desai and A. C. Lau, Measuring forces in liver cutting: New equipment and experimental results, *Annals of Biomedical Engineering* **31**(11), 1372–1382 (2003).
29. M. C. Gemici and A. Saxena, Learning haptic representation for manipulating deformable food objects. In *Proceedings of the 2014 IEEE/RSJ International Conference on Intelligent Robots and Systems (IROS),* pp. 638–645 (2014).
30. A. Atkins, X. Xu and G. Jeronimidis, Cutting, by 'pressing and slicing,' of thin floppy slices of materials illustrated by experiments on cheddar cheese and salami, *Journal of Materials Science* **39**(8), 2761–2766 (2004).
31. D. Zhou, M. Claffee, K. Lee and G. McMurray, Cutting,'by pressing and slicing', applied to the robotic cut of bio-materials, Part II: force during slicing and pressing cuts. In *Proceedings of 2006 IEEE International Conference on Robotics and Automation (ICRA)*, pp. 2256–2261 (2006).
32. E. Reyssat, T. Tallinen, M. Le Merrer and L. Mahadevan, Slicing softly with shear, *Physical Review Letters* **109**(24), 244301 (2012).
33. M. Mahvash and V. Hayward, Haptic rendering of cutting: A fracture mechanics approach, *Haptics-e* **2**(3), 1–12 (2001).
34. G. Arnold, L. Leiteritz, S. Zahn and H. Rohm, Ultrasonic cutting of cheese: Composition affects cutting work reduction and energy demand, *International Dairy Journal* **19**(5), 314–320 (2009).
35. INSEE, Industrie agroalimentaire. http://www.insee.fr/fr/themes/document.asp?ref_id=T10F181 (Accessed April 22, 2013).
36. J. Billingsley, A. Visala and M. Dunn, Robotics in agriculture and forestry. In *Springer Handbook of Robotics, B.* Siciliano and O. Khatib (eds). Springer-Verlag (2008).
37. C. Sang, G. Zhang, T. Fuhlbrigge, T. Watson and R. Tallian, Applications and requirements of industrial robots in meat processing. In *Proceedings of the 2013 IEEE International Conference on Automation Science and Engineering (CASE)*, pp. 1107–1112 (2013), doi:10.1109/CoASE.2013.6653967.
38. L. Hinrichsen, Manufacturing technology in the danish pig slaughter industry, *Meat science* **84**(2), 271–275 (2010).
39. G. Guire, L. Sabourin, G. Gogu and E. Lemoine, Robotic cell with redundant architecture and force control: application to cutting and boning In *Proceedings of the 2010 IEEE 19th International Workshop on Robotics in Alpe-Adria-Danube Region (RAAD)*, pp. 99–104 (2010a).

40. G. Guire, L. Sabourin, G. Gogu and E. Lemoine, Robotic cell for beef carcass primal cutting and pork ham boning in meat industry, *Industrial Robot: An International Journal* **37**(6), 532–541 (2010b).

41. Y. Kusuda, The use of robots in the japanese food industry, *Industrial Robot: An International Journal* **37**(6), 503–508 (2010).

42. P. Long, W. Khalil and P. Martinet, Modeling and control of a meat-cutting robotic cell. In *Proceedings of the 2013 16th International Conference on Advanced Robotics (ICAR)*, pp. 1–6 (2013).

43. W. Khalil and J. Kleinfinger, A new geometric notation for open and closed-loop robots. In *Proceedings of the 1986 IEEE International Conference on Robotics and Automation.*, vol. 3, pp. 1174–1179 (1986).

44. N. Hogan, Impedance control: An approach to manipulation: Part ii Implementation, *Journal of Dynamic Systems, Measurement, and Control* **107**(1), 8–16 (1985).

45. F. Chaumette and S. Hutchinson, Visual servo control, Part I basic approaches, *IEEE Robotics & Automation Magazine* **13**(4), 82–90 (2006).

46. P. Long, W. Khalil and P. Martinet, Force/vision control for robotic cutting of soft materials. In *Proceedings of the 2014 IEEE/RSJ International Conference on Intelligent Robots and Systems (IROS)*, pp. 4716–4721 (2014).

47. B. Yang, H. Wang, W. Chen and Z. Wang, Vision-based cutting control of deformable objects. In *Proceedings of the 2016 IEEE International Conference on Real-time Computing and Robotics (RCAR)*, pp. 650–655 (2016).

48. B. Thuilot, P. Martinet, L. Cordesses and J. Gallice, Position based visual servoing: keeping the object in the field of vision. In *Proceedings of the 2002 IEEE International Conference on Robotics and Automation (ICRA)*, vol. 2, pp. 1624–1629 (2002).

49. P. Long, W. Khalil and P. Martinet, Robotic cutting of soft materials using force control & image moments. In *Proceedings of the 2014 13th International Conference on Control Automation Robotics & Vision (ICARCV)*, pp. 474–479 (2014).

© 2020 World Scientific Publishing Company
https://doi.org/10.1142/9789811222849_0011

Chapter 11

Collaborative Robots for Assembly of Large-Scale Structures

Ashis G. Banerjee

11.1 Introduction

Traditionally, industrial robots have operated in an independent manner regardless of the industry sector, where none of the robots' actions have any impact on the other robots or humans working on the factory floors. Such independent operations have been realized by keeping the robots sufficiently far apart from each other, completely separated from humans inside different work cells, and making them perform well-defined tasks repetitively while often keeping them stationary. This mode of operation has worked well for straightforward tasks such as welding and painting assembly structures, as for example, in automotive lines, by enhancing the overall production yield or efficiency while practically eliminating all forms of safety risks.

However, this mode is less useful for more complex assembly tasks such as bonding, fastening, and riveting of large, non-planar structures. Such tasks would benefit from the robots *collaborating* with each other and potentially, even humans, while still ensuring full safety of all the involved agents (both humans and robots). The benefits would come in the form of both quality and quantity considerations. Collaborating robots would be able to achieve a higher degree of accuracy and precision in terms of maintaining strict dimensional tolerances and avoiding flaws or defects. Simultaneously, they would increase the yield even further by working concurrently, rather than sequentially as done usually for the independent robots, and assisting each other as well as the humans in completing the tasks left over due to failures and boredom or fatigue conditions, respectively.

Due to all these reasons, collaborative robots, or *co-bots*, in short, are increasingly becoming popular in large-scale structures assembly operations. The co-bots are either controlled automatically but rely on human guidance for cognitively challenging tasks, or act in a semi-autonomous manner with limited human inputs, or may even be completely autonomous with no human intervention required. Interestingly though, the related literature is still sparse, and has only gained some traction over the past six-seven years. This relative paucity of literature can be attributed to the additional perception, planning, scheduling, and control challenges imposed by multiple robots sensing and acting in different, but overlapping, regions of the same workspace. The robots often use different types of actuators, and have varying degrees of freedom and configuration spaces. The challenges are pronounced not only because of the increase in the dimensionalities of the robots' state-action spaces but also owing to the overarching need of avoiding collisions with all the agents at any cost without sacrificing the overall yield substantially. All the challenges are exacerbated if humans are involved in-the-loop for operation execution and/or decision making.

In this chapter, we focus on the recent advances in addressing these challenges as broken down according to the application sector. Note that we do not discuss other works that cover the use of co-bots to assemble structures in non-industry settings, such as in space[14,20] or in marine environments.[10] Before discussing the advances, it is, however, useful to briefly review some of the original works on this topic, and point the reader to a new survey article that describes the different assembly metrics and strategies for multi-robot systems.

One of the earliest works in this regard was reported in Simmons et al.[13] Here, a team of three robots with widely different configurations was used to successfully perform a docking task with high precision, something that could not be accomplished by any of the robots individually. The main contribution was in the development of a generic software architecture, comprising planning, executive, and behavioral layers for goal-level decision making, task synchronization, sequencing and execution, and, sensor and actuator-level interfacing, respectively. This architecture allowed the robots to act autonomously while explicitly coordinating their actions with each other.

The same group of three robots was later used in Sellner et al.[11] to study the usefulness of sliding autonomy, a concept that bridged the gap between complete teleoperation and pure autonomy. The novel aspect of this study was in the consideration of mixed human-robot teams, where a remote operator had the option of joining and leaving the team, as and when desired, to assist in performing certain tasks or aspects of the tasks without adversely affecting the robots' coordination. The robots decided for themselves when to seek help from the remote operator.

The robot team and the assembled test structure are shown in Fig. 11.1. Two sets of experiments, one enumerating the team's performance across four different collaboration strategies and the other comparing a variety of user interface designs to facilitate the human's responses to help requests, demonstrated that the inclusion of the human operator had a positive impact in increasing the robustness and efficiency of the overall team. The benefits of this architecture and mixed human-robot team were further shown via more large-scale space structures assemblies in Simmons et al.[12]

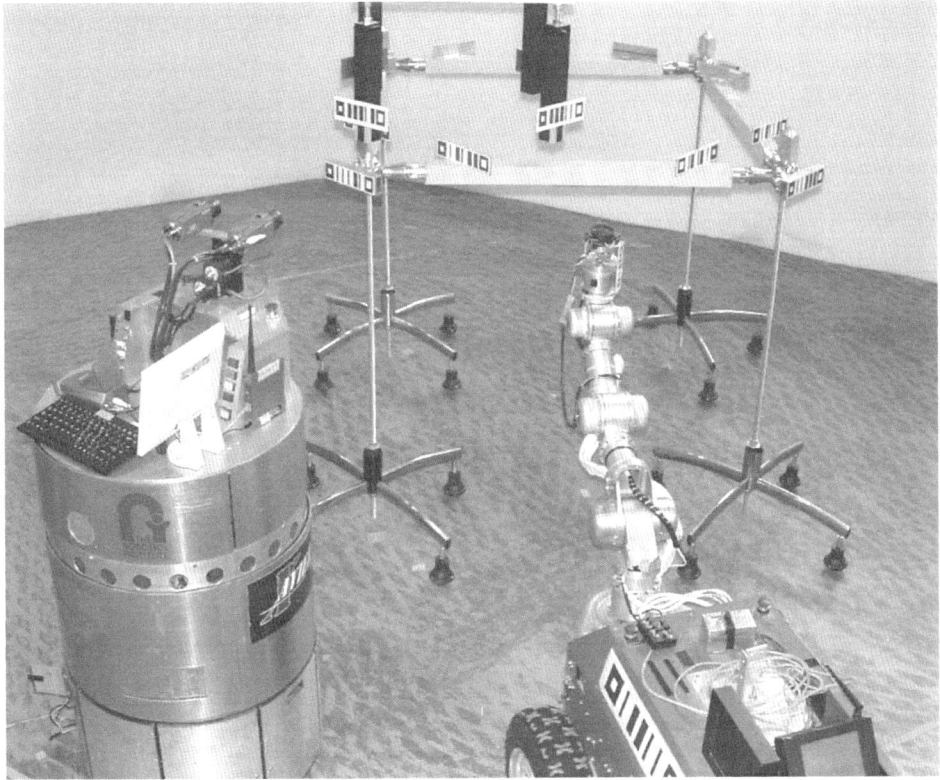

Fig. 11.1. A team of three collaborating robots completing the assembly of a square structure (reused with permission from Sellner et al.[11]) The left robot is used purely for perception, the crane robot (only black tentacles are visible toward the top portion of the structure) is used for heavy-duty manipulation, and the mobile manipulator on the bottom right provides weaker but more precise manipulation.

Very recently, a comprehensive review of different assembly strategies and quality and performance metrics for multi-robot teams was presented in Marvel et al.[7] Each team consisted of two or more robots, which included industrial robot arms, dexterous robot hands, and autonomous mobile platforms such as guided vehicles. It is worth noting here that the strategies differed based on the types of assemblies, and included different search-based, tilting, meshing, offsetting, contour matching, visual servoing, and dynamic fixturing algorithms to synchronize the motions of the robots. The metrics are summarized in Fig. 11.2 and span a wide range from strategy computation and assembly process time and efficiency to resultant forces and energy consumptions.

Metric	Category	Measurement	Unit
Efficiency	Computational complexity	Assembly strategy	O notation
		Impact of using alternative assembly strategies	O notation
		Single versus multiple robots	O notation
	Effort efficiency	Programming time	Seconds
		Optimization/parameter tuning time	Seconds
		Commissioning versus use time	Seconds
		Single versus multiple robot programming time	Seconds
		Single versus multiple robot cost	Monetary unit
	Process quality	Ratio of assembly successes to failures	Dimensionless
		Mean time to failure	Seconds or cycles
Time	Process time	Average time to complete a single assembly	Seconds
		Minimum time to complete a single assembly	Seconds
		Maximum time to complete a single assembly	Seconds
		Standard deviation of assembly completion times	Seconds
		Sensitivity to parameter changes	Seconds
		Time spent for assembly versus other operations	Seconds
		Single versus multiple robot assembly times	Seconds
Motion	Displacement	Average positional error in final assembly pose with respect to initial assembly pose	Meters
	Motion effort	Distance traveled during assembly	Meters
		Joint displacement during assembly	Radians/degrees
		Energy expended during assembly	Watts
		Distance traveled for assembly versus other operations	Meters
Force	Force transfer	Maximum force measured by robot on any axis	Newtons/Newton-meters
		Average force measured by robot on any axis	Newtons/Newton-meters
		Independently measure maximum and average forces at the tool, assembly part, and fixture	Newtons/Newton-meters

Fig. 11.2. Example metrics to measure the performances of multi-robot teams in assembly tasks (adapted from Marvel et al.[7])

11.2 Aircraft Assembly

Aircraft assembly operations have started investigating the role of co-bots only in the last couple of years, largely driven by the need of the large manufacturers to start producing long-lasting and extremely reliable aircraft at lower costs or faster rates. One of the first published literature on this topic can be found in Dogar et al.[2] where a comprehensive multi-scale assembly system was presented.

Figure 11.3 shows a bird's eye view of the entire system. Such assembly operations require the successful completion of a variety of tasks with different parts sizes, completion times, and precision requirements. Consequently, the researchers developed a hierarchical planning approach to link multi-scale perception with multi-scale manipulation where the visual perception resolution was matched to the desired gripper manipulation resolution. The approach could detect and recover from failures by reverting to wider field-of-view sensing to achieve re-localization. Collaboration among the robots ensured that they transported heavy objects together and co-localized the assembly contact locations on the parts. Experiments with four KUKA youBot robots on wing fastener insertion operations demonstrated an extremely high success rate, indicating the tremendous potential of co-bots to execute (speed up without sacrificing quality) complex aircraft assembly tasks autonomously.

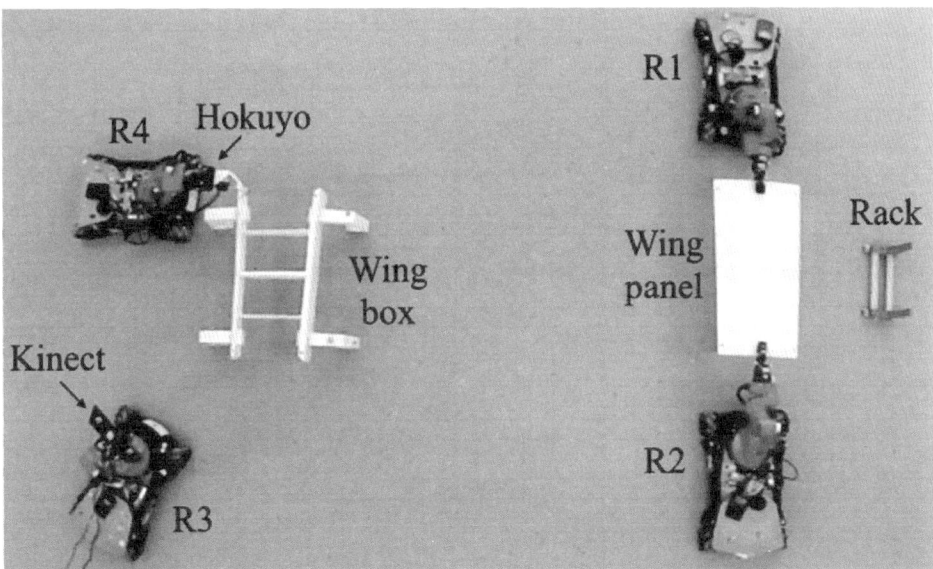

Fig. 11.3. A top view of the overall four collaborative robot system for aircraft wing-like structure assembly (reused with permission from Dogar et al.[2])

A similar case study involving four collaborative ABB robots, shown in Fig. 11.4, for aircraft wing drilling operations was reported in Tereshchuk et al.[17] In this work, a multi-robot scheduling algorithm was presented to allocate the hole drilling tasks so as to maximize the overall operation efficiency. The algorithm had two stages. The first stage consisted of a geometric partitioning-based robot workload balancing method combined with intuitive, staggered robot trajectories to

ensure collision avoidance under nominal conditions with no failures. The second
stage comprised a market-driven auction-based method to assign the leftover holes,
arising due to task failures, among the robots so as to again balance their workload
(and, thereby, complete the operation faster) as much as possible without causing
any collision. Both simulation and physical experiments demonstrated promising
performance with very low scheduler run-times and high efficiency values. However, further investigation is required to evaluate the algorithm's performance for
actual aircraft assembly operations involving full-sized wing structures and a considerably larger number of co-bots.

Fig. 11.4. An aircraft wing assembly work cell (scaled down to 15% of actual size) comprising four
autonomously controlled collaborative robots

11.3 Automotive Assembly

While stationary, non-collaborative robots have been used in automotive assembly
lines for several decades, collaborative robots have only been in action over the
past decade or so. One of the earliest works is found in Gravel et al.,[4] where
collaboration between the Ford Motor Company, ABB Robotics, and BrainTech
Inc. led to the development of vision-guided robotized assembly of transmission
torque converters, transmission body valves, engine heads, and engine pistons. The
ABB robot was equipped with a dampener, low pass filter and PI-based controller

of all the three force and moment components, and the BrainTech system used a proprietary calibration and template matching software named eVisionFactory™ for 3D visual guidance. A suitable design of experiments (DOE) was also used to obtain the optimal set of force control parameters. The deployment of this system led to the removal of ergonomic problems in Ford factory lines, thereby, avoiding worker injuries. Simultaneously, it caused accumulation of domain knowledge to develop even better robotic assembly solutions for ABB.

The need for synergistic collaboration between humans and robots in automotive assembly lines was highlighted as a key research direction in Michalos et al.[8] Subsequently, the topics of safety and stability in human-robot collaborative environments for materials handling operations were investigated from a control system and interface development perspective in Surdilovic et al.[15] This investigation led to the design of a controller for a physically passive co-bot manipulator that redirected the human operator force from assembly task motion. Such redirection worked well for relatively small payloads with limited power assistance to reduce the physical strain on the humans while simultaneously increasing productivity and quality. However, this redirection was not sufficient for large payloads greater than 50 kg. Instead, an admittance display-based impedance controller was designed to address this issue. The controller was embedded inside a human-robot interface that provided different admittances to the human and introduced virtual obstacles in the workspace to constrain and guide or slide the motions of the manipulated parts. As a result, the operator experienced substantially reduced effort in completing the task with the remaining force/torque balance compensated by a heavy-duty power-assist system.

A comparison of traditional fixture-based robotic cell and cooperating robot-based work cell for spot welding of automobile floor panels with floor central panels was presented in Papakostas et al.[9] Although this comparison was done only in a simulated environment, the authors argued that the operational cost and time assessment would be equally applicable to actual production systems. Unsurprisingly, the authors concluded that the traditional set-up is simple to operate and inexpensive to install, whereas, cooperating robots would enable far greater versatility in assembling different kinds of large-scale structures in the same work cell. However, this study did not address how to control the cooperating robots and realize multi-robot coordination in real time.

More recently, a foundational framework was proposed in Djuric et al.[1] to facilitate the design, development and integration of co-bots in smart factories with an emphasis on automobile assembly. The proposed framework had a four-tier structure: system, work cells, machines, and human workers. The idea of Zachman Framework,[24] an ontology often used for enterprise architectures, was then adapted to come up with a matrix of all the factors that need to be considered in order to increase the adoption of co-bots in factories in a safe and reliable manner. The matrix consisted of four rows, corresponding to the what (data), how (function), where (inter-connection), and why (motivation) interrogatives, and five columns, corresponding to contextual and conceptual (both system-level), logical and physical (both embodiment-level), and details-based implementation requirements.

Based on this matrix, the authors developed a set of key performance attributes (see Fig. 11.5), and argued that they would be the same regardless of the co-bot type and capabilities. However, the interactions of the co-bots with the manipulated parts or components should be domain specific and need to account for not only parts geometries and processing conditions, but also the factory topology in terms of the layouts of the work cells and machines. Accordingly, the co-bots interfaces and communications between the framework tiers would become especially important. Furthermore, redundant safety measures in the form of risk analysis, motion prediction, worker training, and fail safe controllers would have to be included as appropriate at each framework tier, and particularly for the physical and details layers. However, the study was purely conceptual, and no actual validation results were reported.

A related topic, which has become increasingly important in the recent past, is safety in the context of physical human-robot interaction. A representative example of this kind of work, motivated by automotive engine assembly, is found in Unhelkar et al.[21] Here, the authors developed a single-axis, human-assisting co-bot system that included human motion prediction during temporal planning to ensure both efficiency and safety of the executed motions. A combination of physical and simulation experiments demonstrated statistically significant improvements over an industry standard-emulating baseline with respect to quantitative interaction measures during mobile manipulation tasks. These results are promising, and it would be useful to generalize the approach for previously unseen human motions, multi-axes robot motions, and (partial) completion of assembled structures.

11.4 Construction Structures

Over the past few years, co-bots have become popular in the construction sector to assemble freeform spatial structures. Such structures, made of glass or carbon fibers, are produced using filament winding that does not require cores or molds,

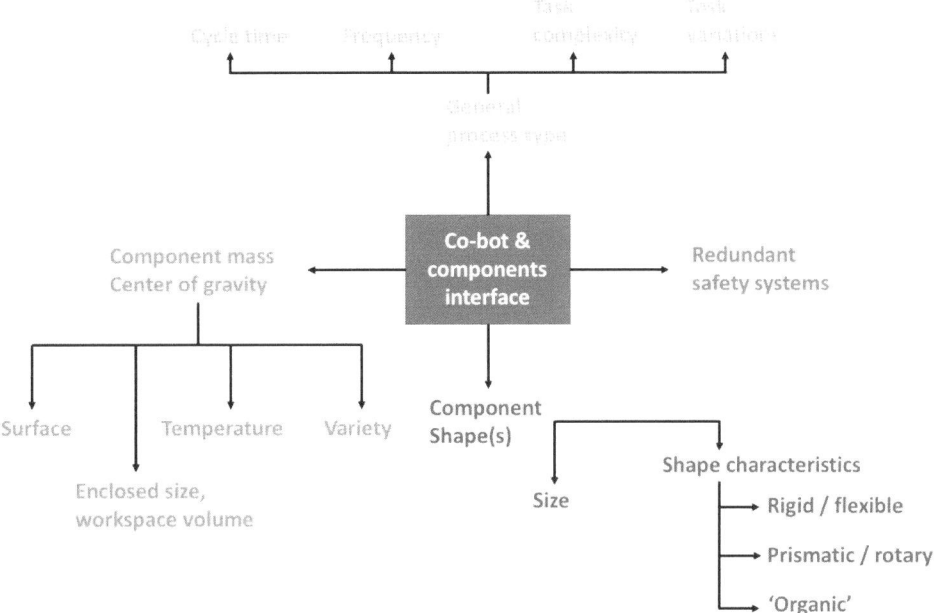

Fig. 11.5. Co-bot interactions with automotive assembly processes and components (adapted from Djuric et al.[1])

unlike in the aerospace and automotive sectors. One of the first published works on this topic appeared in Vasey et al.[22] where a large team of multi-disciplinary researchers developed an end-to-end system to evaluate the benefits of human-robot collaboration to assemble intricate and large-scale structures. Their system comprised a custom end effector, a generic inverse kinematics solver, and a tension control mechanism for the robot, an assembly instruction generation interface using a wearable device, computational methods for fiber layout generation and robot motion planning that accounted for reachability and collisions, and wireless communication among all the hardware and software modules. The system, therefore, could be used to investigate how to deal with off-nominal situations arising due to human errors or the use of non-standard materials. Furthermore, it provided a useful platform to study certain fundamental aspects of human-robot collaboration in construction settings, particularly the separation of tasks between humans and robots, and the central role of coordination and communication in ensuring better control over the fabrication processes.

Another recent use of human-robot collaboration in the construction sector appeared in Lindemann et al.,[6] where a human operator and a robot teamed up for more precise control of adaptive molding of non-standard, double-curved, fiber-reinforced concrete panels. Such collaboration laid out the foundation for fabrication of customized concrete panels much faster than using conventional molding while avoiding any wastage of formwork materials. The fabrication process involved a suite of six steps, ranging from formwork generation and digital pattern creation to adaptive concrete thickness variation and laying out of fibers, all of which required close-knit interactions between a 6 degree of freedom robot with multiple end effectors and a human operator. The results were promising in terms of both the quality and variety of panels produced, thereby, opening up an avenue for more widespread adoption of human-robot collaboration in architecting both aesthetically pleasing and functionally beneficial large-scale structures.

A very interesting use of co-bots in constructing non-regular spatial structures was explored recently in Yablonina et al.[23] This work considered the trajectories of the entire ABB robot arms to avoid obstacles using a rapidly-exploring random tree (RRT)-based motion planner. The planner computed non-intuitive and collision-free trajectories using a high fidelity simulator of the physical set-up. As a result, the co-bots could operate in close spatial proximities to the structural elements. Following the work done in Gramazio et al.,[3] only two co-bots were used at any point of time. One of the robots stabilized the already-assembled structure, whereas the other manipulated (picked and placed) new structural elements. Furthermore, if a robot assembled steel tubes, the other robot acted as a structural support to keep the assembly stable before it could be fixed. Such effective collaboration led to the construction of highly differentiated frame structures that could be put together without requiring additional support structures.

Very recently, researchers reported the use of robotic collaboration for timber construction in Zurich (2018).[25] Both prefabrication of the load-bearing timber modules and precise positioning of the beams according to the spatial structure arrangement were performed using two collaborative robots. Similar to the previous work, the robots employed a path planning method to avoid collisions with already-assembled structural elements. The final bolting process was, however, carried out manually. As in the case of the non-regular spatial structures, this form of collaboration would enable construction of more customized residential units that would be expected to last longer than conventionally built structures.

11.5   Miscellaneous Products

Apart from all the applications in the aerospace, automotive, and construction sectors, collaborative robots have found some use in assembling miscellaneous large-scale structures. One such use was described in Knepper et al.[5] where a team of heterogeneous robots completed furniture assembly tasks based just on an initial user-provided list of parts geometry specifications. To do so, the robot team first analyzed the computer aided design (CAD) files of the components, inferred the relations (coordinate transforms) to mate sub-assembly pairs, and performed a depth-first search over the space of feasible matings. Second, a symbolic planner was employed to compute the sequence of assembly operations that would satisfy all the mating precedence conditions. The plans were executed by the KUKA youBot robots in a distributed manner. The robots were equipped with customized grippers to facilitate screwing operations. Experimental demonstrations, an example of which is shown in Fig. 11.6, were very promising, but limited to table assembly and flipping-type manipulations. Moreover, the work did not consider failure detection and recovery.

Fig. 11.6. Two robots collaborating to assemble a table (reused with permission from Knepper et al.[5])

Another miscellaneous assembly (motivated by manual automotive assembly lines) case study is found in Tsarouchi et al.[19] where a hybrid human-robot collaboration framework and work cell design was presented to build hydraulic pumps. The framework included a basic task allocation method between humans and robots by taking into account their respective capabilities, and using mean resource utilization and flowtime as the performance criteria. It then used gesture-based communication to coordinate the allocated tasks and ensure that task switching occurred seamlessly. The different software and hardware modules interacted with each other by exchanging Robot Operating System (ROS) messages. The reported results, an example of which is shown in Fig. 11.7, were limited but quite promising. This indicates that human-robot collaboration could lead to improved resource utilization for many assembly operations provided dynamic task allocation and gesture recognition for concurrent task execution are implemented. Another noticeable shortcoming was the separation of human and robot workspaces, which needs to be removed to make the framework broadly useful in assembly shop floors.

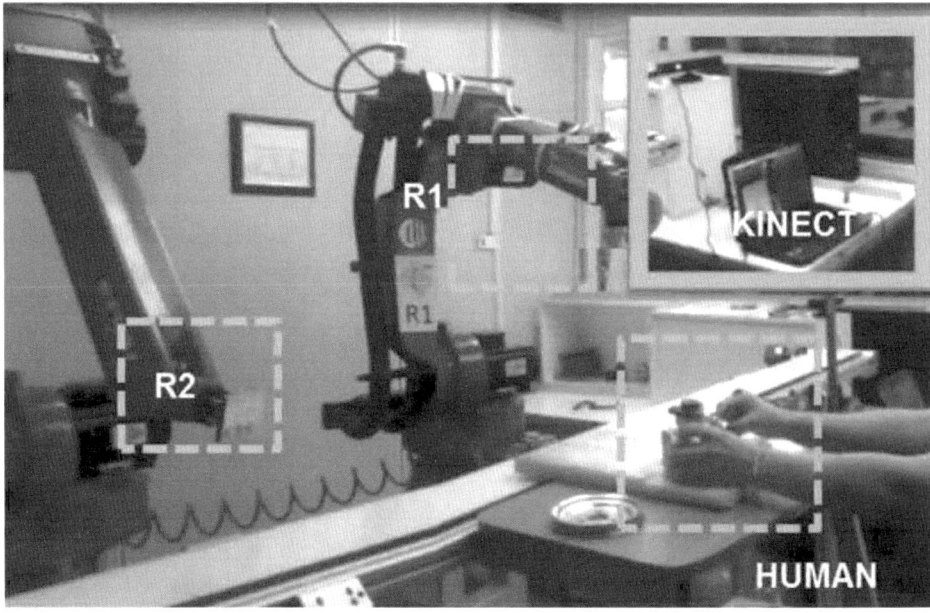

Fig. 11.7. Two robots collaborating with a human operator to assemble a hydraulic pump (reused with permission from Tsarouchi et al.[19])

11.6   Conclusions

As discussed in the previous sections, there is a growing trend toward autonomous assembly operations, with and without humans in-the-loop, using collaborative robot teams. This trend is discussed in details in the context of assembling structures in Tibbits (2017).[18] As pointed out in the article, fabrication of structures, is quite different from many other forms of manufacturing in the sense that the products are often highly customized, need to satisfy strict quality requirements, and are expensive and time consuming to build. These characteristics are particularly true in the aerospace and architecture/construction sectors, and less important for automobiles, furniture, and other industrial equipment. Correspondingly, the need for autonomy through robot-robot as well as human-robot collaboration is felt more strongly in the first two sectors. Quite naturally, we see more published literature on co-bots in these sectors over the past few years.

Even in practice, it is, therefore, hardly surprising that the aerospace and construction sectors have started adopting co-bots more extensively in their production facilities as compared to the other sectors. Taking the aerospace industry as the example, we now see large teams of robots playing prominent roles in all aspects of aircraft assembly operations, from joining the wings to the main body and putting the wings together by attaching the ribs and spars with the skins to connecting the electrical wires and devices. Figure 11.8 shows an example of a typical Airbus aircraft assembly operation involving the complex choreography of stationary robot manipulators, mobile robot manipulators, automated guided vehicles, and workers in the middle of already-assembled and to-be-assembled components.

Another different but equally interesting example of co-bots performing assembly operations, in the form of riveting tasks, happens within a Boeing 777 fuselage. The fact that co-bots are being used both for exterior (unconfined space) and interior (confined space) assembly tasks requiring varying levels of precision, speaks volumes about their versatility, deployment ease, and trustworthiness. The common thread running through all these applications is the benefit of allocating more cognitively challenging but ergonomically safer tasks to humans, who can assist the robots, when they fail or do not know how to act, in a supervisory capacity. Such re-allocation of tasks, therefore, enables one worker to supervise multiple robots, increasing productivity, allows the works to perform interesting jobs keeping them engaged and motivated, and perhaps most critically, reduces their long-term health risks as they do not have to carry out 'dirty' and 'dangerous' jobs (e.g., riveting) repetitively.

The increasing adoption of co-bots in certain assembly production facilities and the corresponding (moderate) growth in the number of related research publications, however, does not imply that all the challenges, as laid out in Section 11.1, have been addressed satisfactorily. In fact, more Research and Development (R&D) work needs to be done to bring co-bots to every assembly floor where they can yield benefits. The main outstanding R&D issues are outlined below:[a]

---

[a]It is worth noting that many of these issues are the same for other applications of industrial collaborative robots.

Fig. 11.8. The process of assembling an Airbus A-380 with a large number of collaborative robots and humans in the presence of both stationary and moving components (reused with permission from Tibbits[18]).

- Perception or situational awareness is one of the key ingredients for the successful use of (semi)-autonomous co-bots in assembly floors. Perception quality, of course, depends on the type and quality of the measurements recorded by the sensors. The sensors can be fitted on the robots, installed in the workspace, or even worn by the human operators. While there are plenty of options in selecting the sensors, cameras, both standard Red, Green and Blue (RGB) and augmented RGB plus Depth (RGB-D), and laser-based Light Imaging, Detection and Ranging devices (LIDARs) are the popular choices. With proper calibration, modern cameras and LIDARs can provide extremely high-quality images. However, each sensor type has its own set of limitations, as for example, visible light cameras cannot detect occluded objects. These limitations can be overcome to reconstruct complete workspaces through suitable fusion of images from multiple sensor sources of different types. Determining optimal sensor locations and types as well as performing accurate image fusion in real time, however, pose significant challenges that have not yet been addressed satisfactorily in actual production settings.

- While it is true that many human-robot interfaces and communication modes have been designed and analyzed in the co-bot literature (see Tan et al.[16] for a recent survey), no consensus has been reached yet regarding the most suitable choices. The reason is quite simple: none of the interfaces or communication modes have been consistently effective across different industry sectors or even among different assembly production facilities within the same sector. Considering that factory floors tend to be noisy environments from an auditory perspective, it is reasonable to believe that gestures would be the most effective communication medium. However, a standardized set of gestures with widely understood interpretations, analogous to what exists for aircraft taxiing, is currently missing for assembly operations. Similarly, there is a lack of standard requirements or templates in developing the interfaces. A comprehensive end user study, spanning a variety of assembly operations types, user profiles, and robot capabilities, might be useful in generating such standards.

- Many large-scale structures, such as aircraft wing and automobile body, are deformable. Yet, such deformations are often completely neglected while planning robot motions or scheduling robot tasks during the assembly process. Even though the robot controller might be able to compensate for such deformations (as, for example, by adjusting the end effector configuration) online to ensure that the assembly tasks are carried out precisely, this might lead to the generation of sub-optimal plans and schedules. The adverse effects are magnified for a team of collaborative robots as each robot's plan or schedule affects the others leading to an overall decrease in operation efficiency. Therefore, it is important to include reasonably high-fidelity deformation models, either analytical or finite element method (FEM)-based, within the planning and scheduling algorithms. While such inclusion is completely non-trivial and may require development of novel algorithms, the payoff should be well worth the time and effort.

- An overwhelming majority of multi-robot task allocation methods work well in practice under nominal conditions where there are no failures to recover from and the assembly structures do not change over long time periods. However, the methods encounter difficulties owing to their large run times whenever the structure geometry changes and robot/task failures occur. In such off-nominal scenarios, it would be tremendously beneficial to be able to re-allocate the tasks efficiently by only updating the affected plans and schedules. Storing a library of potential task switches that could be quickly searched should help significantly in this regard. It might even be possible to 'learn' how the tasks should be allocated given a set of collaborative agents and assembly conditions.

To summarize, while considerable progress has been made in the past few years on investigating the benefits and addressing the technical challenges of deploying collaborative robots to assemble large-scale structures, the progress varies depending on the industry sector. Some sectors have demonstrated a more keen interest to adopt the robots as compared to others based primarily on the competitive nature of their product markets, production volumes, and the ergonomic risks of their employees. Further work, preferably as joint industry-academia teams, is needed to ensure that the benefits are reaped more uniformly across all industry sectors regardless of the size and capacity of the enterprises.

References

1. A. Djuric, R. Urbanic and J. Rickli, A framework for collaborative robot (CoBot) integration in advanced manufacturing systems, *SAE International Journal of Materials and Manufacturing* **9**(2), 457–464 (2016).
2. M. Dogar, R.A. Knepper, A. Spielberg, C. Choi, H.I. Christensen and D. Rus, Multiscale assembly with robot teams, *The International Journal of Robotics Research* **34**(13), 1645–1659 (2015).
3. F. Gramazio, M. Kohlet and J. Willmann, *Aerial Constructures*. Park Books (2014).
4. D. Gravel, F. Maslar, G. Zhang, S. Nidamarthi, H. Chen and T. Fuhlbrigge, Toward robotizing powertrain assembly. In *7th World Congress on Intelligent Control and Automation,* pp. 541–546, Chongqing, China (2008).
5. R.A. Knepper, T. Layton, J. Romanishin and D. Rus, IkeaBot: An autonomous multi-robot coordinated furniture assembly system. In *IEEE International Conference on Robotics and Automation*, pp. 855–862, Karlsruhe, Germany (2013).
6. H. Lindemann, J. Petri, S. Neudecker and H. Kloft, *Process Chain for the Robotic Controlled Production of Non-standard, Double-curved, Fiber-reinforced Concrete Panels with an Adaptive Mould*. UCL Press (2017).
7. J.A. Marvel, R. Bostelman and J. Falco, Multi-robot assembly strategies and metrics, *ACM Computing Surveys* **51**(1), 14:1–14:32 (2018).
8. G. Michalos, S. Makris, N. Papakostas, D. Mourtzis and G. Chryssolouris, Automotive assembly technologies review: Challenges and outlook for a flexible and adaptive approach, *CIRP Journal of Manufacturing Science and Technology* **2**, 81–91 (2010).
9. N. Papakostas, G. Michalos, S. Makris, Z. Dimitris and G. Chryssolouris, Industrial applications with cooperating robots for flexible assembly, *International Journal of Computer Integrated Manufacturing* **24**(7), 640–650 (2011).
10. J. Paulos, N. Eckenstein, T. Tosun, J. Seo, J. Davey, J. Greco, V. Kumar and M. Yim, Automated self-assembly of large maritime structures by a team of robotic boats, *IEEE Transactions on Automation Science and Engineering* **12**(3), 958–968 (2015).

11. B. Sellner, F.W. Heger, L.M. Hiatt, R. Simmons and S. Singh, Coordinated multi-agent teams and sliding autonomy for large-scale assembly, *Proceedings of the IEEE* **94**(7), 1425–1444 (2006).

12. R. Simmons, S. Singh, F.W. Heger, L.M. Hiatt, S. Koterba, N. Melchior and B.P. Sellner, Human robot teams for large-scale assembly. In *Proceedings of the NASA Science Technology Conference*, pp. 1–6, Largo, MD, USA (2007).

13. R. Simmons, S. Singh, D. Hershberger, J. Ramos and T. Smith, First results in the coordination of heterogeneous robots for large-scale assembly. In *Experimental Robotics VII, D. Rus and S. Singh (eds)*. Springer (2001).

14. A. Stroupe, T. Huntsberger, A. Okon, H. Aghazarian and M. Robinson, Behavior-based multi-robot collaboration for autonomous construction tasks. In *IEEE/RSJ International Conference on Intelligent Robots and Systems,* pp. 1495–1500, Edmonton, Canada (2005).

15. D. Surdilovic, G. Schreck and U. Schmidt, Development of collaborative robots (COBOTS) for flexible human-integrated assmbly automation. In *41st International Symposium on Robotics and 6th German Conference on Robotics,* pp. 1–10, Munich, Germany (2010).

16. Q. Tan, Y. Tong, S. Wu and D. Li, Anthropocentric approach for smart assembly: Integration and collaboration, *Journal of Robotics* **2019**, 3146782, (2019).

17. V. Tereshchuk, J. Steward, N. Bykov, S. Pedigo, S. Devasia and A.G. Banerjee, An efficient scheduling algorithm for multi-robot task allocation in assembling aircraft structures, *IEEE Robotics and Automation Letters* **4**(4), 3844–3851 (2019).

18. S. Tibbits, From automated to autonomous assembly, *Architectural Design* **87**(4), 6–15 (2017).

19. P. Tsarouchi, A.-S. Matthaiakis, S. Makris and G. Chryssolouris, On a human-robot collaboration in as assembly cell, *International Journal of Computer Integrated Manufacturing* **30**(6), 580–589 (2017).

20. H. Ueno, T. Nishimaki, M. Oda and N. Inaba, Autonomous cooperative robots for space structure assembly and maintenance. In *International Symposium on Artificial Intelligence, Robotics and Automation in Space,* Nara, Japan (2003).

21. V.V. Unhelkar, P.A. Lasota, Q. Tyroller, R.D. Buhai, L. Marceau, B. Deml and J.A. Shah, Human-aware robotic assistant for collaborative assembly: Integrating human motion prediction with planning in time, *IEEE Robotics and Automatic Letters* **3**(3), 2394–2401 (2018).

22. L. Vasey, L. Nguyen, T. Grossman, H. Kerrick, D. Nagy, E. Atherton, D. Thomasson, N. Cote, D. Benjamin, G. Fitzmaurice and A. Menges, Collaborative construction: Human and robotic collaboration enabling the fabrication and assembly of a filament-wound structure. In *Proceedings of the 36th Annual Conference of the Association for Computer Aided Design in Architecture*, pp. 184–195, Ann Arbor, Michigan, USA (2016).

23. M. Yablonina, M. Prado, E. Baharlou and T. Schwinn. *Mobile Robotic Fabrication System for Filament Structures*. UCL Press (2017).

24. J.A. Zachman, Zachman Framework™, (2008). Available at https://www.zachman.com/about-the-zachman-framework. (Accessed August 15, 2018).

25. E. Zurich, Dfab house, (2018). Available at https://www.ethz.ch/en/news-and-events/eth-news/news/2018/03/spatial-timber-assemblies.html. (Accessed August 15, 2018).

© 2020 World Scientific Publishing Company
https://doi.org/10.1142/9789811222849_0012

Chapter 12

Robotic Finishing of Geometrically Complex Parts

Ariyan M. Kabir, Prahar M. Bhatt, Brual C. Shah, and Satyandra K. Gupta

12.1   Introduction

Finishing processes are one of the four basic classes of manufacturing. It is required in many different manufacturing applications. Surface finishing includes tasks such as cleaning, sanding, polishing, superfinishing, deburring, grinding, and paint-stripping. These tasks account for up to 25% of the manufacturing cost. Automating these tasks can improve efficiency, and significantly reduce manufacturing costs. Finishing processes are often highly non-repetitive in small and medium volume productions. Many parts with intricate interior regions require finishing operations. The finishing process automation needs to adapt to the changes in individual part geometry, scale, surface, and tools. A unique tool trajectory is required to be generated for every new part. Experiments need to be carried out to set the right operation parameters (e.g. force, velocity, stiffness, oscillation) for the desired finish performance.

Traditionally, robots have been used in manufacturing for the repetitive material handling and assembly tasks. Employing robots on non-repetitive finishing tasks is difficult, as the robot cannot use preprogrammed motions. An advanced impedance controller needs to be used instead of a position controller to ensure that the robot can deal with part position uncertainty caused by registration errors. In addition, processing the entire complex target surface from one relative pose between the robot and the part may not be possible. Often, the part must be moved and re-grasped to ensure access to the entire surface. Moreover, in small production volume runs, it is economically not feasible to build custom fixtures to hold the parts during finishing processes. In order to finish a part without fixtures, we need to dynamically generate motion plans for a robot or mechanism to manipulate the part in space, while a second robot performs the finishing task. Parts may also be delicate and cannot withstand arbitrarily large forces, requiring that the applied force be monitored and controlled to ensure that the part being processed is not damaged. Finally, finishing tasks require continual autonomous monitoring and assessment of the surface. As a result of these complexities, tedious and time consuming finishing tasks of geometrically complex parts with interior features are traditionally performed by hand. Automating the finishing process on such parts is expected to provide the following benefits:

(1) Performing finishing operations on complex parts is often an ergonomically challenging task. Automating the finishing operation can reduce the potential for risk to human health.
(2) Automated finishing process can provide consistent quality and reduce the risk of part damage caused by human error.
(3) Finishing is often a time consuming operation. Automated finishing can increase the productivity by reducing the touch labor.

We have developed a system for non-repetitive finishing of user-specified parts. The automated system is capable of finishing complex parts. Our system is applicable to non-repetitive finishing tasks in small and medium manufacturing industries, where hand-coded robot programs are not feasible. Our system automates the mundane tasks of finishing to improve productivity. The system architecture of our method is sufficiently general to permit scaling to meet the requirements of different industries where finishing is an important part of manufacturing processes.

12.2   Related Work

Robotic polishing, superfinishing, cleaning, grinding etc. are examples of robotic finishing. These surface processing tasks share the same core technologies. A significant number of research works have been done on robotic finishing. Research focus has been given to path planning and optimization,[1–8] force and impedance control,[3,4,9–13] knowledge transfer from human,[9,14,15] model of task and material removal,[4,10–13,16,17] identification and optimization of key process parameters,[4,6,12,15,18–22] tool design,[23] vision based performance analysis,[24–26] work-cell calibration,[27] setup-planning,[28,29] learning part deformation model,[30–32] etc.

In most of the works, a five-dimensional tool path has been generated using CNC machining software. Nagata et al. developed a surface following controller for industrial robots to follow the polishing tool path.[6] Takeuchi et al. developed a robot controller for following tool paths in polishing applications.[1] Tam et al.

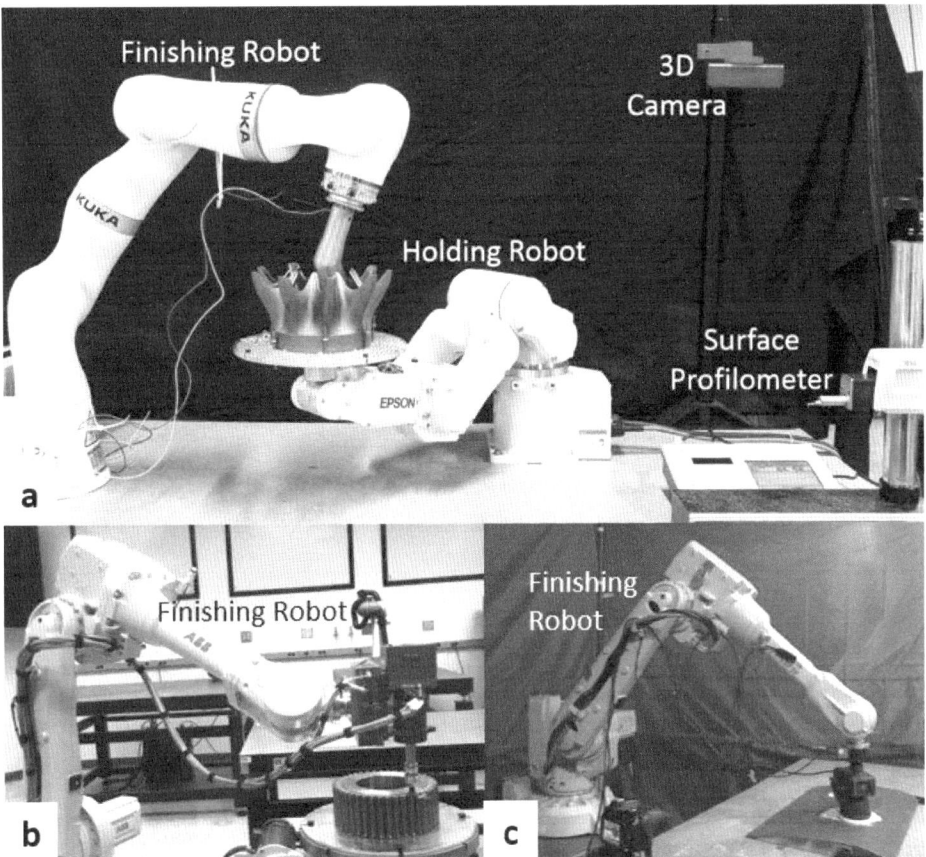

Fig. 12.1. On-going (a) metal surface polishing, (b) metal surface grinding, and (c) composite surface sanding at our robotic finishing cells.

studied the polishing performance using scanning, bi-scanning, Hilbert, and Peano paths.[7] Nagata et al. studied trajectories made of zigzag paths, whirl paths, or their combination.[3] They developed a scheme to adapt the pattern based on the shape of workpieces. Huang et al. devised an adaptive path planning approach using a passive compliant tool.[4]

Works have been done on modeling the contact force and contact stress between the tool and the workpiece. Researchers have also developed force and impedance controllers to maintain a desired contact force or stress. Feng et al. developed a force controller for polishing curved surfaces.[13] They studied the relationship between the pressure distribution model and the displacement of the of elastic disk tool to realize the controller. Impacts of contact stress on polishing was studied by Roswell et al.[11] They concluded that constant force does not guarantee constant contact stress between tool and workpiece. They also modeled how contact stress needs to be controlled for polishing. Huang et al. devised a method to control the passive force coming from the compliant tool for grinding and polishing.[4] Nagata et al. used impedance control in their wooden furniture polishing application to maintain uniformity.[3] They also developed an impedance controller for a joystick based teaching system for polishing robots.[9, 14] The human operator controlled the tool orientation during the training phase, while the tool path and contact force were controlled automatically. Pagilla et al. developed position and force controllers for three phases of robot motion in surface finishing.[10] The phases are free motion phase (when a robot is approaching the workpiece), transition phase (when a robot touches the workpiece), and constrained motion phase (when a robot is following trajectory on the workpiece).

Several groups have worked on developing models for material removal to ensure desired performance. These works are based on geometrical analysis of tool, workpiece, and their contact points. Tian et al. investigated effects of polishing pressure on removal rate.[16, 17] Based on their studies, they developed algorithms to adjust the position and orientation of a tool locally on the surface. The force control was decoupled from the tool pose control in their approach. Feng et al. developed a material removal model based on the contact force, displacement of a polishing tool, and contact zone.[13] Jin et al. combined linear velocity and rotation speed of a tool with the contact force to determine a material removal model.[12]

Research focus has been given to optimizing process parameters to improve finish quality. Kalt et al. worked on knowledge transfer from human to robot for improving performance.[15] They developed a mechatronic device to capture the effects of force, torque, vibration, polishing pattern, and feed rates on polishing. Jin et al. investigated the effects of tool inclination angle, rotation speed, contact size, contact force, stress field, and linear velocity on the polishing performance.[12] Huang et al. experimentally determined the effects of contact force, belt speed, and feed rate on grinding and polishing performance.

In our earlier works,[18–20] we developed an online-learning method to optimize the process parameters in robotic finishing applications. Our method minimized the number of experiments required to find the optimal set of parameters. We posed the problem as an optimization problem with black-box constraints. We have also developed an online-learning method for part deformation models.[30–32] Our algorithm enabled us to clean or finish compliant parts without damaging them. The algorithm also determined the optimal sequence of grasp location to minimize finishing the part.

We have also developed setup planning algorithm[28,29] to minimize robotic finishing time in our earlier works. Due to kinematic constraints, a robot cannot finish the complete surface of the part for a fixed relative pose of the part. Our algorithm determined the optimal sequence of reposition and reorientation of the part to minimize overall finishing time.

A robotic finishing system needs to incorporate the following modules: trajectory planner, setup planner, tool selector, process parameter selector, process monitoring, contingency handling module, and user interface to transfer knowledge from human operator to the automated robotic system. The earlier works on robotic finishing addressed the challenges in some of the modules. In this chapter, we have proposed an integrated system that is capable of taking high level inputs from user and addressed the challenges in robotic finishing using low level automated routines.

12.3 Requirements for Robotic Finishing System

An automated robotic finishing system will need to have certain hardware and software components to interact with the part and the human operator.

12.3.1 *Hardware*

We are listing down the hardware components below with brief descriptions.

(1) *Finishing Robot:* A robotic finishing system will need to have a robotic manipulator to operate the finishing tool on the part.
(2) *Holding Mechanism (or Robot):* For a fixed pose of the part, the finishing robot may or may not be able to reach all the regions on it due to kinematic and dynamic constraints. Therefore, the system may need a mechanism (or a second robot) to hold the part and change its pose (setup) relative to the finishing robot.
(3) *Part Fixture:* Most of the surface finishing operations are non-repetitive in nature. It is economically not feasible to build custom fixtures for each part in low and medium volume production. An automated system for robotic finishing needs to have a reconfigurable fixture to mount a large variety of parts on the holding mechanism.
(4) *Finishing Tools and Tool Changer:* Different geometry and material requires different kinds of finishing tools. The system needs to have a set of finishing

tools available in the work cell to work on different parts. A tool changing mechanism is required to automatically change the tools between processes.

(5) *Sensors for Localization:* An appropriate sensor system needs to be integrated with the system to localize the part with respect to the robots.

(6) *Sensors for Performance Evaluation:* An appropriate sensor system needs to be integrated with the system for performance evaluation and feedback.

12.3.2 *Software*

We are listing down the required software components below with brief descriptions.

(1) *Tool Selection Module:* Depending on part geometry, it may not be possible to use the same finishing tool on the entire surface of a part. This is due to the constraints posed by part and tool geometry. The robotic finishing system needs to have a tool selection module that will determine the right tools to use for different regions of the part.

(2) *Trajectory Planner for Finishing Robot:* The system needs to have a trajectory planner that is capable of generating collision free insertion, finishing, and retraction trajectories in real time for the finishing robot. The trajectories need to meet the process constraints (e.g. constraint on finishing time).

(3) *Setup Planner:* We call the pose of the part relative to the finishing robot to be a setup. The part needs to be placed in a certain setup based on the reachable workspace of the finishing robot. The system needs to have the capability of determining the setup to maximize reachability and minimize finishing time.

(4) *Process Parameter Selection Module:* The process parameters influence the performance of robotic finishing. These parameters include velocity, tool speed, normal and shear force, stiffness and damping parameters, etc. The system needs to be capable of selecting the optimal process parameters.

(5) *Process Monitoring and Contingency Handling Module:* An automated performance measurement module needs to be integrated with the system for evaluating finishing performance and monitoring progress. The system also needs to be able to detect contingencies that may arise. Based on performance feedback and contingencies, the system needs to be capable of auto-adjustment. It should seek human help when the auto-adjustments are not enough to resolve contingencies.

(6) *User Interface:* The robotic finishing system needs an intuitive user interface through which the human operator can interact with the system and provide

high level instructions. He/she should be able to perform the following operations through the interface.

(a) Import Computer-Aided Design (CAD) model of the part
(b) Select desired regions on the surface to finish
(c) Select process parameters
(d) Initiate trajectory generation for the finishing robot
(e) Verify the system generated trajectory for the finishing robot
(f) Provide seeds for the part setup
(g) Verify the optimized setup by the system
(h) Execute robot motion
(i) Remotely monitor the process

12.4 System Design

We have developed an automated finishing system to complete non-repetitive finishing tasks for parts with complex geometries, especially concave interiors. Our system takes high level commands from human operator, and transforms them into low level instructions for the robot. The inputs to our system are a CAD model, task specifications, desired finishing performance constraints, and process parameter bounds. The output of the system is a finished part with desired performance.

(1) *Design of Workcell:*

(a) *Robots:* We designed multiple robotic finishing workcells with one or two robots (see Fig. 12.1). In the workcell shown in Fig. 12.1(a), one of the two robots is a 7 degree-of-freedom (DOF) KUKA iiwa7 that is used as a finishing robot which manipulates the finishing tool required for the finishing task. The second robot in the same workcell is a 6-DOF Epson C3 which is used for manipulation of the part that needs to be finished. Ideally, any mechanism that can change the parts' position and orientation in space can be used as the holding mechanism. In the workcells shown in Fig. 12.1(b) and (c) only one 6-DOF ABB IRB 2600 robot is used for finishing with a constant part placement.

(b) *Finishing Tools:* The finishing robot is equipped with custom tools to finish a wide range of geometries. The housings of the custom tools are additively manufactured. DC motors with appropriate ratings are attached to the housing to create tools with desired specifications. The speed controllers of the motors are operated directly from a host computer. We selected the tool heads based on application requirements.

Recent Advances in Industrial Robotics

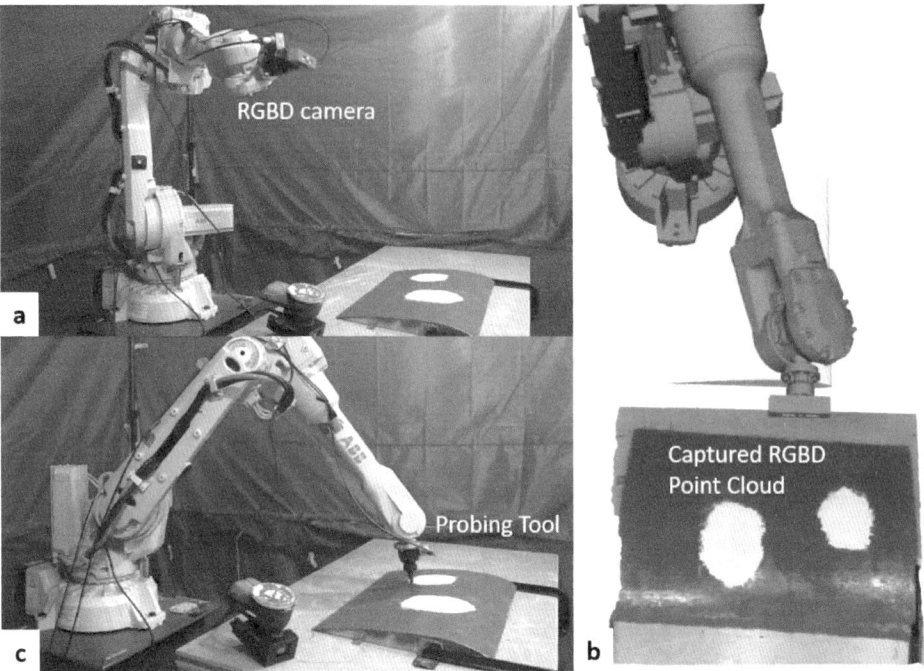

Fig. 12.2. (a) Registering the part with a eye-in-hand RGBD (red green blue depth) vision system, (b) Captured RGBD point cloud in the robot workspace, and (c) Improving registered point cloud accuracy using contact-based probing.

(c) *Finishing Tool Changer:* We have designed and integrated a custom tool changer in our system. It helps to quickly install and remove different tools for having different applications. A permanent magnet and a linear actuator is used to securely hold the tool in position. All the parts used in the assembly are additively manufactured with Polylactic Acid (PLA) material. To restrict the linear motion of the tool or the direction from where tool can fall from the attached part, a mechanism using a permanent magnet and a linear pull solenoid actuator is used. Fig. 12.3(a)-(d) illustrates the tool latching mechanism in CAD environment, the Fig. 12.3(e)-(f) shows the robot grasping the tool in the physical environment.

(d) *Reconfigurable Fixture:* We attached a platform (made out of acrylic sheet) for part placement on the holding robot. This platform was designed to be a flexible universal fixture. Having flexible fixtures can facilitate small volume manufacturing where tasks are highly non-repetitive in nature. Parts of a wide variety of geometry can be mounted using our simple clamping mechanisms.

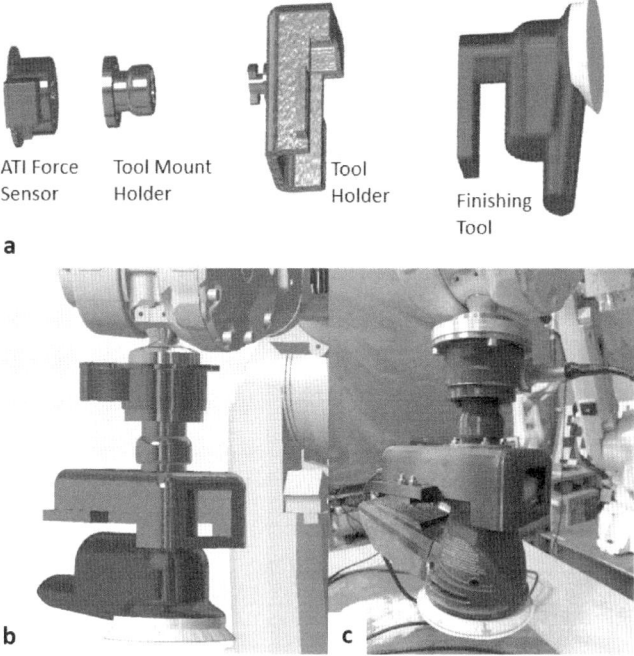

ATI Force   Tool Mount   Tool
Sensor   Holder   Holder
                                      Finishing
                                      Tool

a

b   **c**

Fig. 12.3. (a) Exploded view of the tool changing mechanism in CAD environment. (b) The tool being mounted on the finishing robot using the designed tool changer in the CAD environment, and (c) The tool being mounted on the finishing robot using the designed tool changer in the physical cell.

(e) *Perception:* We have integrated visual and tactile perception modules in our system to automate part registration and performance measurements.

i. *Visual:* We have used the Ensenso N10 camera to acquire the point cloud of the part during part registration. We have used Iterative Closest Point (ICP) algorithm in our system to register the point cloud of the part to the CAD model. The human operator provided input to improve the accuracy of the part registration, and reduce the computation time required to compute the parts' pose. After the part registration, the system knows the pose of the part with respect to the finishing robot as the holding mechanism changes the pose of its end-effector. The part needs to be registered every time it is placed at a different location on the platform. Fig. 12.2 illustrates an example of part registration.

ii. *Tactile:* We have integrated a Mitutoyo SJ-410 surface profilometer to measure surface roughness accurately when needed. The holding robot in our system takes the target surface under the probe of this device to take measurements. Fig. 12.9 illustrates some images taken from a footage of automated performance measurement. Due to complex part geometries, it is not always possible to automate the process of taking measurements. In our experiments, the human operator manually measured the performance of the parts with complex internal regions using the surface profilometer. Moreover, the operator used an external CMM to take approximate measurements for regions where a surface profilometer could not reach.

(2) *Software Architecture:* We have developed our own software architecture to connect all the hardware components and user-interface together. The communication to the robots and measurement devices were done using TCP/IP and serial communication. A central computer acts as the master (or host) device and all the hardware components act as slave devices. The master (or host) device takes user input from the user interface, runs all the algorithms (e.g. trajectory planning, parameter optimization, etc.) in the background, and transfers the instructions to the robots, measurement devices, sensors, and motor drives. We used the ROS framework as part of our architecture. It is mainly used for the simulation and visualization environments.

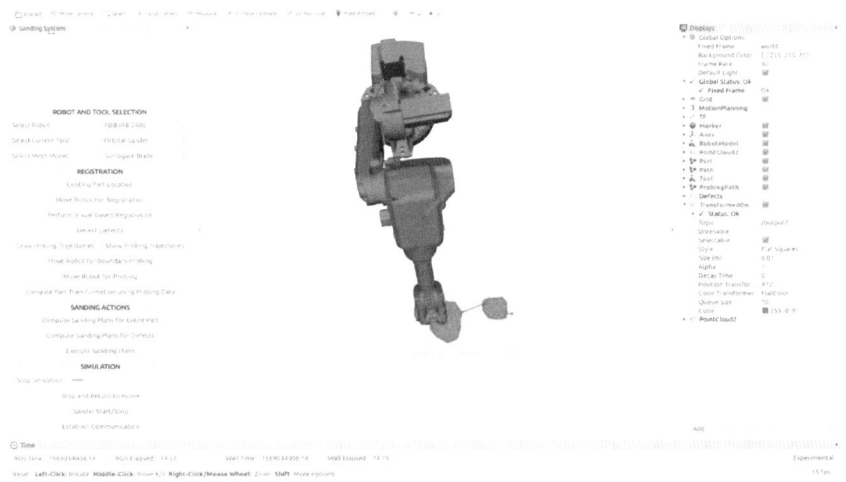

Fig. 12.4. Human Machine Interface with the options to robot, tool, and part selection, part registration, trajectory generation, trajectory simulation, and trajectory execution.

(3) *User Interface:* We developed a Qt-based application for the user-interface. The human operator can import the CAD model through this interface and select regions on the surface that needs to be finished. The selection can be made either by drawing lines on the surface or by selecting surface patches. For line selections, the user only selects the start and end points. We used a

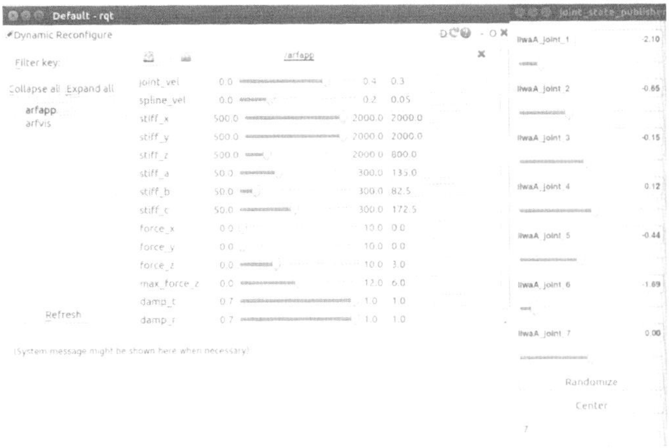

Fig. 12.5. Human Machine Interface with the options to process parameter selection.

geodesic curve generation algorithm to generate the complete scribe line as a shortest path on the surface. Fig. 12.6 illustrates an example of drawing scribe lines for trajectory generation. We have modified the open source application Meshlab to create the interface for surface patch selection. Fig. 12.7 illustrates an example of selecting surface patches for trajectory generation.

(4) *User Interaction with the System:* Once the CAD of the part is imported and the desired surface area has been selected, the user goes through the following steps to interact with the system.

  (a) *Part placement with aid of Mixed Reality:* We have integrated a Microsoft Hololens in our system that can guide an inexperienced user in mixed reality. It projects a hologram of the part on the platform during part placement and is capable of guiding the user through clamping sequence. This way the user will not mistakenly place the wrong part on the platform. Our current mixed reality system uses markers for detecting different objects. It is also restricted by the viewing angle of Hololens camera. Fig. 12.10(a) illustrates an example of the mixed reality interface.

  (b) *Tool Selection:* After placing the part on the holding robot, the operator initiates the tool selection module through the user interface. We use a search-based algorithm to determine which tools will be optimal to use on different regions of the part's surface. The search-based algorithm uses the tool geometry as a part of the cost function to minimize the finishing time and to detect collision with part features. The operator verifies the system generated selection of tools and makes modifications if needed. In our

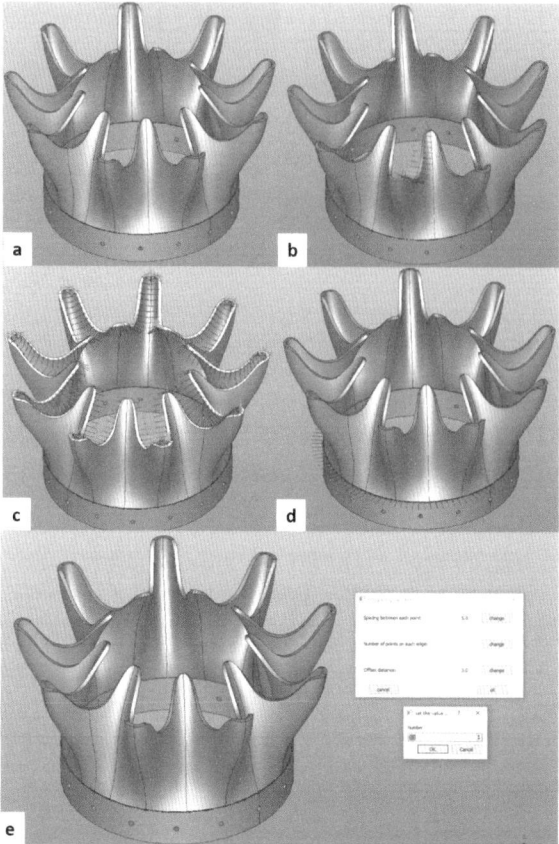

Fig. 12.6. Example of trajectory generation by selecting CAD edges. (a) Imported CAD model in the user interface, (b) operator selected edge surrounding a face, (c) operator selected edge wire on multiple faces, (d) operator selected edge between two intersecting faces, and (e) trajectory generation pop-up menu to select the edge parameters.

current system, we are only able to accommodate the tools with cylindrical geometry. The operator manually selects the regions for the tools with complex geometry in the scenarios where the automated algorithm fails to provide a solution.

(c) *Setup Planning:* In Section 12.3, we defined the setup to be a pose of the part with respect to the finishing robot. The pose of the part is six-dimensional with three translation, and three rotation components. It is not feasible to analytically determine the optimal setup for a part to be finished in six-dimensional space by considering the kinematic and dynamic constraints of a 7-DOF manipulator. Therefore, we designed our system to take some sample seeds for the setups from the human operator. The

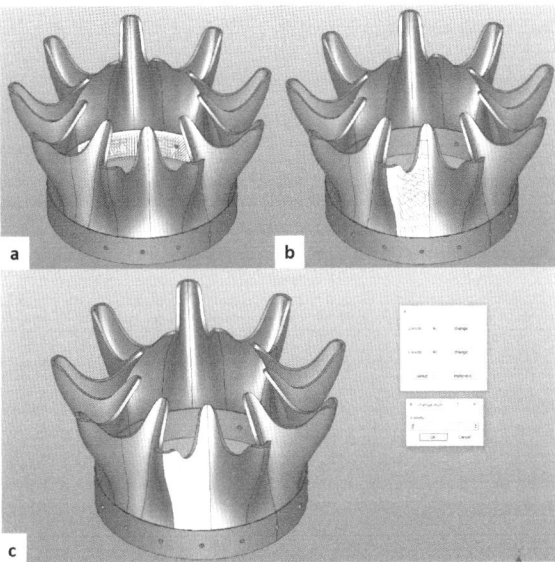

Fig. 12.7. Example of trajectory generation by selecting CAD faces . (a) Selected inner face to finish, (b) selected outer face to finish, and (c) trajectory generation pop-up menu to select the face parameters.

operator can input multiple setups (or pose of the part) by articulating the holding robot through the user interface. Our setup planner[29] runs search and optimization algorithms on the user provided seeds to find the optimal setup or sequence of setups.

(d) *Trajectory Planning:* After setup planning, the user can initiate the trajectory generation module from the interface. The trajectory generation module generates insertion, process, and retraction trajectories for the finishing robot. It also generates repositioning and setup changing trajectories for the holding robot. The trajectories are generated based on the inputs provided by the user. Fig. 12.8 and 12.9 illustrates some images taken from a footage of an insertion trajectory execution by the finishing robot and repositioning trajectory execution by the holding robot respectively. We have described the details on trajectory planning in Section 12.5.

(e) *Trajectory Verification and Execution:* Once the trajectory is generated, the operator can simulate and visualize the motion of the robots in the user interface. The operator can modify waypoints on the trajectory if needed. We integrated the RViz visualization environment with our user interface. Once verified, the operator can then deploy the trajectories on the physical system and initiate execution. Our interface provides an option to monitor

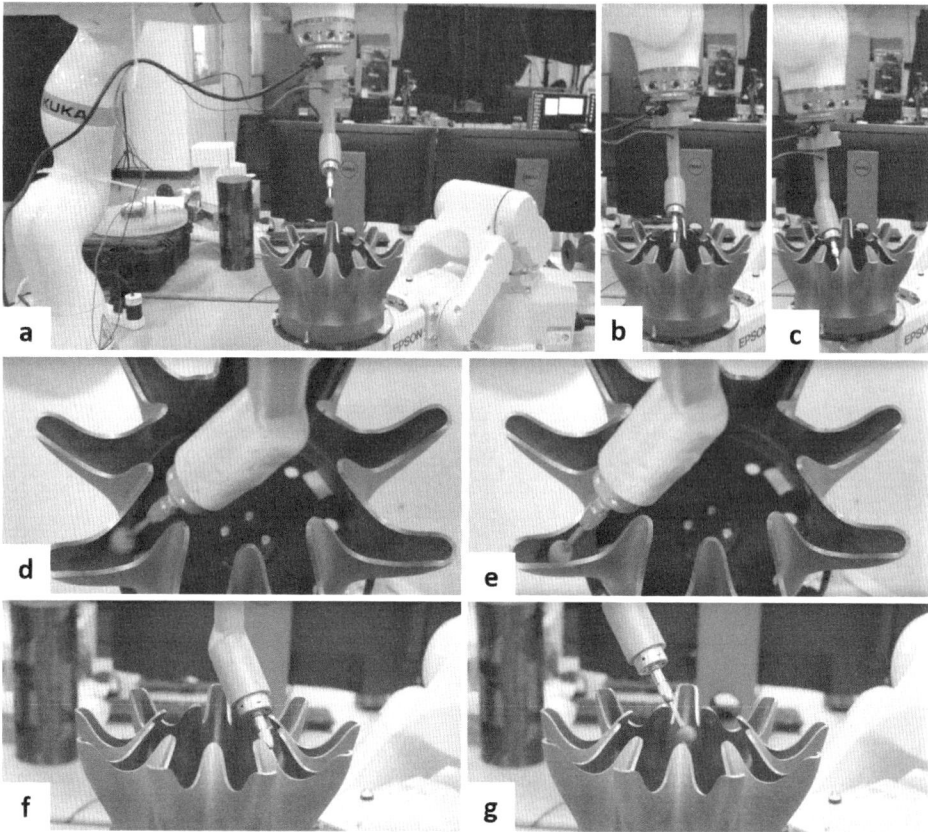

Fig. 12.8. (a)-(c) Snaps from a footage of insertion trajectory on a test part. (d)-(f) Execution of finishing trajectory. (g) Ending the finishing operation.

the physical system remotely. It imitates the live motion of the robot and tool in a virtual environment so that the operator can monitor the process without being present close to the finishing cell.

(f) *Process Parameter Selection:* We have integrated a module for process parameter selection within the RViz environment. Figure 12.5 illustrates the RViz environment. The user can manually tune the of the process parameters through this interface and observe their effects.

(g) *Performance Measurements and Feedback-based Adjustments:* The user can specify a schedule for taking performance measurements. To measure the performance of the finishing process, we have developed a module that can support and take feedback from laser scanners, probe-based CMMs, and surface profilometers. The user can decide the type of measurement device, the required feedback, and the interval to take performance mea-

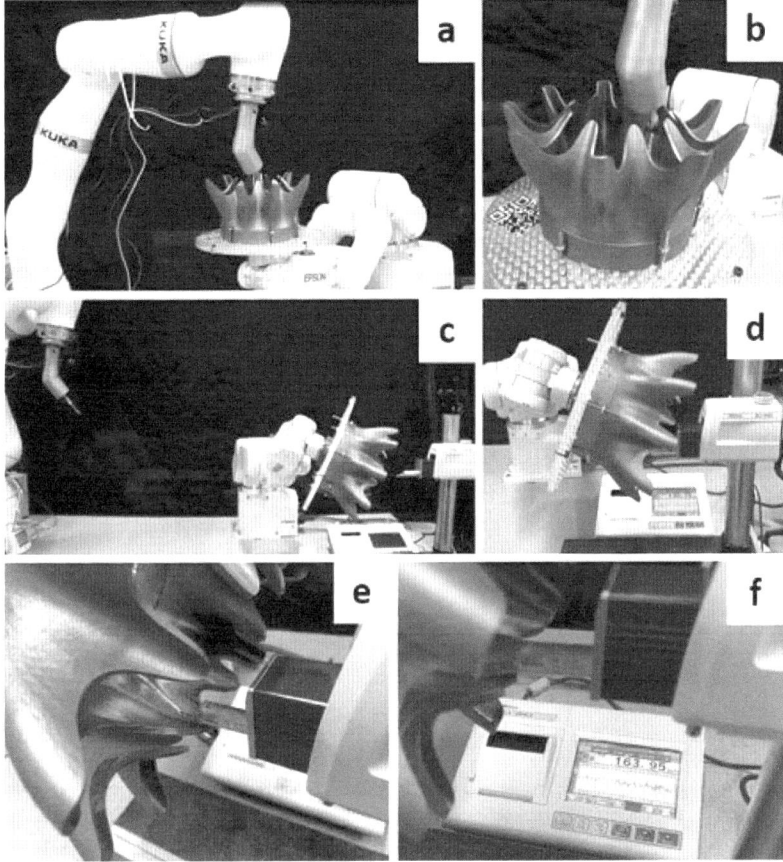

Fig. 12.9. Snapshots from a footage of performance measurement using surface profilometer. (a),(b) Ongoing robotic finishing of a part, (c),(d) Holding robot takes the part to the surface profilometer to measure surface roughness, (e),(f) Ongoing surface roughness measurement. The result is sent back to the system as feedback.

surement. Based on the feedback, the operator can adjust process parameters and trajectories through the interface. We used surface profilometer for performance measurement in our experiments. Human assistance might be required to take performance measurements manually for very complex internal geometries. A mixed reality system can be used to help the operator by highlighting the specific regions on the part to take the measurements at right locations.

(h) *Contingency Handling and Smart Notifications:* Depending on the task profile, the finishing operation can take a long time to complete. Contingencies may arise during the process and human inputs are sometimes crucial to resolve them quickly. However, it is not effective for the human

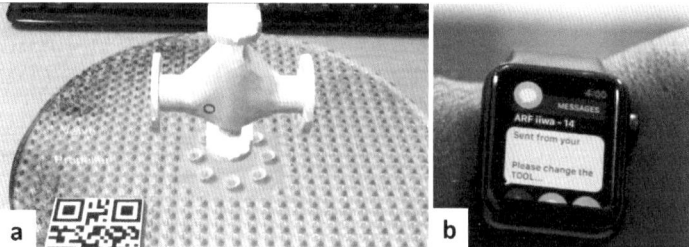

Fig. 12.10. (a) A view through Hololens during part placement. Hologram of the part guides the operator while mounting the part. (b) A notification sent to the operator for contingency handling.

operator to stand next to the robotic finishing cell the entire time. We have developed a smart notification module in our system. It can send text messages to the operator's phone or wearable devices (e.g. smart watch) when the robot needs help from the operator or when any other human input is required by the system. Fig. 12.10(b) illustrates an example of a notification sent to the wearable device of the operator.

12.5 Trajectory Planning

Performing robotic finishing operation on a part requires automated generation of robot trajectories. Given a surface patch $\mathbb{S}$ on the workpiece that requires finishing using tool $\mathbb{T}$, we use the following approach to generate the trajectory.

(1) The first step is to identify the tool trace curves on $\mathbb{S}$. These curves are selected such that tool center motion along these curves can cover S and hence complete the finishing operation. These curves are generated by placing an initial curve, and then offsetting the curve using the selected strategy. There are many different strategies such as zig-zag, contour following, spiraling etc. The best strategy depends on the geometry of $\mathbb{S}$ and tool size. The human operator needs to select the strategy.

(2) The next step is to determine the relative location of the workpiece with respect to the robot so that the tool held by the robot can access all points on tool trace curves on $\mathbb{S}$ in the desired orientation without violating constraints of the robot workpiece (e.g., joint limits and singularity). This problem is solved by explicitly constructing the robot workspace and using non-linear optimization techniques to find the workpiece pose(s) in the robot workspace that allow the robot mounted tool $\mathbb{T}$ to reach all points on the selected tool trace curves. The human operator gives the initialize pose to the system.

(3) The next step is to find robot trajectories in the joint space that can move the tool along the tool trace curves. These trajectories need to be executed without robot or tool colliding with the workpiece or the fixture holding part. The tool will also need to avoid collision with the robot. In order for the tool to follow a trace curve, three trajectory components are needed. The first trajectory component is the insertion component. This component enables the robot to move the tool from its initial location to the start point on the trace curve. The second component of the trajectory is tracing component. This allows the tool to move along the trace curve. The final component of the trajectory is extraction component that allow the robot to move the tool from the end point on trace curve to the tool rest position. Our approach generates all three types of trajectories. We expect that robots used in this application will be either six or seven degrees of freedom robots. We generate initial trajectories using discrete search-based method. This search method performs search in the joint space to find near-optimal trajectories. We designed a library of maneuvers that enables the search method to handle commonly found concavities in computationally efficient manner. These maneuvers represent a sequence of joint motions and hence speed up the search. Once a trajectory has been found by discrete search, we use a collision detection tool to estimate free space around the trajectory. We use a non-linear optimization method to refine the initial trajectory and a smoothing algorithm to smoothen the computed trajectory.

(4) The final step is to identify the optimal process and trajectory parameters that will ensure desired finishing performance. The set of parameters include force, velocity, tool speed, stiffness used by impedance controller, etc. The optimal values for these parameters are different for different task profiles. The parameters are selected by human operator if they are known. For a new material, surface, and tool profile, the optimal values of the process parameters might be unknown to the operator. However, the operator can provide the boundary values for the parameters and an initial feasible seed. This seed is used to iteratively optimize the parameters within the bounds using a probabilistic decision making approach on a sample part using the human input.

Due to space limitation describing the mathematical formulation of trajectory planning is beyond the scope of this chapter.

Table 12.1. Robotic finishing performance on different parts.

Part	Ra Value (μm)	
	Before	After
Shaft Housing	1.29	0.52
Lobbed Flow Mixer	12.75	1.62
Miniature Turbine with Epicyclic Gear Train	2.87	1.64
Fuel Injection Nozzle	7.95	1.64
Pump Impeller	4.70	0.44
Gear Bearing	5.88	3.28
Jet Engine Bracket	13.81	3.08

12.6 Results

We have conducted experiments of robotic finishing on a set of representative parts with complex geometries. These parts require finishing of internal regions for functionality. The names and brief description of the test parts are given below.

(1) Housing for supporting the load bearing shaft
(2) Exhaust flow mixer for mixing exhaust gases with cold air in turbofan engines
(3) Miniature turbine structure with epicyclic gear loading for greater torque output
(4) Nozzle for fuel injection in gas turbines
(5) Impeller for centrifugal pumps
(6) Gear bearing for improved performance over traditional ball bearings
(7) Bracket for jet engines

Figure 12.11 illustrates the representative parts we used in our experiments. The surface roughness measurements(before and after finishing) for these parts are summarized in Table 12.1. Figures 12.12 and 12.13 visually illustrate the surface roughness difference on the impeller blade and flow mixer respectively. A short video of robotic finishing process for the housing and flow mixer can be viewed at https://www.youtube.com/watch?v=HJGdn1Wrg3s

The internal surface area of the load bearing shaft housing and exhaust flow mixer was 0.0903 m^2 and 0.0784 m^2 respectively. Our robotic finishing system took 24 mins. to finish 0.0326 m^2 of the internal surface of the housing part and 58 mins. to finish 0.0094 m^2 of the internal surface of the flow mixer. However, the surface area of the tool used for flow mixer was significantly smaller compared to the tool used for the housing. The finishing time is governed by the geometry of the part and tool. It is also constrained by the optimum velocity required to achieve the desired surface finish. We determined the velocity requirement using our process parameter selection module.

Fig. 12.11. Some of the parts with complex geometry we used for robotic finishing. (a) Shaft Housing, (b) Lobbed Flow Mixer, (c) Miniature Turbine with Epicyclic Gear Train, (d) Fuel Injection Nozzle, (e) Outer Teeth Gear, (f) Helicopter Blade, (g) Pump Impeller, (h) Gear Bearing, (i) Jet Engine Bracket, (j) Inner Teeth Gear, and (k) Motorbike Fender.

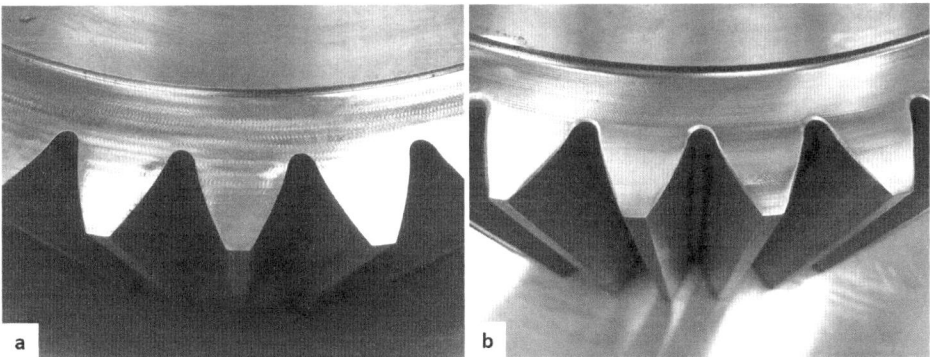

Fig. 12.12. Surface of the external teeth gear (a) before and (b) after finishing.

12.7   Conclusions

In this chapter, we have shown that the collaborative system involving the human operators and the robotic assistants for complex finishing operations can be realized. We have developed a planning algorithm, that takes the CAD model of the part and high-level user input, and generates the motion plans for the finishing robot. This significantly reduces the programing time and improves the efficiency of the system. Secondly, we have developed a parameter optimization routine that iteratively selects the process parameters until the system reaches the satisfactory finishing performance. We have evaluated the system on a representative set of parts with complex geometries. The system was able to perform finishing operations on the test parts satisfactorily. Manual finishing operations are tedious and time consuming. Our system helps the human operators by reducing their work load and eliminating tasks that are ergonomically challenging. It enables them to utilize their time more effectively and increase their productivity.

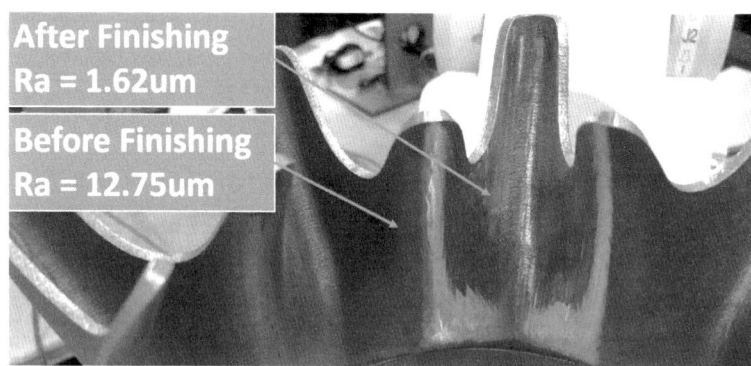

Fig. 12.13. Surface roughness of finished and unfinished segments of the lobbed flow mixer.

Currently the system takes human inputs for initial setup seeds and process parameters. It then optimizes the setup and process parameters in discrete space. In future, we plan to automate the process of setup planning and process parameter selection in continuous space to find the globally optimal solutions. Custom designed tools are often required to finish very complex geometries. We aim to develop a planner for simultaneous design of tool geometry and trajectory to optimize the overall time taken for robotic finishing. In future, we will also study the quality consistency of robotic finishing and develop methods to consistently maintain desired performance over production batches.

12.8   Acknowledgment

This work is supported in part by National Science Foundation Grant #1634431. Opinions expressed are those of the authors and do not necessarily reflect opinions of the sponsors.

References

1. Y. Takeuchi, D. Ge and N. Asakawa, Automated polishing process with a human-like dexterous robot. In *Proceedings of the 1993 IEEE International Conference on Robotics and Automation*, pp. 950–956 (1993).
2. H. Tam, O. C. Lui and A. C. Mok, Robotic polishing of free-form surfaces using scanning paths, *Journal of Materials Processing Technology* **95**(1), 191–200 (1999).

3. F. Nagata, K. Watanabe and K. Izumi, Furniture polishing robot using a trajectory generator based on cutter location data. In *Proceedings of the 2001 IEEE International Conference on Robotics and Automation (ICRA)*, Vol. 1. pp. 319–324 (2001).

4. H. Huang, Z. Gong, X. Chen and L. Zhou, Robotic grinding and polishing for turbine-vane overhaul, *Journal of materials processing technology* **127**(2), 140–145 (2002).

5. Z. Yang, F. Xi and B. Wu, A shape adaptive motion control system with application to robotic polishing, *Robotics and Computer-Integrated Manufacturing* **21**(4), 355–367 (2005).

6. F. Nagata, Y. Kusumoto, Y. Fujimoto and K. Watanabe, Robotic sanding system for new designed furniture with free-formed surface, *Robotics and Computer-Integrated Manufacturing* **23**(4), 371–379 (2007).

7. H. Tam and H. Cheng, An investigation of the effects of the tool path on the removal of material in polishing, *Journal of Materials Processing Technology* **210**(5), 807–818 (2010).

8. N. Jayaweera and P. Webb. Measurement assisted automated robotic edge deburring of complex components. In *Proceedings of the 9th WSEAS International Conference on Signal Processing, Robotics and Automation (ISPRA'10)*, pp. 133-138, Wisconsin, USA (2010).

9. F. Nagata, K. Watanabe, K. Kiguchi, K. Tsuda, S. Kawaguchi, Y. Noda and M. Komino, Joystick teaching system for polishing robots using fuzzy compliance control. In *Proceedings of the 2001 IEEE International Symposium on Computational Intelligence in Robotics and Automation,* pp. 362–367 (2001).

10. P. R. Pagilla and B. Yu, Robotic surface finishing processes: modeling, control, and experiments, *Transactions-American Society of Mechanical Engineers Journal of Dynamic Systems Measurement and Control* **123**(1), 93–102 (2001).

11. A. Roswell, F. J. Xi and G. Liu, Modelling and analysis of contact stress for automated polishing, *International Journal of Machine Tools and Manufacture* **46**(3), 424–435 (2006).

12. M. Jin, S. Ji, L. Zhang, Q. Yuan, X. Zhang and Y. Zhang, Material removal model and contact control of robotic gasbag polishing technique. In *2008 IEEE Conference on Robotics, Automation and Mechatronics,* pp. 879–883 (2008).

13. D. Feng, Y. Sun and H. Du, Investigations on the automatic precision polishing of curved surfaces using a five-axis machining centre, *The International Journal of Advanced Manufacturing Technology* **72**(9–12), 1625–1637 (2014).

14. F. Nagata and K. Watanabe, Teaching system for a polishing robot using a game joystick. In *Proceedings of the 39th SICE Annual Conference (SICE 2000),* pp. 179–184 (2000).

15. E. Kalt, R. P. Monfared, and M. R. Jackson. Towards an automated polishing system: capturing manual polishing operations, *International Journal of Research in Engineering and Technology* **5**, 182–192 (2016).

16. F. Tian, C. Lv, Z. Li and G. Liu, Modeling and control of robotic automatic polishing for curved surfaces, *CIRP Journal of Manufacturing Science and Technology* **14**, 55–64 (2016a).

17. F. Tian, Z. Li, C. Lv and G. Liu, Polishing pressure investigations of robot automatic polishing on curved surfaces, *The International Journal of Advanced Manufacturing Technology* **87**(1-4), 639–646 (2016b).

18. A. M. Kabir, J. D. Langsfeld, C. Zhuang, K. N. Kaipa and S. K. Gupta, Automated learning of operation parameters for robotic cleaning by mechanical scrubbing. In *ASME 11th Manufacturing Science and Engineering Conference*, Blacksburg, Virginia, USA (2016).

19. A. M. Kabir, J. D. Langsfeld, C. Zhuang, K. N. Kaipa and S. K. Gupta, A systematic approach for minimizing physical experiments to identify optimal trajectory parameters for robots. In *2017 IEEE International Conference on Robotics and Automation (ICRA)*, Singapore (2017). doi:10.1109/ICRA.2017.7989045.

20. A. M. Kabir, J. D. Langsfeld, K. N. Kaipa and S. K. Gupta, Identifying optimal trajectory parameters in robotic finishing operations using minimum number of physical experiments, *Integrated Computer-Aided Engineering, special issue on "Enabling Robot Autonomy"* **25**(2), 111–135 (2018), doi:10.3233/ICA-180563.

21. J. D. Langsfeld, K. N. Kaipa and S. K. Gupta, Selection of trajectory parameters for dynamic pouring tasks based on exploitation-driven updates of local metamodels, *Robotica* **36**(1), 141–166 (2018), doi:10.1017/S0263574717000212.

22. R. K. Malhan, Y. Shahapurkar, A. M. Kabir, B. C. Shah and S. K. Gupta, Integrating impedance control and learning based search scheme for robotic assemblies under uncertainty. In *ASME 13th Manufacturing Science and Engineering Conference*. College Station, Texas, USA (2018).

23. L. Liao, F. J. Xi and K. Liu, Modeling and control of automated polishing/deburring process using a dual-purpose compliant toolhead, *International Journal of Machine Tools and Manufacture* **48**(12), 1454–1463 (2008).

24. X. Li, L. Wang and N. Cai, Machine-vision-based surface finish inspection for cutting tool replacement in production, *International journal of production research* **42**(11), 2279–2287 (2004).

25. B. Y. Lee, S. F. Yu and H. Juan, The model of surface roughness inspection by vision system in turning, *Mechatronics* **14**(1), 129–141 (2004).

26. G. A. Al-Kindi and B. Shirinzadeh, An evaluation of surface roughness parameters measurement using vision-based data, *International Journal of Machine Tools and Manufacture* **47**(3), 697–708 (2007).

27. F. Leali, A. Vergnano, F. Pini, M. Pellicciari and G. Berselli, A workcell calibration method for enhancing accuracy in robot machining of aerospace parts, *The International Journal of Advanced Manufacturing Technology* **85**(1-4), 47–55 (2016).

28. A. M. Kabir, J. D. Langsfeld, S. Shriyam, V. S. Rachakonda, C. Zhuang, K. N. Kaipa, J. Marvel and S. K. Gupta, Planning algorithms for multi-setup multi-pass robotic cleaning with oscillatory moving tools. In *2016 IEEE International Conference on Automation Science and Engineering (CASE)*. Fort Worth, Texas, USA, pp. 751–757 (2016), doi:10.1109/COASE.2016.7743478.

29. A. M. Kabir, K. N. Kaipa, J. Marvel and S. K. Gupta, Automated planning for robotic cleaning using multiple setups and oscillatory tool motions. In *IEEE Transactions on Automation Science and Engineering* **14**(3), 1364–1377 (2017), doi:10.1109/TASE.2017.2665460.

30. J. D. Langsfeld, A. M. Kabir, K. N. Kaipa and S. K. Gupta, Online learning of part deformation models in robotic cleaning of compliant objects. In *ASME 11th Manufacturing Science and Engineering Conference*, Blacksburg, Virginia, USA (2016a).

31. J. D. Langsfeld, A. M. Kabir, K. N. Kaipa and S. K. Gupta, Robotic bimanual cleaning of deformable objects with online learning of part and tool models. In *2016 IEEE International Conference on Automation Science and Engineering (CASE)*. Fort Worth, Texas, USA, pp. 626–632 (2016b), doi:10.1109/COASE.2016.7743460.

32. J. D. Langsfeld, A. M. Kabir, K. N. Kaipa and S. K. Gupta, Integration of planning and deformation model estimation for robotic cleaning of elastically deformable objects, *IEEE Robotics and Automation Letters* **3**(1), 352–359 (2018), doi:10.1109/LRA.2017.2749280.

© 2020 World Scientific Publishing Company
https://doi.org/10.1142/9789811222849_0013

Chapter 13

Advancing Capabilities of Industrial Robots Through Evaluation, Benchmarking, and Characterization

Adam Norton, Elena Messina, and Holly Yanco

13.1 Introduction

Industrial robots are designed to operate in many different environments and perform tasks with varying requirements. These parameters influence the manner in which industrial robots are able to operate in a given domain. To understand the relationship between these parameters and the robot's capabilities, the robot and the domain in which it operates must be properly characterized. Characterization of an industrial robot is achieved by evaluating its performance and capturing the conditions (i.e., context) under which that performance was achieved. Characterizing an industrial robot domain or use case is accomplished by recording the factors particular to it that may influence required robot capabilities. Proper characterization can foster better understanding of industrial robot capabilities and how they can be transferred between domains to promote reconfigurability and reusability.

There are many resources available that can be used to conduct performance evaluations of industrial robots. These resources include testing protocols, data sets, and benchmarks, which are available through published standards, competitions, and online repositories. Benchmarks typically refer to use of structured evaluation to determine whether a technology or system can achieve the required performance in a specific domain, functionality, or task. Many of these resources have associated performance metrics, which are either connected with more generic properties of an industrial robot (e.g., lift capacity) or those more specific to a scenario (e.g., time taken to navigate through a confined space while avoiding obstacles). In both instances, the context under which the evaluation takes place is needed such that the performance metrics are meaningful and properly interpreted.

Context is also needed to ensure replicability and comparisons of results.

Throughout this chapter, many of the aspects of industrial robot evaluation are discussed and resources that can be used to conduct evaluations are provided. This is presented as a process, starting with the methods by which to determine what aspects of performance are important (i.e., key performance indicators and parameters). The evaluation resources that are currently available and elements of contextualization are discussed, with examples given from robotic systems in industrial domains as well as other applications. A few non-industrial cases are included as evidence of successful approaches that could be leveraged for industrial robots. Considerations for industrial robot evaluation are reviewed, such as variability (for real world applicability), statistical significance (for reliable performance), replicability (for validation and comparison of results), and generalizability (for transferability of evaluation results to other domains). Technology readiness levels – or the evaluation of industrial robot maturity – are also discussed, particulary with respect to the connections to performance evaluation. Gaps in the research and available evaluation resources are explored throughout the chapter.

13.2   Related Work

The landscape of available resources for evaluating the performance of industrial robots spans formal and informal methods. On the formal side, there are consensus standards that specify methods by which to measure a robot's capabilities. Informal methods of measuring and comparing performance include emerging benchmarks, metrics, and test methods aimed at the research community.

Currently available standards include foundational ones for industrial robot performance, such as.[1] Perhaps the most commonly referenced standards for industrial robots, including mobile robots or automatic guided vehicles (AGVs), are those pertaining to safety.[2,3] There are a few other performance-oriented standards that exist or are under development which are relevant to industrial robots. These standards include industrial vehicle performance,[4] machine vision systems,[5] 3D sensors,[6] and exoskeleton technology.[7]

Several benchmarking efforts targeting different levels of capabilities exist or are under development. For example, benchmarks to advance performance of industrial robots, such as in achieving a higher-level goal (e.g., assembly of a drive axel), are being developed in the European Union through the Robot Competitions Kick Innovation (RoCKin) effort.[8] The overall assembly goal is decomposed into sub-benchmarks for tasks, such as drilling, and functionalities, such as object perception. On a different front, a benchmarking scheme for bipedal locomotion for humanoid robots and exoskeletons has been developed[9] to organize the existing published benchmarks in the research community. The scheme decomposes the various characteristics of bipedal locomotion in order to assist researchers in finding relevant resources.

Performance standards are also being developed for robot systems in non-industrial domains. These include robots for use in emergency response and law enforcement applications, such as urban search and rescue, bomb disposal, fire fighting, and nuclear plant incidents. ASTM Subcommittee E54.09 on Response Robots has produced almost two dozen standards, with an additional fifty under development.[10,11] Given the range of conditions and missions covered by the umbrella of response applications, this effort provides a good framework to consider applying to robots in the manufacturing domain. The process used for the response robots standards began with a focus on urban search and rescue operations. The rather complex performance space was decomposed into a set of capability categories to be evaluated, while at the same time, a set of deployment or mission scenarios for the robots was defined.[12] The key point is that, ideally, the same test method could be used to capture performance data for a wide range of robots, e.g., from small, throwable robots that have limited mobility to larger robots for wide area situational awareness. The acceptable performance range for the speed of traversal of a small robot in a confined space is very different than that for a wide area robot which must cover a large area quickly in order to help responders assess a potentially hazardous situation, such as from a train derailment. The same test methods can be used to measure both robots' performance, but their results are interpreted differently. Beyond characterization of robot capabilities to guide procurements, it has been shown that the test methods, which are also used in the RoboCup Rescue International competitions (e.g., Ref. 13), help advance the capabilities of response robots. As noted in Refs. 14 and 15, the developer of the robot that made the greatest progress in responding to the Fukushima nuclear plant disaster credits the E54.09 test methods for providing concrete performance targets to guide the engineering of their robot towards achieving better performance in challenging environments.

Beyond robotics, benchmarks have been useful for many research communities, serving to provide common means of evaluating and comparing performance. In the case of computational performance, the maturity of benchmarks has progressed to the point that there are industry standards. For example, the System Performance Evaluation Cooperative, now named the Standard Performance Evaluation Corporation (SPEC), develops benchmarks for computing.[16] This organization began by evaluating desktop computers and workstations, but has expanded to include cloud-based, high-performance, graphics, and many other computing technologies. Most benchmarks are less formal than standards, yet still provide a valuable service to their stakeholders. Examples include the Text REtrieval Conference (TREC),[17] benchmark tracks,[18] and the additive manufacturing benchmarks.[19]

13.3   Key Performance Indicators (KPIs) and Parameters (KPPs)

Before embarking on a process for evaluating a system or a component of a system, one must first understand what performance aspects are most important. It is instructive to consider the approach to performance measures that many potential adopters of new robotic system technologies use during their operations, known as key performance indicators (KPIs). These concepts drive business decisions, including acquisitions and implementation of new equipment. KPIs are quantifiable and strategic levels of achieving a critical objective that are derived from aggregated physical measurements, data, or other KPIs.[20]

KPIs may represent business, productivity, or efficiency performance and are often compared to benchmarks for similar plants, equipment, or processes. Examples of types of KPIs include asset utilization, equipment availability, avoided cost, and customer satisfaction. The appropriate selection and deeper understanding of the KPIs can help achieve desired business results. With the advent of smart manufacturing and the Internet of Things (IoT), sensing and measurements are proliferating throughout manufacturing enterprises. These measurements offer the possibilities of the derivation of new KPIs that utilize this additional data.[21]

When considering the definition of industrial robot performance metrics, one can start by examining existing broadly-scoped KPIs to determine what performance metrics contribute to those KPIs. An example would be to start with a KPI of product quality. One can analyze the type of product(s) that a robot would be involved in helping to manufacture. Depending on the process that the robot would perform, performance thresholds would be established in order to attain the desired quality. These performance thresholds are then key performance parameters (KPPs), in that measured performance should fall within the parameters to be considered successful or acceptable. If the robot is performing a surface finishing operation to leverage its dexterity and compliance, enabling it to maintain uniform pressure on the surface, the number and types of defects would be measures of the resulting quality contribution of the robot. Therefore, one would quantify maximum deviations from ideal surface finish (e.g., root mean square of the roughness) and compare it to a benchmark surface finish value to decide if implementing a robot is advantageous. Of course, implementation decisions should also factor in other KPIs, such as throughput, scrap costs, and employee ergonomic issues.

There are some documented examples of the processes used to derive performance requirements – and hence performance metrics – from the equivalent of key performance indicators. Among these are the domain and task-driven derivations (e.g., Ref. 22), which focus on intelligent autonomous vehicles, starting with a cognitive perspective to guide the application and domain examination. The derivation of robot performance requirements from urban search and rescue task force members is detailed in Ref. 12. In Ref. 23, a manufacturing-relevant examination focuses on assembly in order to derive the metrics to guide development of test methods for evaluating robot systems or sub-components. The term KPI is not used in these prior examples, but there are underlying similarities. All of these examples begin with consideration of what attributes are valued by the end user in the deployment of the robotic system, whether safety, effectiveness in carrying out missions, or applicability to a wider range of tasks. The common approach to deriving performance requirements and the corresponding metrics and test methods is shown in Fig. 13.1.

In the case of performance requirements for urban search and rescue (US&R) robots, the process was initiated with a series of workshops with US&R experts who were members of the Federal Emergency Management Agency (FEMA) US&R Task Force network. FEMA Task Forces are deployed in response to large-scale disasters. During the workshops, the responders enumerated over a dozen deployment situations where robots could be useful, e.g., robots that could be thrown into confined spaces for initial inspection or those that could carry chemical sensors for remote detection of hazards. In the deployment scenarios, responders detailed the different stages or roles within response and the tasks entailed, such as the principal tasks for the reconnaissance role: initial detection, structural assessment, mapping (3D), hazardous materials identification, mitigation, and forensics. Analysis of these tasks produced a set of requirements (i.e., KPPs) categories, such as real-time remote visual observation, adjustable wide angle zoom, and adjustable illumination for cameras on the robot.[12] These initial requirements and metrics formed the foundation for development of the ASTM E54.09 standard test methods.

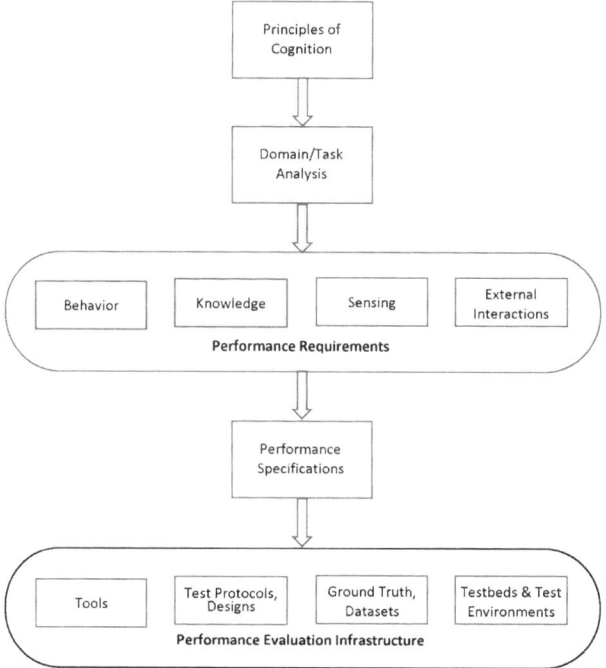

Fig. 13.1. Generalized method for deriving performance requirements and the performance evaluation framework (from Ref. 22. Principles of cognition form the foundation since the robotic system is expected to emulate aspects of human cognitive behavior, including sensing, modeling, planning, acting, and reacting.

In the industrial domain, a similar process for deriving performance requirements has occurred, although not in the same open format. The stakeholders for
industrial operations are centered around business, potentially dealing with sensitive information and processes (i.e., intellectual property concerns), so it is understandable that explicit KPIs and KPPs for a particular industrial process may not
be made public. However, the high-level desirable aspects of industrial operations
are fairly universal: high quality, high throughput, low cost, and, increasingly popular, high flexibility. Each of these aspects leads to KPIs such as high accuracy
and repeatability, each of which can be more specifically defined for a particular
manufacturing process. There are also increasing desires for human-robot collaboration operations, which will inform another set of KPIs and KPPs. The resources
available for evaluation that are discussed throughout this chapter can be used to

measure performance for particular KPIs and KPPs, but development is needed to address performance evaluation of more complex and specific operations.

13.4   Technology Readiness Levels

In considering methodologies to assess the performance of a robotic system or component, it is useful to examine the concept of technology readiness levels (TRLs) and how to assess the maturity of a given technology. TRLs were developed for evaluating the readiness of technologies for deployment in space applications[24] and have been adopted and adapted by a wide range of other programs.

Technology readiness levels range from 1, wherein basic principles are observed and reported, to 9, where an actual system is proven through successful mission operations within actual operating conditions. Attaining readiness at lower levels begins through publications and limited laboratory experiments. Many organizations consider TRL 6 to be a crucial milestone, at which point a system or subsystem model or prototype is successfully demonstrated in a relevant environment. The significance of attaining TRL 6 is due to the "relevant environment" qualifier. In other words, the system performs under conditions where its mission and environment approximate the required context of the target deployment. A salient example of TRL evaluation of robotic systems is the in-depth TRL 6 assessment of a military scout vehicle's autonomous navigation system (ANS).[25] The experimental design sought to test the ANS in a range of "relevant environments" studying five factors: terrain difficulty, speed, line-of-sight, mission, and operator team/vehicle. These criteria led to 646 missions that were conducted covering approximately 560 km at three different test sites. The vehicle was able to operate autonomously (without human assistance) in 96% of the distance covered. The relevant environments were selected in consultation with subject matter experts (military officers). For each of the three relevant environments (arid, vegetated, and urban), missions were run on courses through terrains deemed to have two different levels of difficulty. The in-depth experimentation provided the U.S. Department of Defense with statistically significant performance data that is contextual: if the vehicle failed to operate autonomously in a given region, the terrain, line-of-sight, and other factors that impeded it were known, allowing for decision-making in real-world deployments to reduce risk of failures.

The U.S. Department of Defense, which relies heavily on TRLs to make procurement decisions, has also developed a manufacturing readiness level (MRL) assessment to determine the risks associated with adopting a particular technology, product, or process.[26] Manufacturing USA is public-private partnership to advance innovation and competitiveness through a set of institutes to enable the transition of targeted technologies from MRL 4 and 5 through 6 or 7.[27] Paralleling the TRL scale, MRL 4 and 5 are demonstrated in laboratory environments, whereas MRL 6 and 7 are assessed in production-relevant or production-representative environments. Of particular relevance to this chapter is the Advanced Robotics for Manufacturing (ARM) Institute,[28] which seeks to accelerate the advancement of transformative robotic technologies from lower technology or manufacturing readiness levels through to TRL and MRL 6 or 7 with demonstrations in relevant or representative environments respectively.

Despite gaining popularity in some domains, technology readiness level assessments are not commonly applied to industrial robotics. Even with the TRL/MRL focus of the ARM Institute, there are no defined practices or approaches to guide the readiness evaluation of industrial robotic technologies, but there have been explorations from a TRL perspective for robotic bin picking.[29,30] Participants in a workshop session devoted to the topic concluded that there needs to be a clearer definition of measures or quantification of bin picking context (i.e., how complex is the specific bin picking scenario) and of metrics for bin picking performance (for the overall robotic system as well as for the contributing technologies such as perception, planning, grasping, and manipulation). A proposed way forward was to classify the readiness levels of the main technologies underlying bin picking solutions at a coarse grain. Four levels of readiness were defined ("highly fragile prototypes" through "solved problem robust in many applications") and assessed with respect to perception, grasping, movement, and planning in the context of the types of parts ("uniform rigid with limited configurations" through "flexible with varying size and configurations") and the bin environment ("structured arrays" through "fully random part placement"). This example highlights the value of identifying clearly the context in which a system and its component technologies are evaluated in order to determine readiness for implementation in a given application and environment.

13.5   Performance Evaluation Resources

Working groups and standards committees have sought to develop common testing protocols, test artifacts, and metrics for evaluating industrial robot performance. Committees such as the ASTM F45 Committee on Driverless Automatic Guided Industrial Vehicles[4] and ISO/TC 299 Robotics[31] develop standards, performance criteria, and test methods for mobility platforms and manipulators. Competitions such as RoboCup have several leagues focused on developing robots for industrial environments,[32] home,[33] and logistics.[34] Through these organizations, common evaluation methods, test apparatuses, and metrics are produced and made available to the industrial robotics community. Published benchmarks,[35,36] shared data sets,[37,38] and common metrics[39] are also available.

Many of the performance evaluation resources currently available are presented in Tables 13.1–13.5 as a catalog, organized along three axes:

- **System**: Higher-level groupings for an industrial robot and/or its components,
- **Characteristic**: Property or capability of the system type that can be measured, and
- **Level**: The extent of the evaluation performed, defined by the number of components engaged and the characteristic(s) being evaluated.

The catalog is also available online and will continue to be updated as new resources for evaluation become available: http://nerve.uml.edu/EvaluationCatalog/.

13.5.1 *System Type*

System type is divided into four main categories: mobility, manipulation, sensor, and interaction. See Fig. 13.2 for examples of evaluation resources in each category.

- Mobility systems are those that can locomote and traverse through spaces, which could comprise an entire industrial robot whose primary function is to navigate around a warehouse or just the mobility base of a larger system such as a mobile manipulator robot.
- Manipulation systems have articulated limbs or other actuators with varying degrees of freedom that are intended to physically interact with objects, such as robot arms and hands performing pick and place tasks in a factory line. These two categories can be combined for evaluation resources that involve both aspects, which is the case for many robotics competitions.
- Sensor systems measure and detect characteristics of the environment; this includes both the sensor(s) and the computation to process the sensor input.
- Interaction systems refer to the manners in which human agents engage with the robot, including control methods, programming/teaching, and human-robot collaboration. Note that there is considerable work on robot-

robot interaction, but achieving collaboration among robots does not necessarily rely on external interactions, but rather can be accomplished via
other commmunication protocols or higher-level planning and decision-
making.

The categories are not mutually exclusive from one another, but instead are
meant to refer to the main aspect of the robot that is to be evaluated in the resource.
For example, the ASTM F3244 standard test method for navigation[40] would be categorized under mobility as it evaluates the capability of a mobile robot to traverse
through a space. The robot being evaluated will use sensors to assist in navigating
through the space, but the test is ultimately evaluating the robot's mobility characteristics. Some resources are also very particular to the system type to which
they pertain, such as the ASTM E3064-16 standard test method for optical tracking
system performance,[41] which only pertains to sensor systems and not how they are
used in coordination with other systems on the robot to perform a task.

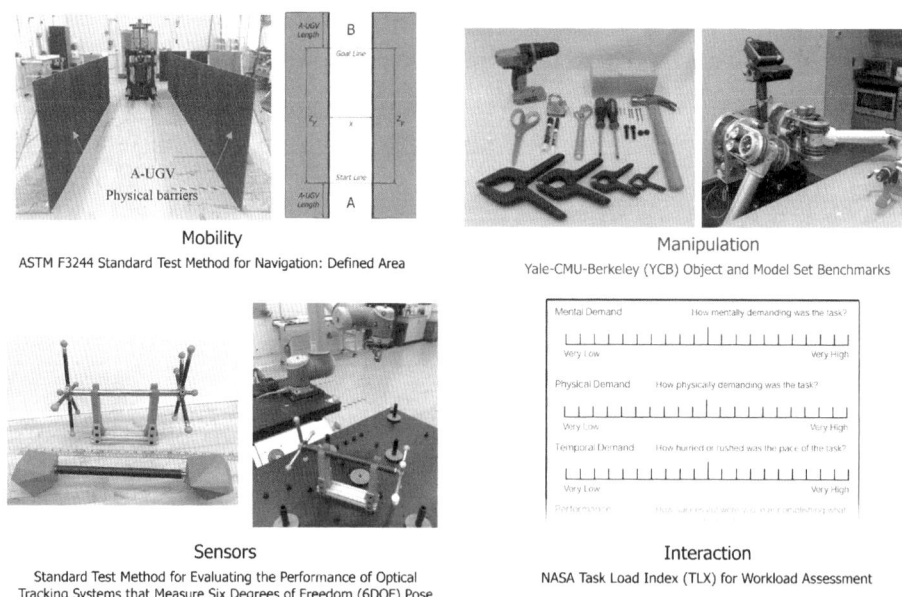

Mobility
ASTM F3244 Standard Test Method for Navigation: Defined Area

Manipulation
Yale-CMU-Berkeley (YCB) Object and Model Set Benchmarks

Sensors
Standard Test Method for Evaluating the Performance of Optical
Tracking Systems that Measure Six Degrees of Freedom (6DOF) Pose

Interaction
NASA Task Load Index (TLX) for Workload Assessment

Fig. 13.2. Examples of evaluation resources for each system type in the catalog: Mobility,[40] Manipulation,[37] Sensors,[41] and Interaction.[42]

13.5.2   *Characteristics*

The characteristics noted throughout the catalog are those associated with or used towards accomplishing tasks in an industrial setting. Rather than define all of the possible characteristics noted in the catalog, we use generic terms or those generally accepted throughout the robotics community. Examples of characteristics include properties of robot components such as the strength of a robot finger and battery life of a mobile robot, or capabilities of a robot system such as detecting and avoiding collisions with obstacles. Characteristics are listed in the catalog only if an evaluation resource is available.

13.5.3   *Level*

The level at which an evaluation takes place refers to whether one or more components (combined to form a robot system) are being evaluated and in what capacity. We specify three different levels: elemental, functional, and operational; see Fig.13.3 for examples of evaluation resources at each level. The levels are hierarchical, in that the evaluation of an elemental test can inform the evaluation of a functional test and so on. An operational evaluation can also be decomposed into smaller pieces to determine functional and elemental evaluations that could be performed prior to the operational evaluation. Some resources in the catalog (see Tables 13.1–13.5) are not tagged with a level because the property is not applicable; this is largely the case for common data sets and models that are made available to the research community because they are agnostic to the type of evaluation for which they are utilized.

- Elemental level evaluations are used to determine a property of a component of a robot system. The property of a component does not refer to a specific task, but it may have implications for tasks that rely on that property. An example of an elemental evaluation resource is the finger strength test method developed by the National Institute of Standards and Technology (NIST).[43] This test method evaluates the maximum force that a finger on a robotic hand can exert on a test artifact. The property of finger strength will have implications for grasping tasks at both the functional and operational levels. Another example would be the ASTM E2566[44] standard test method for visual acuity which evaluates the smallest details able to be resolved in a camera image.

- Functional level evaluations are used to evaluate a capability of a set of components or a robot system. The capability of a robot system refers to competencies needed to perform tasks. An example of a functional evaluation resource is the ASTM F3265 [45] standard test method for obstacle measurement, wherein a mobile system detects an obstacle while driving down an aisle. The reference task is to traverse down an aisle while navigating through an industrial warehouse space; the capability needed is obstacle detection to limit collisions while performing the task.

- Operational level evaluations use application-relevant tasks performed by a robot system that are evaluated using task-based metrics, such as throughput and mean time between failures. The ability for a robot system to perform tasks is dependent upon the properties of its components (determined by elemental evaluations) and its capabilities (determined by functional evaluations). An example of an operational-level test is the series of assembly test methods being developed by NIST.[43] These tests evaluate abstracted pick-and-place and peg-in-hole performance, as well as more real-world assembly operations. A series of assembly task boards are being designed to provide concrete benchmarks on how well robots can assemble and disassemble commercially-available connectors, pulleys, and wire harnesses.

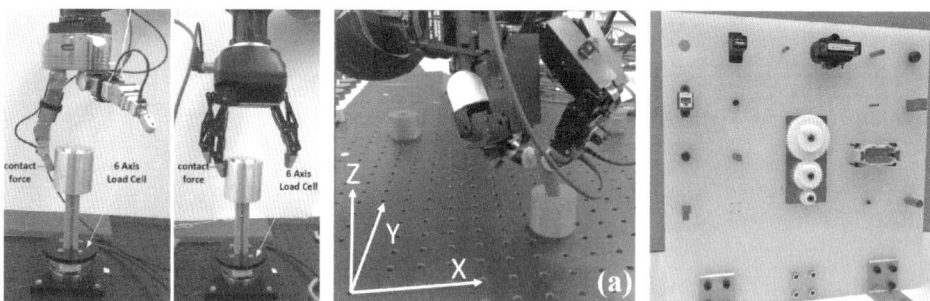

Fig. 13.3. Examples of evaluation resources at each evaluation level in the catalog. Left to right: elemental (touch sensitivity), functional (peg-in-hole insertion, operational (insertion, meshing, and threading assembly).[43]

Resources in the catalog such as benchmarks and data sets can be used towards evaluations at multiple levels and are tagged as such. An example is the Yale-Carnegie Mellon-Berkeley (YCB) object and model set.[37] The YCB set specifies a set of common objects that can be used for evaluating many aspects of grasping capabilities of a manipulator system. The objects could be used at an elemental level to evaluate sensor detection and object identification. At a functional level, the ability for a robotic arm and end effector to grasp the objects can be evaluated (e.g., Ref. 46). For an operational level test, the objects could be used as part of a human-robot collaboration study for evaluating pointing gestures for conveying task directions.[47]

Table 13.1. Catalog of evaluation resources for system type: Mobility.

System type: Mobility			
Characteristic	**Resource**	**Reference**	**Level**
Locomotion	ISO 18646-1:2016, Robotics – Performance criteria and related test methods for service robots – Part 1: Locomotion for wheeled robots	48	Functional
Navigation	ASTM F3244-17, Standard Test Method for Navigation: Defined Area	40	Functional
Navigation	ISO/DIS 18646-2, Robotics – Performance criteria and related test methods for service robots – Part 2: Navigation	49	Functional
Obstacle detection and avoidance	ASTM F3265-17, Standard Test Method for Grid-Video Obstacle Measurement	45	Functional
Obstacle detection and avoidance	ASTM F3381-19, Standard Practice for Describing Stationary Obstacles Utilized within A-UGV Test Methods	50	Elemental, Functional, Operational
Navigation, obstacle detection and avoidance	Intelligent Ground Vehicle Competition (IGVC)	51	Functional
Safety, obstacle detection and avoidance	ANSI/ITSDF B56.5 - 2012, Safety Standard for Driverless, Automatic Guided Industrial Vehicles and Automated Functions of Manned Industrial Vehicles	3	Functional
Positioning, docking	ASTM WK57000, Standard Test Method for Docking Driverless Automatic Guided Industrial Vehicles	52	Functional, Operational

Table 13.2. Catalog of evaluation resources for system type: Manipulation.

System type: Manipulation			
Characteristic	**Resource**	**Reference**	**Level**
Positioning	ISO 9283:1998, Manipulating industrial robots – Performance criteria and related test methods	1	Elemental
Grasping	RHGM Metrics WG test methods, artifact designs, and data	43	Elemental
Grasping	Proposed standard performance metrics for robotic hands	53	Elemental
Grasping	Yale-CMU-Berkeley (YCB) Object and Model set	37	Elemental, Functional, Operational
Grasping, placing	Universal picking comparison via Mean Picks Per Hour	54	Functional, Operational
Grasping, placing	SHAP: Southhampton Hand Assessment Procedure	55	Functional
Dexterity	Lafayette Dexterity Tests	56	Functional
Dexterity	Benchmark Tasks for Robotic Manipulation	57	Elemental, Functional
Assembly	Metrics and Benchmarks to Advance the State of Robotic Assembly	43	Functional, Operational
Safety	ISO/TS 15066:2016, Robots and robotic devices – Collaborative robots	58	Functional

Table 13.3. Catalog of evaluation resources for two system types: Mobility and Manipulation

System types: Mobility and Manipulation			
Characteristic	**Resource**	**Reference**	**Level**
Logistics tasks	European Robotics Challenge (EuRoC)	59	Operational
Logistics tasks	RoCKIn@Work Competition	8	Operational
Logistics tasks	RoboCup@Work Competition	32	Operational
Logistics tasks	RoboCupLogistics Competition	34	Operational
Logistics tasks	Agile Robotics for Industrial Automation Competition (ARIAC)	60	Operational
Home and service tasks	RoCKIn@Home Competition	61	Operational
Home and service tasks	RoboCup@Home Competition	33	Operational
Assembly and manu-facturing tasks, home and service tasks	European Robotics League (ERL)	62	Operational
Assembly and manu-facturing tasks, home and service tasks	World Robot Summit	63	Functional, Operational

Table 13.4. Catalog of evaluation resources for system type: Sensor.

Characteristic	System type: Sensor		
	Resource	Reference	Level
Acuity, resolution	ASTM E2566-17a, Standard Test Method for Evaluating Response Robot Sensing: Visual Acuity	44	Elemental
Simultaneous localization and mapping (SLAM)	Benchmarking and evaluation tools for SLAM	35, 36, 64	Elemental, Functional, Operational
Mapping	IEEE 1872-2015 Standard for Robot Map Data Representation for Navigation	65	Elemental, Functional, Operational
Object recognition	CORe50: Dataset and Benchmark for Continuous Object Recognition	38	Elemental, Functional, Operational
3D imaging range measurement	ASTM E2938-15, Standard Test Method for Evaluating the Relative-Range Measurement Performance of 3D Imaging Systems in the Medium Range	66	Elemental
Pose Determination	ASTM E2919-14, Standard Test Method for Evaluating the Performance of Systems that Measure Static, Six Degrees of Freedom (6DOF), Pose	67	Functional
Motion tracking	ASTM E3064-16, Standard Test Method for Evaluating the Performance of Optical Tracking Systems that Measure Six Degrees of Freedom (6DOF) Pose	41	Functional
Human detection and tracking	Quantitative measures of human detection and tracking systems	68, 69	Functional
Communication	ASTM WK54421, Standard Practice for Performance Testing of an A-UGV Under Varied Communication Conditions	70	Functional

Table 13.5. Catalog of evaluation resources for system type: Interaction.

System type: Interaction			
Characteristic	**Resource**	**Reference**	**Level**
Human-Robot Interaction	Common Metrics for HRI	39	Functional, Operational
Situation aware-ness	Situation Awareness Global Assessment Technique (SAGAT)	71	Functional, Operational
Workload	NASA Task Load Index (NASA-TLX)	42	Functional, Operational
Safety	ISO 13482:2014, Robots and robotic devices – Safety requirements for personal care robots	72	Functional, Operational

13.5.4 *State of Available Evaluation Resources*

Automatic guided vehicles (AGVs) and mobile robots are common in the industrial world, so it is not surprising that the majority of evaluation resources available for mobility are mature enough to be supported by standards committees. Manipulation is also common, so has some support from standards, but largely in regards to characteristics of safety and repeatable positioning. Many common test protocols exist for human hand dexterity and are applicable for robot evaluation, but are basic in their application. More domain-driven and task-specific methods need to be developed, so research groups such as the IEEE Robotic Hands, Grasping, and Manipulation Technical Committee[73] have been proliferating their designs. While not a standard, a metric for mean picks per hour (MPPH) and basic testing protocol for robot picking has been developed via an open online document that researchers can contribute to Ref. 54. This type of consensus-driven development can be used in the potential formation of standard test methods around robotic manipulation, although none exist just yet. Sensor evaluation resources are available as either benchmarks and data sets that can support other robot tasks – such as benchmarking tools for simultaneous localization and mapping (SLAM) that can support navigation – or standard test methods for evaluating 3D sensor equipment.

However, the methods that exist for interaction are more generally accepted measurement techniques and not supported by standards. There are efforts to develop human-robot interaction (HRI) evaluation standards, such as the series of Evaluation Methods Standardization for HRI (EMSHRI) workshops,[74] but typically only common metrics for evaluating HRI[39] are used throughout the research community. The rise of human-robot collaboration in industrial environments calls for more evaluation techniques to be developed in this area.

Wearable robots, such as exoskeletons, are also becoming a more prevalent area for development and integration into industrial environments, evidenced by standards groups such as ASTM F48 Committee on Exoskeletons and Exosuits[7] and the IEEE/RAS Technical Committee on Wearable Robots.[75] Evaluation resources particular to exoskeletons are in development in these committees, in which industrial environments and tasks are considered.

A core element of a robotic system is its computing, meaning the processes that form the robot's autonomous behaviors and artificial intelligence that are used to make decisions and plan its actions. The evaluation resources that currently exist assume a level of computational functionality, and the performance characteristic that is measured is representative of that functionality. For example, performing a navigation task will potentially exercise a robot's ability to plan paths, calculate trajectories, etc., to perform the most effective traversal. Thus, a performance metric for a navigation task, such as time to complete, is informed by autonomous functionality that is driven by algorithms and other computational elements, but does not specifically measure that computational performance. Any performance measurement is in the context of that task or actions that were performed. There have been efforts to characterize a robot's autonomy, such as the Autonomy Levels for Unmanned Systems (ALFUS) framework,[76] and human-centric measures of autonomy (e.g., neglect time, interaction time, robot attention demand[77]). However, explicit evaluation methods for the computing characteristics of an industrial robot do not exist, and may be desirable given how integral this aspect is to robot performance.

Of the resources presented in Tables 13.1–13.5, a majority of them can be used for functional level evaluations. Functional level evaluations are likely easier to develop as they are focused specifically only on one or a few robot capabilities, and also easier to implement and conduct.

There are not many elemental evaluations methods that have been formalized, as typically the properties of robot components that can be evaluated are done so using more basic means. The speed of a robot's traversal, for instance, can be measured using well-established distance and time measurements. Such a measure is also typically devoid of context and therefore requires less specificity. The few resources that are at the elemental level, such as the test methods for finger and grasp strength[43,78] are those that require unique test artifacts to be evaluated properly, and therefore also need documentation.

The majority of operational level evaluation resources are specified through competitions, such as the many leagues in RoboCup.[79] These operational level evaluations are essentially a series of functional evaluation methods used to form a scenario. The scenarios used in competitions, though, are typically limited in their applicability to the real world due to restrictions on variability in order to balance difficulty inherent in the application domain and ensure fairness in terms of currently-available technologies used by the competitors. The tasks and metrics used in these competitions are still viable evaluation methods and can be used to model tasks in other domains that the competition may not explicitly cover. More operational level evaluation methods need to be developed to satisfy increasing technology readiness level (TRL) requirements for industrial robot developments, which is discussed in Section 13.4.

13.6   Contextualization

The context in which an industrial robot is used is important. Context includes many factors that can influence performance, such as environmental conditions, variability of task parameters, and interactions with other agents and humans. Evaluating industrial robot performance will produce metrics that are only meaningful if they are framed properly. Therefore, the results of an evaluation must be contextualized such that the understanding of performance is meaningful and its relevance to a specific application can be understood. Recording the context for an evaluation will also make it easier to replicate the results. Conversely, the context of a particular target use case, scenario, or domain can also be characterized in order to tune the parameters of how an evaluation is to be conducted. It can also set thresholds on performance metrics to determine if a recorded measure is acceptable or not per the context.

For example, the environmental difficulty with which a material transport vehicle (e.g., an AGV) has to contend can vary depending on where it is deployed. Some factories have aisleways that are flat, clean, and kept clear at all times for the AGVs, therefore these systems are not expected to traverse rough or uneven terrain, or deal with clutter and obstacles that must be avoided. Performance test results of travel speed and navigation evaluation conducted under pristine conditions would therefore be relevant when making purchasing decisions about an AGV for factories which offer clear, clean, flat aisles. This is not the case if an AGV is intended for use in an environment that has cluttered aisles, holes in the floor, and varying flooring materials. An applicable resource for this example is the ASTM F3244 [40] standard test method for navigation where the dimensions of a defined area and the average traversal speed through that area are measured. The dimensions of the area provide a context for the performance measurement and can be defined to determine a more generic characteristic of the robot (e.g., the narrowest passage able to be traversed) or tuned to fit the conditions of an intended deployment environment. The context under which the above navigation test is run can be further defined by use of a complementary Standard Practice for Recording Environmental Effects for Utilization with Automatic, Automated, or Autonomous Unmanned Ground Vehicle (A-UGV) Test Methods.[80] This practice provides a standard way to define the environmental conditions – or context – under which testing of an A-UGV is conducted.

This section reviews contextualization factors that should be considered and can be referenced when performing evaluations. A summary of the factors is presented in Table 13.6. This table is also available online and will continue to be updated as new resources for contextualization become available: http://nerve.uml.edu/EvaluationCatalog/.

13.6.1 *Contextual Characteristics*

In order to define context, the relevant characteristics must first be determined and measured. While there is no comprehensive list of these characteristics, many efforts have sought to organize the relevant parameters. For example, the IEEE Robot Task Representation Study Group is developing an ontology to represent the relationships between aspects of robot automation tasks.[81] In addition to other defined terms, they present two groups of distinct characteristics of context: the environment (things that are not part of the robot system) and the platform (things that are part of the robot itself). The characteristics of the environment can be expressed as characteristics that the robot requires in order to perform the task. There are also frameworks for robot performance, such as the PerMFUS[82] framework, which was developed to facilitate characterizing performance requirements for an unmanned system, and metrics to measure performance to meet those requirements, focusing on military applications. The framework is built on three axes: mission complexity, environmental complexity or difficulty, and independence from humans (as related to autonomy). Each axis can be taken as a group of relevant characteristics that are used to define context. The characteristics of the robot itself are also important for context. The hardware and software configuration of an industrial robot will vary based on many factors and is particularly important to record if the robot is configurable for multiple jobs. From these sources, four high-level contextual characteristic groups can be defined that fit the industrial robotics space: task complexity, environmental conditions, human-robot interaction, and robot configuration.

Task complexity characteristics pertain to the actions required to be performed by the robot in order to complete a task, such as picking and placing objects or delivering a payload by traversing through a warehouse. The characteristics of individual tasks are relevant for functional level evaluations, whereas those for an entire job or combination of tasks are relevant for an operational level evaluation. Some generic characteristics include accuracy, repeatability, throughput, speed, and completeness, each of which can have associated performance metrics as relevant to the task. There are also factors relating to task composition, such as the *a priori* knowledge needed to perform a task, any adaptation to unplanned events that is required, etc. More specific characteristics can pertain to artifacts that are part of the task, such as objects that are manipulated by an end effector or carried as a payload (e.g., dimensions, texture, fragility, weight). Some existing taxonomies of industrial tasks exist, such as,[23] which distills assembly tasks into robot actions and their associated parameters.

Environmental conditions are characteristics of the operating space where the tasks will be performed. Examples of these characteristics include the dimensions of operating space, lighting, sensor interference, ground surfaces, air particulates, and obstacles. There are many environmental characteristics that can be measured, but they should be limited to those that can impact performance. For example, operating in a clean room environment will require any human agents to wear personal protective equipment which may impact any human-robot interaction components of the system. Conversely, operation in a low-light environment may have fewer implications for a robot system that relies solely on light detection and ranging (LIDAR) data to operate. Many environmental conditions are not static and may involve transitions between conditions, such as a vehicle delivering goods into and out of a freezer, or lighting changes for day/night operations. Tools such as lux meters for lighting and temperature sensors can be used to explicitly measure environmental characteristics. A good resource for environmental conditions and their pertinent qualities is ASTM F3218,[80] which provides a method for recording environmental characteristics.

Human-robot interaction (HRI) characteristics are particular to instances where humans and robot(s) are collocated and/or collaborating. These characteristics include the roles of the human agent (e.g., supervisor, operator, mechanic, peer, bystander,[83]) the frequency of interaction (e.g., simultaneously performing a collaborative task, sequentially performing tasks that are dependent on each other), and the protocols for interaction (e.g., conveying failures, adapting task processes due to unplanned events). The context of HRI in the industrial domain also sees human agents teaching robots to perform tasks, doing so kinesthetically, teleoperating with a teach pendant, or more traditional programming. Each of these characteristics is important to note for functional (single tasks) and operational evaluations (combinations of tasks). There are existing taxonomies and surveys of common HRI metrics and relevant characteristics, such as[39,84,85] and,[86] that can be used to guide evaluation. Operator workload is a major consideration for characterization of HRI as well. The taxonomy presented in[87] categorizes the drivers of workload into environment, task, equipment, and operator characteristics.

Robot configuration refers to the hardware and software characteristics of the industrial robot that is being evaluated. Industrial robots are designed to be integrated into many different types of environments and to perform a variety of tasks, meaning they are highly reconfigurable. Mobility platforms can provide many options for localization methods, such as using cameras to detect fiducials in the environment, LIDAR data for SLAM, or following magnetic tape on the ground. Manipulator systems are typically comprised of a combination of arms, end effectors, and sensors. There are also tunable software settings for each hardware component and for how the entire robot system will use them to function. To this end, capturing the pertinent robot configuration characteristics that were used to conduct an evaluation is necessary. The ASTM F3327[88] standard provides a practice for recording the configuration of an industrial mobile vehicle, noting relevant characteristics including hardware parameters (e.g., make and model, steering type, loaded/unloaded), software parameters (e.g., velocity, acceleration, stand-off distances), capabilities (e.g., localization method, sensors used, safety-rated equipment), and task-relevant characteristics (e.g., environment maps, changes in software during a test). A published standard does not yet exist for recording the relevant characteristics of a robot manipulator, but[54] discusses several important aspects including the robot's computer system, arm, grippers/hands, sensors, and controller.

13.6.2 *Communicating Context*

Given the many characteristics of context that can impact robot performance, presenting the context under which an evaluation took place must be done in an understandable manner. The first step is to use a standard nomenclature when describing the context of an evaluation. Evaluation resources that are produced by standards committees will typically adhere to their own terminology standards. Relevant standard terminology documents include:

- ISO 8373 Robots and Robotic Devices – Vocabulary[89]
- OSHA Technical Manual, Section IV: Safety Hazards, Chapter 4: Industrial Robots and Robot System Safety[90]
- ASTM F3200 Standard Terminology for A-UGVS[91]
- ISO/TS 15066 Standard Terms for Collaborative Robots[58]
- Proposed Standard Terminology for Robotic Hands and Associated Performance Metrics[78]

Many of these standards documents reference one another so as to not provide conflicting definitions of terms.

The evaluation resources described in Section 13.5 specify pieces of information which are relevant to an evaluation that must be recorded. This includes the exhibited performance metrics and contextual information related to the four groups described previously. Many of the evaluation methods provide methods by which to record this data in a standard format and present it alongside the performance metrics. For example, the YCB Benchmarks website[92] hosts community-generated protocols that utilize the YCB objects and each protocol has fields for providing contextual information such as the initial and target poses of each object, description of the environment, and *a priori* information provided to the robot. Standard test methods such as ASTM F3244 for navigation[40] require that relevant characteristics of context be presented, including shapes, dimensions, and boundary types used to define the area being navigated. These evaluation methods, as well as the previously described standard practices for recording environmental characteristics[80] and robot configuration,[88] provided sample test forms that can be used to record and present the relevant contextual characteristics in a standard format. See Fig. 13.4 for a suggested example report form that can be used with ASTM F3218 standard.

13.6.3 *Conducting Relevant Evaluations*

When conducting evaluations, evaluation resources at the elemental level are typically devoid of explicit context as they evaluate more generic properties of robots. Evaluations at the functional and operational level, however, will be conducted in a more specific context that can be relevant to a particular use case, scenario, or application domain. In this case, one can conduct a relevant evaluation by matching the contextual characteristics of the target use case to that of the evaluation context.

A robotic food-handling application for sorting and inspection for deformities, for example, may involve manipulation of soft, fragile materials, with camera-enabled computer vision, performed in a clean environment. There may also be HRI considerations to the application wherein an operator will have to reprogram the system several times a day to change which job it is performing. These contextual characteristics will impose performance requirements on the robot, in addition to desired performance thresholds such as throughput and accuracy, that will inform how to evaluate the robot.

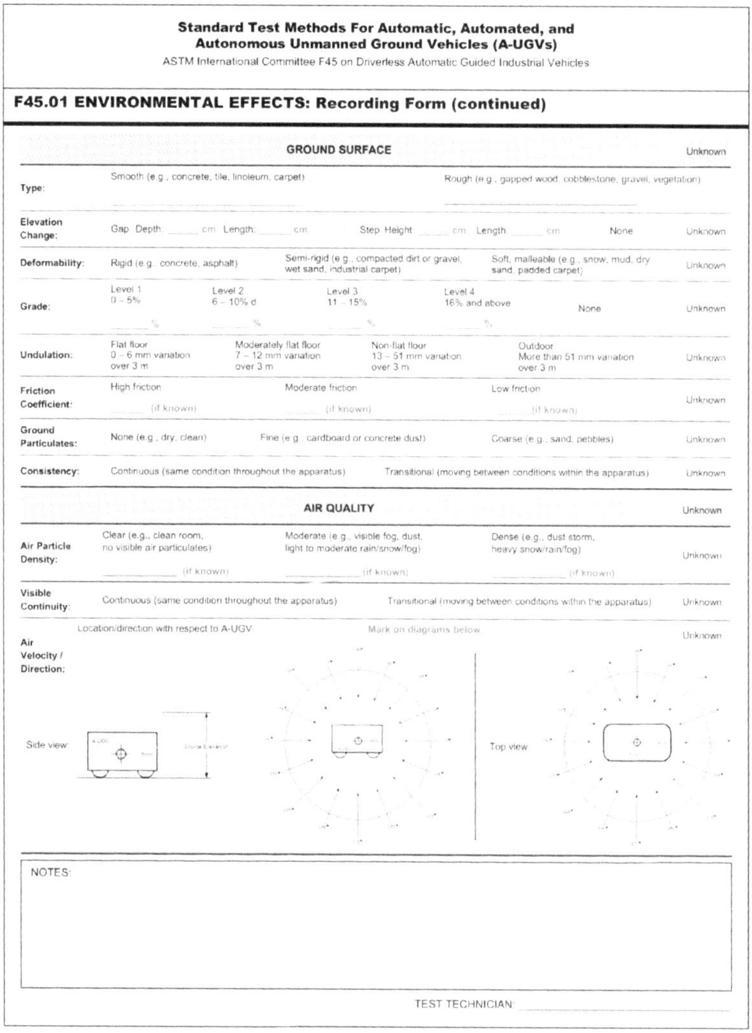

Standard Test Methods For Automatic, Automated, and Autonomous Unmanned Ground Vehicles (A-UGVs)
ASTM International Committee F45 on Driverless Automatic Guided Industrial Vehicles

F45.01 ENVIRONMENTAL EFFECTS: Recording Form (continued)

	GROUND SURFACE				Unknown
Type:	Smooth (e.g., concrete, tile, linoleum, carpet)		Rough (e.g., gapped wood, cobblestone, gravel, vegetation)		
Elevation Change:	Gap Depth: ____ cm Length: ____ cm		Step Height ____ cm Length ____ cm	None	Unknown
Deformability:	Rigid (e.g. concrete, asphalt)	Semi-rigid (e.g., compacted dirt or gravel, wet sand, industrial carpet)	Soft, malleable (e.g., snow, mud, dry sand, padded carpet)		Unknown
Grade:	Level 1 0 – 5% ____ %	Level 2 6 – 10% d ____ %	Level 3 11 – 15% ____ %	Level 4 16% and above ____ % None	Unknown
Undulation:	Flat floor 0 – 6 mm variation over 3 m	Moderately flat floor 7 – 12 mm variation over 3 m	Non-flat floor 13 – 51 mm variation over 3 m	Outdoor More than 51 mm variation over 3 m	Unknown
Friction Coefficient:	High friction ____ (if known)	Moderate friction ____ (if known)	Low friction ____ (if known)		Unknown
Ground Particulates:	None (e.g., dry, clean)	Fine (e.g. cardboard or concrete dust)	Coarse (e.g., sand, pebbles)		Unknown
Consistency:	Continuous (same condition throughout the apparatus)		Transitional (moving between conditions within the apparatus)		Unknown
	AIR QUALITY				Unknown
Air Particle Density:	Clear (e.g., clean room, no visible air particulates) ____ (if known)	Moderate (e.g., visible fog, dust, light to moderate rain/snow/fog) ____ (if known)	Dense (e.g., dust storm, heavy snow/rain/fog) ____ (if known)		Unknown
Visible Continuity:	Continuous (same condition throughout the apparatus)		Transitional (moving between conditions within the apparatus)		Unknown
Air Velocity / Direction:	Location/direction with respect to A-UGV		Mark on diagrams below		Unknown

NOTES:

TEST TECHNICIAN: ____

Fig. 13.4. A suggested example report form that can be used to record ground surface and air quality environmental conditions for the ASTM F3218 standard.[80]

By specifying the context under which an evaluation takes place, comparisons between multiple robots can also be made. Experimental results may also be replicated when the same context is used across multiple experiments. This is very important when benchmarks are produced and shared with the research community, as future benchmarks that are generated must be directly comparable to others. However, if sufficient contextual information is not supplied, replications of an experiment may not be possible and comparisons may not be fair or accurately representative of a robot's performance. While there is no explicit requirement for the minimum "amount" of context that must be supplied or adhered to when conducting an evaluation, noting the characteristics that are considered to be potentially impactful on robot performance (across the four categories outlined in Section 13.6.1) is good practice. There are also many characteristics that have been shown to have impacts on robot performance throughout the research community. For instance, the surface quality of an object that is to be avoided in the environment by a mobile robot is highly relevant, particularly if the robot uses LIDAR sensors and the object's surface is flat black[93] or if the robot uses sound navigation ranging (sonar) and the object's surface is highly reflective.[3] Not all contextual characteristics will be presented alongside a performance evaluation, and the values of those missing characteristics should not be assumed. Additional evaluation may be required if the missing characteristics are deemed relevant enough to change the performance outcome.

The capabilities of industrial robots are typically designed to be application-agnostic, meaning they are relevant to many different use cases and domains. Demonstrating a robot's applicability across domains, though, can be difficult, due to the varying characteristics of context particular to each domain. This could imply a desire for more generic test protocols that are devoid of specific context, but such testing will likely miss some of the relevant aspects of a use case that could impact performance. Instead, methods for translating the results of an evaluation between domains could be developed. Proper representation of the relevant contextual characteristics for an evaluation could enable this type of transferability to be demonstrated. If an evaluation has already been conducted, the contextual characteristics that it is presented with could be compared to that of another target domain and the similarity could be assessed. Or if an evaluation is being designed, the shared contextual characteristics of one or more domains could be used to shape the conditions of the evaluation method, finding the overlapping

Table 13.6. Summary of contextualization factors to consider when performing evaluations.

Contextualization Factors			
Categories	**Considerations**	**Examples**	**References**
Task complexity	Metric requirements	Accuracy, repeatability, throughout, speed, completeness	23
	Task composition	Requirements for a priori knowledge, adaptation to unplanned events, sequence of actions	
	Required robot actions	Assembly: detect, align, pick up, insert, slide	
	Task/object physical properties	Dimensions, texture, fragility, weight	
Environmental conditions	Physical properties	Dimensions of operating space, lighting, ground surface	80
	Static vs. dynamic	Changing lighting due to time of day, moving in and out of a freezer	
	Interference	External sensor emission (e.g., LIDAR), electrical interference	
Human-robot interaction	Roles of the human agent	Supervisor, operator, mechanic, peer, bystander	83·84·86
	Frequency of interaction	Simultaneous collaboration, sequential independent task performance	
	Protocols	Communication of failures, adaptation to unplanned events	
	Teaching method	Kinesthetic, teach pendant, computer programming	
	Workload	Drivers: environment, task, equipment, and operator	87
Robot configuration	Hardware	Locomotion method, sensors, arms, end effectors, tooling	88·54
	Software	Velocity, navigation, localization, obstacle avoidance, object detection, decision-making	
	Capabilities	Localization method, sensors used for navigation and obstacles avoidance	
Terminology	Industrial robots and safety	ISO 8373 Robots and Robotic Devices – Vocabulary	89
		OSHA Technical Manual, Section IV: Safety Hazards, Chapter 4: Industrial Robots and Robot System Safety	90
	Industrial mobile vehicles	ASTM F3200 Standard Terminology for A-UGVS	91
	Collaborative robots	ISO/TS 15066 Standard Terms for Collaborative Robots	58
	Robotic hands	Proposed Standard Terminology for Robotic Hands and Associated Performance Metrics	78

characteristics and implementing them. There are also considerations for variability of contextual characteristics to better reflect real world scenarios and evaluate the robustness of a robot's capabilities; these are discussed in Section 13.7. More formal methods need to be developed to properly guide this type of comparative and transferable evaluation.

13.7   Robustness, Significance, and Repeatability

Robustness is defined as "the degree to which a system or component can function correctly in the presence of invalid inputs or stressful environmental conditions".[94] It is an important characteristic to consider when implementing robotic systems, especially in manufacturing operations where production disruptions are extremely costly. A survey found that stopped production costs auto industry manufacturers an average of $22,000 per minute.[95] Characterizing the variability of conditions that an industrial robot will encounter is a daunting task. Lighting levels and hues are classic examples of highly-variable factors that affect vision systems in industrial settings. Performance evaluations should take into account edge cases to determine how the system responds. If the inputs or conditions are outside its performance envelope, at a minimum it should degrade gracefully or raise an alert so that the situation can be remedied. Robustness and variability concerns are part of the context under which a system is evaluated as well as deployed. Representing robustness and variability in meaningful ways will be essential for completing the definition of context. Statistical representations may provide a way forward in capturing the variations in external conditions. Modeling the distribution of conditions, such as lighting intensity, density of traffic, uncertainty in part positions, etc., would provide a starting point for more rigorous characterization of context and also serve to provide ways to evaluate the robotic system robustness by testing how it responds to edge cases or outlier conditions.

Repeatability is an important aspect of industrial robot performance as it demonstrates competency of a capability. One-off performance demonstrations do not wholly represent the capabilities of a system; it must instead be demonstrated to perform reliably many times within a desired threshold. Depending on the task, there may also be implications for safety, such as for a mobile robot reliably avoiding a human in the environment. If the robot cannot reliably avoid collisions with another object in the environment then it may not be deemed safe and therefore will most likely not be deployed. Standard test methods for robots, such as those specified through ASTM, require that repeatable test results be achieved within certain levels of statistical reliability and confidence levels. For example, the standard test method for navigation in a defined area[40] has variable success criteria that are set by the test requestor, such as navigating through an aisle that is five meters wide, without colliding with the boundaries. This task must be repeated several times, successfully, until a certain number of repetitions is reached without any failures (i.e., colliding with the boundaries). See Table 13.7 for the number of repetitions required to achieve different confidence and probability measures for static test settings. For tests involving variability, such as to test for robustness, more statistical analysis is required in order to achieve significance.

Experiment replicability is one of the cornerstones of the scientific method and is necessary in order for a technical field to make measurable progress. Replicability, also referred to as reproducibility, is also essential for enabling industrial application of a new technology. The key is to define as precisely as possible the experimental conditions so that others may reproduce them and conduct the same procedures. It is increasingly acknowledged that the field of robotics in general is hindered by the lack of experimental replicability.[96] One example of response to this need is the creation of a new type of paper within the IEEE Robotics and Automation Society Magazine that is devoted to reproducing the described experiments – "R-papers".[97]

The value of replicability is further increased if there is a way of categorizing the context in which the experiments succeeded. As noted in, Ref. 98 experiments in robotics typically are not necessarily conducted to prove a hypothesis, but rather to demonstrate that a system is working with respect to a reference model and that it works (ideally) better than other similar systems. Due to the complexity of robotic systems, there is also an exploratory aspect to experiments, where they are conducted to bring forth the responses and behavior of the system being tested. Regardless of whether the experimental results are based on evaluating how well a

Table 13.7. The number of repetitions required to achieve different confidence measures against the probability of success thresholds with zero failures. Source: Ref. 40.

		Probability of Success Threshold		
		0.99	0.95	0.90
	0.99	459	90	44
	0.95	299	59	29
Confidence	0.90	230	45	22
	0.85	189	37	19
	0.80	161	32	16

robot works or if they are based on answering a broader question of how a robot responds to a given environment and stimuli, it is important to understand how the results can be extended to other situations. The concept of generalizability is therefore an additional consideration when defining and designing replicable experiments.

Generalizability hinges on defining an experiment's "representativeness".[98] The representativeness of experimental conditions corresponds closely to the context discussed in Section 13.6. In order to realize the potential of replicable experimentation that can be extrapolated to other applications or implementations, it will be necessary to develop more rigorous definitions of contextual elements. Examples of quantitative descriptions of the environment include analysis of building features which were the settings for papers on SLAM in a major robotics conference[98] and metrics for the terrain difficulty that a robot traverses.[99] Having quantitative measures of industrial environmental conditions can help in assessing of whether results reported in a paper or product brochure are applicable to similar scenarios.

Another potentially important resource in supporting reproducibility of experimental results is the open source movement. There are many efforts in the development of software for robotic systems that can be reused and that enable replication of systems for conducting experiments. Examples include Open Robotics, which supports the Robot Operating System (ROS) and the simulation tool Gazebo[100] and the Open Robot Control Software (OROCOS).[101] A variant of ROS that is focused on industrial robotics is being developed through the ROS Industrial Consortium.[102] However, considerations when deciding to adopt existing software need to include under which contexts it is applicable. Grasp planning software developed for picking parts that have already been singulated (isolated) and assumes no collisions will occur in approaching an object will not work if applied to bin-picking.

13.8   Conclusions

This chapter reviews many different facets of industrial robot evaluation, from determining appropriate KPIs and KPPs to contextualizing and evaluating industrial robot capabilities with considerations for variability, reliability, and confidence. While many evaluation resources have been developed and are actively being used throughout the industrial robotics community, there are still areas that require additional work to fill evaluation gaps, particularly in the areas of contextualization and generalization.

The evaluation resources that are available require some level of context to be recorded and presented with the performance data, but it is not clear if the appropriate amount of context is being captured. This issue has larger implications when characterizing the context under which a robot is planned to be used and knowing which factors of context must be properly represented as an evaluation parameter. If a procurement of a robot system is planned, the procurer will need a method to validate the degree to which presented performance data is relevant to their planned use case. At the same time, the intended deployment environments for industrial robots must be effectively characterized so robot manufacturers can develop their systems with a better understanding of the end goal. More context-driven evaluation methods can assist stakeholders on both sides of this scenario.

Different levels of variation and accurate context replication of the target use case(s) will satisfy whether or not an evaluation is considered to have been conducted in a laboratory environment (TRL 4), relevant environment (TRL 5 and 6), or an operational environment (TRL 7). A method by which to connect relevant contextual characteristics to each of the TRLs will be very beneficial in advancing how industrial systems can be evaluated. Guides for how to effectively represent the relevant contextual characteristics of real-world use cases into an evaluation are also needed to ensure proper replication of test results.

Evaluating the performance of an industrial robot's capabilities must be done in a manner that allows for the results of the evaluation to be translatable to multiple domains. The aim is not to develop evaluation methods that lack specificity, but to allow the relevant characteristics of the performance context to connect to the evaluation results. Proper characterization of context will enable this and allow for generalizability metrics to be developed. It will also highlight gaps in an evaluation that need to be addressed before allowing claims to be made about an industrial robot's capabilities in other domains.

Development towards bridging these gaps will address needs for connecting the results of an evaluation to the requirements of a technology readiness level (TRL), which ultimately will allow the field of industrial robotics to progress more rapidly.

References

1. ISO, ISO 9283:1998 - Manipulating industrial robots – Performance criteria and related test methods, Standard, International Organization for Standardization, Geneva, CH (2000).
2. ISO, ISO 10218:2011 - Robots and robotic devices – Safety requirements for industrial robots – Part 1: Robots, Standard, International Organization for Standardization, Geneva, CH (2015).

3. ANSI/ITSDF, ANSI/ITSDF B56.5 - Safety Standard for Driverless, Automatic Guided Industrial Vehicles and Automated Functions of Manned Industrial Vehicles, Standard, American National Standards Institute/Industrial Truck Standards Development Foundation (2012).

4. ASTM, Committee F45 on Driverless Automatic Guided Industrial Vehicles. https://www.astm.org/COMMITTEE/F45.htm (Accessed January 7, 2018).

5. European Machine Vision Association, EMVA 1288. http://www.emva.org/standards-technology/emva-1288/, (Accessed January 7, 2018).

6. ASTM, Committee E57 on 3D Imaging Systems. https://www.astm.org/COMMITTEE/E57.htm (Accessed July 1, 2018).

7. ASTM, Committee F48 on Exoskeletons and Exosuits. https://www.astm.org/COMMITTEE/F48.htm (Accessed July 1, 2018).

8. RoCKin, RoCKin@Work. http://rockinrobotchallenge.eu/work.php (Accessed January 27, 2019).

9. D. Torricelli, J. Gonzalez-Vargas, J. F. Veneman, K. Mombaur, N. Tsagarakis, A. J. del Ama, A. Gil-Agudo, J. C. Moreno and J. L. Pons, Benchmarking bipedal locomotion: A unified scheme for humanoids, wearable robots, and humans, *IEEE Robotics & Automation Magazine* **22**(3), 103–115 (2015).

10. ASTM, Subcommittee E54.09 on Response Robots. https://www.astm.org/COMMIT/SUBCOMMIT/E5409.htm (Accessed May 18, 2018)

11. A. Jacoff, H.-M. Huang, E. Messina, A. Virts and A. Downs, Comprehensive Standard Test Suites for the Performance Evaluation of Mobile Robots. In *Proceedings of the 10th Performance Metrics for Intelligent Systems Workshop (PerMIS'10),* New York, USA (2010).

12. E. Messina, A. Jacoff, J. Scholtz, C. Schlenoff, H.-M. Huang, A. Lytle and J. Blitch, Statement of requirements for urban search and rescue robot performance standards, *NIST Draft Report* (2005). https://www.nist.gov/document-12931 (Accessed May 21, 2018).

13. H. L. Akin, N. Ito, A. Jacoff, A. Kleiner, J. Pellenz and A. Visser, RoboCup Rescue Robot and Simulation Leagues, *AI Magazine* **34**(1), 78 (2012).

14. NIST, At New NIST Facility, Response Robots Must Measure Up. https://www.nist.gov/featured-stories/new-nist-facility-response-robots-must-measure (Accessed May 21, 2018).

15. R. Sheh, A. Jacoff, A.-M. Virts, T. Kimura, J. Pellenz, S. Schwertfeger and J. Suthakorn, Advancing the state of urban search and rescue robotics through the RoboCup Rescue Robot League competition. In *Field and Service Robotics*, M. Hutter and R. Siegwart (eds). Springer, (2014).

16. Standard Performance Evaluation Corporation. https://www.spec.org/ (Accessed May 18, 2018).

17. TREC, Text REtrieval Conference. https://trec.nist.gov/ (Accessed May 18, 2018).

18. E. M. Voorhees and D. K. Harman, *TREC: Experiment and Evaluation in Information Retrieval*, Vol. 1. MIT Press (2005).

19. NIST, Additive Manufacturing Benchmark Test Series (AM-BENCH). https://www.nist.gov/ambench (Accessed May 18, 2018).

20. ISO, ISO 22400-1 - Automation Systems and Integration – Key Performance Indicators (KPIs) for Manufacturing Operations Management - Part 1: Overview, Concepts and Terminology, Standard, International Organization for Standardization, Geneva, CH (2014).

21. M. P. Brundage, W. Z. Bernstein, K. C. Morris and J. A. Horst, Using graph-based visualizations to explore key performance indicator relationships for manufacturing production systems, *Procedia CIRP* **61**, 451–456 (2017).

22. E. Messina, J. Adam and H. Scott, Performance Evaluation of Autonomous Mobile Robots. In *Intelligent Autonomous Vehicle Systems: A 4D/RCS Approach*, R. Madhavan, E.R. Messina, and J.S. Albus (eds). Nova Science Publishers (2007).

23. M. Shneier, E. Messina, C. Schlenoff, F. Proctor, T. Kramer and J. Falco, Measuring and representing the performance of manufacturing assembly robots, Tech. Rep. 8090, National Institute of Standards and Technology (2015).

24. J. C. Mankins, Technology readiness levels, White Paper, April **6** (1995).

25. B. A. Bodt and R. S. Camden, Technology readiness level six and autonomous mobility. In *Unmanned Ground Vehicle Technology VI*, Vol. 5422, G.R. Gerhart, C.M. Shoemaker, and D.W. Gage (eds). International Society for Optics and Photonics, pp. 302–314 (2004).

26. Department of Defense, DoD Manufacturing Readiness Levels. http://www.dodmrl.com/ (Accessed June 18, 2018).

27. Manufacturing USA, Manufacturing USA. https://www.manufacturingusa.com/ (Accessed July 13, 2018).

28. ARM Institute, Advanced Robotics for Manufacturing Institute. http://arminstitute.org/ (Accessed July 1, 2018).

29. J. Marvel, R. Eastman, G. Cheok, K. Saidi, T. Hong, E. Messina, B. Bollinger, P. Evans, J. Guthrie, E. Hershberger, C. Martinez, K. McNamara and J. Wells, Technology Readiness Levels for Randomized Bin Picking, Performance Metrics for Intelligent Systems (PerMIS) 2012 Workshop, Special Session, Report, National Institute of Standards and Technology (2012a), doi:https://dx.doi.org/10.6028/NIST.IR.7876.

30. J. A. Marvel, K. Saidi, R. Eastman, T. Hong, G. Cheok and E. Messina, Technology readiness levels for randomized bin picking. In *Proceedings of the Workshop on Performance Metrics for Intelligent Systems*. pp. 109–113 (2012b).

31. ISO, ISO/TC 299 - Robotics, Standards catalogue (2018).

32. RoboCup, RoboCup@Work. http://www.robocupatwork.org/ (Accessed July 1, 2018).

33. RoboCup, RoboCup@Home. http://www.robocupathome.org/ (Accessed July 1, 2018).

34. RoboCup, RoboCup Logistics League, http://www.robocup-logistics.org/ (Accessed July 1, 2018).

35. B. Bodin, H. Wagstaff, S. Saeedi, L. Nardi, E. Vespa, J. Mayer, A. Nisbet, M. Luján, S. Furber, A. Davison, P. Kelly and M. O'Boyle, SLAMBench2: Multi-Objective Head-to-Head Benchmarking for Visual SLAM. In *Proceedings of The International Conference in Robotics and Automation (ICRA) 2018*, pp. 3637–3644 (2018).

36. S. Ceriani, G. Fontana, A. Giusti, D. Marzorati, M. Matteucci, D. Migliore, D. Rizzi, D. G. Sorrenti and P. Taddei, Rawseeds ground truth collection systems for indoor self-localization and mapping, *Autonomous Robots* **27**(4), 353 (2009).

37. B. Calli, A. Singh, A. Walsman, S. Srinivasa, P. Abbeel and A. M. Dollar, The YCB object and model set: Towards common benchmarks for manipulation research. In *2015 International Conference on Advanced Robotics (ICAR)* pp. 510–517 (2015).

38. V. Lomonaco and D. Maltoni, CORe50: a New Dataset and Benchmark for Continuous Object Recognition, *arXiv preprint arXiv:1705.03550* (2017).

39. A. Steinfeld, T. Fong, D. Kaber, M. Lewis, J. Scholtz, A. Schultz and M. Goodrich, Common metrics for human-robot interaction. In *Proceedings of the 1st ACM/IEEE Conference on Human-Robot Interaction*. ACM, pp. 33–40 (2006).

40. ASTM (2017), ASTM F3244-17, Standard Test Method for Navigation: Defined Area, ASTM International, West Conshohocken, PA (2017).

41. ASTM (2016), ASTM E3064-16, Standard Test Method for Evaluating the Performance of Optical Tracking Systems that Measure Six Degrees of Freedom (6DOF) Pose, ASTM International, West Conshohocken, PA, (2016).

42. S. G. Hart and L. E. Staveland, Development of NASA-TLX (Task Load Index): Results of empirical and theoretical research. In *Human Mental Workload, P.A. Hancock and P. Meshkati (eds)*. Elsevier, pp. 139–183 (1988).

43. NIST, Robotic Grasping and Manipulation for Assembly. https://www.nist.gov/el/intelligent-systems-division-73500/robotic-grasping-and-manipulation-assembly (Accessed July 1, 2018).

44. ASTM (2017a), ASTM E2566-17a, Standard Test Method for Evaluating Response Robot Sensing: Visual Acuity, ASTM International, West Conshohocken, PA (2017).

45. ASTM (2017b), ASTM F3265-17, Standard Test Method for Grid-Video Obstacle Measurement, ASTM International, West Conshohocken, PA (2017).

46. T. Suzuki and T. Oka, Grasping of unknown objects on a planar surface using a single depth image. In *2016 IEEE International Conference on Advanced Intelligent Mechatronics (AIM)* pp. 572–577 (2016).

47. D. Shukla, O. Erkent and J. Piater, Probabilistic detection of pointing directions for human-robot interaction. In *2015 International Conference on Digital Image Computing: Techniques and Applications (DICTA)* pp. 1–8 (2015).

48. ISO, ISO 18646-1:2016 - Robotics – Performance criteria and related test methods for service robots – Part 1: Locomotion for wheeled robots, Standard (2016).

49. ISO, ISO/DIS 18646-2 - Robotics – Performance criteria and related test methods for service robots – Part 2: Navigation, Standard (2017).

50. ASTM (2019), ASTM F3381-19, Standard Practice for Describing Stationary Obstacles Utilized within A-UGV Test Methods, ASTM International, West Conshohocken, PA (2019).

51. IGVC, Intelligent Ground Vehicle Competition. http://www.igvc.org/ (Accessed July 1, 2018).

52. ASTM (2018), Draft Standard WK57000, New Test Method for Standard Test Method for Docking Driverless Automatic Guided Industrial Vehicles, under development of Subcommittee F45.02 on Docking and Navigation.

53. J. A. Falco, K. Van Wyk and E. R. Messina, Performance metrics and test methods for robotic hands (draft), Tech. Rep., National Institute of Standards and Technology (2018). doi:https://doi.org/10.6028/NIST.SP.1227-draft.

54. J. Mahler, R. Platt, A. Rodriguez, M. Ciocarlie, A. Dollar, R. Detry, M. A. Roa, H. Yanco, A. Norton, J. Falco, K. van Wyk, E. Messina, J. J. Leitner, D. Morrison, M. Mason, O. Brock, L. Odhner, A. Kurenkov, M. Matl and K. Goldberg, Robot grasping benchmarks, protocols, and metrics (Guest Editorial), *IEEE Transactions on Automation Science and Engineering* **15**(4), 1440–1442 (2018).

55. C. Metcalf, SHAP: Southampton Hand Assessment Procedure. http://www.shap.ecs.soton.ac.uk/ (Accessed July 1, 2018).

56. Lafayette Instrument Evaluation, Dexterity Tests - Human Evaluation by Lafayette Instrument Company. http://lafayetteevaluation.com/listing/dexterity-tests (Accessed June 1, 2018).

57. A. H. Quispe, H. B. Amor and H. I. Christensen, A taxonomy of benchmark tasks for robot manipulation. In *Robotics Research*, A. Bicchi and W. Burgard (eds). Springer, pp. 405–421 (2018).

58. ISO, ISO/TS 15066:2016 - Robots and robotic devices — Collaborative robots, Standard, International Organization for Standardization, Geneva, CH (2016).

59. EUROC, European Robotics Challenges. http://www.euroc-project.eu/ (Accessed July 1, 2018).

60. NIST, Agile Robotics for Industrial Automation Competition. http://www.nist.gov/ariac/ (Accessed July 1, 2018).

61. RoCKin, RoCKin@Home, http://rockinrobotchallenge.eu/home.php (Accessed July 1, 2018).

62. euRobotics, European Robotics League. https://www.eu-robotics.net/robotics_league/ (Accessed July 1, 2018).

63. World Robot Summit, World Robot Summit. http://worldrobotsummit.org/en/ (Accessed July 1, 2018).

64. A. Handa, T. Whelan, J. McDonald and A. J. Davison, A benchmark for RGB-D visual odometry, 3D reconstruction and SLAM. In *2014 IEEE International Conference on Robotics and Automation (ICRA)* pp. 1524–1531 (2014).

65. IEEE, IEEE Std 1872-2015 - IEEE Standard for Robot Map Data Representation for Navigation, Standard (2015).

66. ASTM (2015), ASTM E2938-15, Standard Test Method for Evaluating the Relative-Range Measurement Performance of 3D Imaging Systems in the Medium Range, ASTM International, West Conshohocken, PA (2015).

67. ASTM (2014), ASTM E2919-14, Standard Test Method for Evaluating the Performance of Systems that Measure Static, Six Degrees of Freedom (6DOF), Pose, ASTM International, West Conshohocken, PA (2014).

68. M. Shneier, T. Hong, G. Cheok, K. Saidi and W. Shackleford, *Performance Evaluation Methods for Human Detection and Tracking Systems for Robotic Applications.* US Department of Commerce, National Institute of Standards and Technology (2015). doi:https://dx.doi.org/10.6028/NIST.IR.8045.

69. W. Shackleford, G. Cheok, T. Hong, K. Saidi and M. Shneier, Performance Evaluation of Human detection systems for robot safety, *Journal of Intelligent & Robotic Systems* **83**(1), 85–103 (2016).

70. ASTM (2018), Draft Standard WK54431, New Practice for Performance Testing of an A-UGV Under Varied Communication Conditions, under development of Subcommittee F45.04 on Communication and Integration.

71. M. R. Endsley, Situation awareness global assessment technique (SAGAT). In *Proceedings of the IEEE 1988 National Aerospace and Electronics Conference (NAECON)* pp. 789–795 (1988).

72. ISO, ISO 13482:2014 - Robots and robotic devices – Safety requirements for personal care robots, Standard, International Organization for Standardization (2014).

73. IEEE, IEEE Robotics & Automation Society, Technical Committee for Robotic Hands, Grasping and Manipulation. http://www.ieee-ras.org/robotic-hands-grasping-and-manipulation (Accessed July 1, 2018).

74. EMSHRI 2017, Third International Workshop on Evaluation Methods Standardization for Human-Robot Interaction. https://sites.google.com/view/emshri2017/home (Accessed July 16, 2018).

75. IEEE, IEEE Robotics & Automation Society Technical Committee for Wearable Robotics. http://www.ieee-ras.org/wearable-robotics (Accessed July 16, 2018).

76. H.-M. Huang, K. Pavek, B. Novak, J. Albus and E. Messina, A framework for autonomy levels for unmanned systems (ALFUS). In *Proceedings of the AUVSI's Unmanned Systems North America* , pp. 849–863 (2005).

77. M. A. Goodrich and D. R. Olsen Jr, Seven principles of efficient human robot interaction. In *IEEE International Conference on Systems Man and Cybernetics*, vol. 4, pp. 3943–3948 (2003).

78. J. A. Falco, K. Van Wyk and E. R. Messina, Proposed standard terminology for robotic hands and associated performance metrics (draft), Tech. Rep., National Institute of Standards and Technology (2018). doi:https://doi.org/10.6028/NIST.SP.1229-draft.

79. RoboCup, RoboCup Federation official website. http://www.robocup.org/ (Accessed July 1, 2018).

80. ASTM (2017), ASTM F3218-17, Standard Practice for Recording Environmental Effects for Utilization with A-UGV Test Methods, ASTM International, West Conshohocken, PA (2017).

81. S. Balakirsky, C. Schlenoff, S. R. Fiorini, S. Redfield, M. Barreto, H. Nakawala, J. L. Carbonera, L. Soldatova, J. Bermejo-Alonso, F. Maikore, P. J. S. Goncalves, E. De Momi, V. R. S. Kumar and T. Haidegger, Towards a robot task ontology standard. In *ASME 2017 12th International Manufacturing Science and Engineering Conference collocated with the JSME/ASME 2017 6th International Conference on Materials and Processing*. American Society of Mechanical Engineers, pp. V003T04A049–V003T04A049 (2017).

82. H.-M. Huang, K. Pavek, M. Ragon, J. Jones, E. Messina and J. Albus, Characterizing unmanned system autonomy: Contextual autonomous capability and level of autonomy analyses. In *Unmanned Systems Technology IX*, Vol. 6561. International Society for Optics and Photonics, p. 65611N (2007).

83. J. Scholtz, Theory and evaluation of human robot interactions. In *Proceedings of the 36th Annual Hawaii International Conference on System Sciences* (2003).

84. H. A. Yanco and J. Drury, Classifying human-robot interaction: an updated taxonomy. In *2004 IEEE International Conference on Systems, Man and Cybernetics,* Vol. 3, pp. 2841–2846 (2004).

85. P. A. Lasota, T. Fong and J. A. Shah, A survey of methods for safe human-robot interaction, *Foundations and Trends® in Robotics* **5**(4), 261–349 (2017).

86. A. Bauer, D. Wollherr and M. Buss, Human-robot collaboration: A Survey, *International Journal of Humanoid Robotics* **5**(1), 47–66 (2008).

87. B. L. Hooey, D. B. Kaber, J. A. Adams, T. W. Fong and B. F. Gore, The underpinnings of workload in unmanned vehicle systems, *IEEE Transactions on Human-Machine Systems* **48**(5), 452–267 (2017).

88. ASTM (2018), ASTM F3327-18, Standard Practice for Recording the A-UGV Test Configuration, ASTM International, West Conshohocken, PA, (2018).

89. ISO, ISO 8373:2012 - Robots and robotic devices – Vocabulary, Standard (2012).

90. OSHA, Technical Manual, Section IV: Chapter 4: Industrial Robots and Robot System Safety, https://www.osha.gov/dts/osta/otm/otm_iv/otm_iv_4.html (Accessed July 1, 2018).

91. ASTM (2018), ASTM F3200-18a, Standard Terminology for Driverless Automatic Guided Industrial Vehicles, ASTM International, West Conshohocken, PA (2018).

92. YCB, YCB Benchmarks – Object and Model Set, http://www.ycbbenchmarks.com/protocols-and-benchmarks/ (Accessed July 1, 2018).

93. L. Kneip, F. Tâche, G. Caprari and R. Siegwart, Characterization of the compact Hokuyo URG-04LX 2D laser range scanner. In *2009 IEEE International Conference on Robotics and Automation (ICRA 2009)*, pp. 1447–1454 (2009).

94. IEEE, Standard Glossary of Software Engineering Terminology (ANSI), *IEEE Software Engineering Standards Collection* (1990).

95. Manufacturing.net, The $22,000-Per-Minute Manufacturing Problem, https://www.manufacturing.net/article/2006/03/22000-minute-manufacturing-problem (2006), (Accessed July 16, 2018).

96. F. Bonsignorio and A. P. Del Pobil, Toward replicable and measurable robotics research [from the guest editors], *IEEE Robotics & Automation Magazine* **22**(3), 32–35 (2015).

97. F. Bonsignorio, A New Kind of Article for Reproducible Research in Intelligent Robotics [From the Field], *IEEE Robotics & Automation Magazine* **24**(3), 178–182 (2017).

98. F. Amigoni, M. Luperto and V. Schiaffonati, Toward generalization of experimental results for autonomous robots *Robotics and Autonomous Systems* **90**, 4–14 (2017).

99. V. Molino, R. Madhavan, E. Messina, A. Downs, S. Balakirsky and A. Jacoff, Traversability metrics for rough terrain applied to repeatable test methods. In *IEEE/RSJ International Conference on Intelligent Robots and Systems (IROS 2007)*, pp. 1787–1794 (2007).

100. Open Robotics, Open Robotics, https://www.openrobotics.org/ (Accessed June 18, 2018).

101. Orocos, The Orocos Project, http://www.orocos.org/ (Accessed June 18, 2018).

102. S. Edwards and C. Lewis, ROS-Industrial: Applying the Robot Operating System (ROS) to industrial applications. Presented at the *International Conference on Robotics and Automation/Robot Operating System Developer Conference (ICRA/ROSCon)*, St. Paul, Minnesota (May 2012).